1001 STORIES
For Children and Children's Workers

1001
STORIES
for CHILDREN
and Children's
Workers

Alice M. Knight

WM. B. EERDMANS PUBLISHING COMPANY

Grand Rapids   Michigan

60,528

To my three lovely daughters

ALICE MARIE, MARY NELL, AND SARAH RUTH

who early in life gave themselves to the wondrous
Saviour, and who have grown into womanhood,
loving and serving Him, this volume is affection-
ately dedicated, with the earnest prayer that God
will use them to bring many "little lambs"
to the gracious Saviour.

Jesus loves the little children,
All the children of the world;
Black, brown, yellow, red, and white,
All are precious in His sight;
Jesus loves the little children of the world!

Introductory Note

Ours is a day of VISUAL AIDS. Is not a racy, imagination-kindling illustration a "visual aid"? What is so effective in aiding children to see and grasp spiritual truths as an aptly chosen illustration or story? How tellingly did the Master Story Teller, Jesus, make use of illustrations to bring down to earth for His hearers heavenly truths!

For more than twenty-five years, the author of this book, 1,001 STORIES FOR CHILDREN AND CHILDREN'S WORKERS, has written the Junior and Primary Sunday school lessons for the Union Gospel Press, Cleveland, Ohio. Too, for many years, she traveled over the nation with her father, the late Dr. R. E. Neighbour, a Bible teacher and evangelist, holding meetings for the boys and girls. She began teaching boys and girls when thirteen years of age, and has worked with them ever since. During these years, she has amassed and used the tangy, heart-warming, character-ennobling illustrative material contained in this book. She is now sharing these stories and illustrations with preachers, teachers, and other workers with children. Their up-to-dateness; their brevity; their to-the-pointedness; their splendid classification; their Bible and Christ-centeredness; their easy-to-understand style, make them most valuable to all who obey the Saviour's gracious words of invitation: "Suffer little children, and forbid them not to come unto Me: for of such is the kingdom of heaven" (Matt. 19:14).

WALTER BROWN KNIGHT,
Author and Compiler of
3,000 *Illustrations for Christian Service.*

CONTENTS

1001 STORIES

For Children and Children's Workers

ASSURANCE

"My Anchor Holds"

A sailor was wounded in a wreck. He was brought ashore by his comrades and cared for in a little hut. His fever ran high. A few days later he was dying. The physician had said, "He can't live long now!" He did not know any of his friends who were gathered around him. Just a few minutes before his death, he opened his eyes and looked around calmly. He knew every one, for his mind was now clear. He told each one of his comrades goodby, calling them by their names. One of the sailors asked, "Mate, how are you now?" He looked up into the face of his friend and said, "My anchor holds!"

How wonderful it is to know that, "My anchor holds!"

Sightless but Sure

An aged Christian man called his daughter to him after breakfast one morning. He said, "Daughter, my Master calleth me!" At this moment, his sight failed. He called for his Bible, and, being unable to read, he said to his daughter, "Turn to the eighth chapter of Romans, and put my finger on verse thirty-nine!" The daughter did as he requested. She read the verse which says, "Nor height, nor depth, nor any other creature, shall be able to separate us from the love of God, which is in Christ Jesus our Lord!" The man asked, "Is my finger on it?" The daughter assured him that it was. Then he said, "God be with you, my child. I have had breakfast with you. I shall sup with the Lord Jesus Christ tonight!" Immediately, after saying this, he died!

A Safe Harbor

The old captain of the *Merrimac* was an inmate of the Pennsylvania Soldiers' Home. He was a skeptic, an unbeliever. The chaplain in the Home tried to get him to read the Bible, but he would not. At last the chaplain said to the old captain, "Read the Bible and mark in red any thing that you do not believe. Begin with the Gospel of John." The captain accepted the challenge. He was sick at the time and confined to his bed. Every few hours, the chaplain, passing his door, would come in and ask, "Have you marked anything yet, captain?" The old captain would grin and answer nothing.

Several days later, when the chaplain stepped into the old captain's room, he found him dead, with his Bible open beside him. The chaplain leafed through the Gospel of John. Nothing was marked in red in the first chapter, or the second, or the third, until John 3:16. This verse was circled in red, and beside it was written, "I have cast my anchor in a safe harbor, thank God!"

She Knew

A great choir was preparing to give a public rendering of "The Messiah" (an oratorio written by Handel). They were having their final rehearsal. The choir had sung through to the point where the soprano solo takes up the refrain, "I

15

know that my Redeemer liveth." A young lady was the soloist. She sang the part through. Her notes were flawless. After she had finished, all eyes were fixed on Reichel, the conductor, to catch his look of approval. Instead, he walked over to the soloist, and asked, "My daughter, do you really *know* that your Redeemer liveth? Do you?" She blushed, and replied, "Why, yes, I think I do!" "Then sing it," cried Reichel; "tell me and all who hear you that you really *know* that your Redeemer liveth!" Then he motioned for the part to be sung again. This time, the soloist sang the truth as she *knew* it, as she had *experienced* it in her own soul. All who heard her wept. The old master, with tear-dimmed eyes, approached her and said, "My daughter, you do know it, you do know it! You have told me so!"

Fanny Crosby's Faith

One day, Mrs. Joseph Knapp was chatting with Fanny Crosby in her home. She told the blind hymn writer that she had composed a new tune. She played the tune on the piano several times. She asked Fanny Crosby to write a poem to go with the tune. As Fanny Crosby listened to the music, her face was suddenly lighted. "Why," said she, "that music says:

'Blessed assurance Jesus is mine!'"

Then Fanny Crosby gave the following beautiful words to the hymn:

"Blessed assurance, Jesus is mine!
O what a foretaste of Glory Divine!
Heir of salvation, purchase of God,
Born of His Spirit, washed in His Blood!"

These words express the great faith and assurance which Fanny Crosby had. She had been blind from babyhood. She always thought of her handicap as a blessing. One day, a minister mentioned her blindness to her and she surprised him by saying that she was sometimes glad to be sightless. "You see," she said, "when I get to Heaven, the first face that shall ever gladden my sight will be the face of my Saviour!"

The Need of the World

One cold, winter afternoon, Thomas Carlyle was sitting in his library. The door opened, and the new paster of the local church entered the room. Carlyle and the young minister visited together for a few minutes. Then, the young minister asked Carlyle, "What do you think this parish needs most?" Instantly, Carlyle replied, "What this parish needs is a man who *knows* God otherwise than by hearsay."

This whole world needs men and women, boys and girls, who *know* God for themselves. How wonderful it is to have *real* assurance concerning God, and God's Word, the Bible.

Resting on Certainties

When the great Christian and scientist, Sir Michael Faraday, was dying, some men questioned him about his speculations (or guesses) concerning the soul and death. Said the great chemist, "I know nothing about speculations. I am resting on *certainties*: '*I know* whom I have believed, and am persuaded that He is able to keep that which I have committed unto Him against that day.'"

The Seven Stones

In a humble cottage near the ocean, a fisherman lay dying. His pastor sat beside him. "Are you *sure*?" the pastor asked the old man. The old seaman looked through the open window. "Are the Seven Stones still there? Is the Wolf Rock still there?" "Yes, yes," replied the pastor, "they are still there." The dying man then folded his hands reverently, and quoted, "The mountains shall depart, and the hills be removed; but My kindness shall not depart from thee, neither shall the covenant of My peace be removed, saith the Lord that hath mercy on thee."

Knowing the Shepherd

Some years ago, at a social function in England, a great actor was asked to recite something for the pleasure of his fellow guests. He consented. He asked if there was anything special which his audience would like to hear. An aged minister who was present arose and said, "Could you, sir, recite the 23rd Psalm?"

The great actor replied, "I can, and will, if you, my friend, after I have finished, will do the same." The minister consented. Impressively, the great actor recited the Psalm. His voice was perfect. His intonation was flawless. The audience was spellbound! As he finished, the guests applauded.

Then, the aged minister arose and began to recite the Psalm. His voice was not remarkable. His intonation was not faultless. When he finished, there was no sound of applause. There was *silence*. There was not a dry eye in the room. Many heads were bowed in reverence.

The great actor again arose to his feet and, with great emotion, he said, "My friends, I have reached your eyes and ears. But the minister has reached your *hearts*. The difference is this: I know the 23rd Psalm, but he knows the Shepherd!"

BIBLE

The Leper

A leper at a mission station in China loved Jesus. He loved God's Word. He learned much of God's Word by heart. Because of his disease, he had only one finger left. His ears were big, for they were swollen to twice their normal size. His feet were so swollen that he could hardly walk. His voice was only a hoarse whisper. He was blind. But still, he wanted to hear more of God's Word, and learn more of it by heart. One day, he surprised the missionary. He wanted to recite the Gospel of Matthew. He began to quote the verses from the first chapter. He went on through the second, the third, fourth and fifth chapters.

Before he stopped, he had recited *all* twenty-eight chapters of the Book of Matthew from *memory*! The missionary said, "You have worked hard to learn God's Word. It is in your heart. You cannot see it and read it, but you know it in your heart. Are you glad?" The leper said, "Yes, God's Word has given me *peace*. God's Word has given me *joy*. God's Word has given me *faith*! Now, if death comes to me, I am not afraid. I belong to Jesus, and I can see Heaven in my mind!"

The Dog Who Ate the Bible

One day, a little boy in Africa came to Dr. Moffat, the great missionary. The little boy had his big dog with him. He was filled with sorrow, because the dog had gotten hold of his Bible, and eaten some of the pages. Dr. Moffat told the little boy that he would get him another Testament. The little boy was not comforted. Sorrowfully, he said, "But think of the dog!" Dr. Moffat laughed and said, "Your dog can crunch and eat an ox bone. He will not be hurt by some paper!" Then, the little African boy cried out, "Oh, Papa Moffat, I am not afraid that the dog will get sick. But I was once a bad boy. I had an enemy and I hated him. I wanted to kill him. Then, I got the Bible in my heart, and I began to love everybody. I forgave my enemies. And now my big hunting dog has got the Book in him, and he will begin to love the lions and tigers. He will let them help themselves to the sheep and oxen!"

Why His Life Was Spared

In Africa, there once lived a tribe of cannibals. These cannibals ate human flesh. One day, a missionary carried God's Word to these cannibals. He told them about the Lord Jesus who saves from sin. As the cannibals heard the Word of God, they accepted Jesus Christ as Saviour, and their hearts and lives were changed. They no longer ate human beings. Soon, they learned to read the Bible for themselves. One day, a white man, a trader from Europe, came into the village. He saw one of the men reading his Bible. He asked what he was reading. "I am reading the Bible," was the reply. "Oh, you don't believe that Book?" asked the trader. "If I didn't believe this Book," said the African, "you would be cooking for my dinner now!"

A Horrible Dream

A young man dreamed that he went to consult his Bible about something. To his amazement, he found every page *blank*! He rushed to his neighbor's house, aroused him from his sleep, and asked to see the Bible. When he looked at that Bible, he found that every page in it was also blank. Together, he and his neighbor sought other Bibles. To their great sorrow, they found every page in them blank also. Then, they went to the library, thinking that from the great books there, they could gather many quotations from the Bible and try to remake the blessed Book. But, when they examined all the books on the shelves of the library, they found that wherever a quotation from the Bible had been, that part of the book was blank. Then the man awoke from his dream. He was wet with cold perspiration, so great had been his agony while he dreamed that the Bible was gone from the earth. Oh, how dark would this world be without the Bible, God's Word!

All in One

A Christian man was packing his suitcase, preparing for a journey. A friend was watching him. Said the Christian, "Well I have a little corner left in the suitcase. In it, I am going to pack a guidebook, a lamp, a mirror, a telescope, a book of poems, some biographies, a bundle of letters, a hymn-book, a sharp sword, a small library of books — *all* in a space of about three by two inches!" "How are you going to do that?" asked the friend. "Very easily," replied the Christian, "for my Bible contains *all* these things!"

The Effect of a Small Portion

An American missionary in Burma traveled far from the coast to an inland village. To his surprise, he heard prayer being made to the *true* and *living* God. The name of Buddha was not mentioned. He knew that no missionary, or white man, had ever visited that village before. He began to ask questions. He found that several years before the head man of that village had gone down to another village some miles away to buy some things. An article of food, which he had bought, had been wrapped up in printed paper. The paper happened to be a chapter from the Word of God. This chapter told about Jesus the Saviour. He read this little portion of God's Word. He believed it. He put sin away. He found the Lord Jesus to be his Saviour. Then he called his friends together and read to them the small portion of Scripture on the paper. They, too, believed the Word. They put away their idols, and trusted in Jesus to save them from sin. For six years, they had all been praying to the Lord Jesus as the Saviour from sin. How happy the missionary was that he had come to this village, and could now give them *more* of God's precious Word!

Mighty in Influence

In Argentina, a woman bought a Spanish Bible. She was much afraid of her husband, because he was an enemy of God, and an unbeliever. Every day, she read the Bible in his absence. One night, she forgot to hide the Bible. When her husband came home, he saw it on the table. Without saying anything, he began to read it. After awhile, he told his wife that it appeared to be a good Book. Every night after that, when he returned home, he went on reading his wife's Bible. Soon, a great change came into the lives of the wife and the husband. One day, the wife suggested that they go together to see her parents to whom they had not spoken for two years. They went and asked forgiveness. Now, both families are reading their Bibles, and following the Lord.

How mighty is the Word of God in its influence.

From the Author

A little girl bought a Bible as a gift for her father on his birthday. She wondered what to write on the flyleaf. "From Maggie" seemed too cold. "From your little daughter" would not do either, for she was getting to be a big girl. "From one who loves you" would not do either, for many others, too, loved him. Finally, she went to her father's library. There she found written on the flyleaf of one of his books, "From the author." These words appealed to her greatly, and she wrote them on the flyleaf of the Bible. When the father opened his gift, and saw the words, *"From the Author,"* written on the flyleaf, he realized that he did not know the Author of the Bible. He began to study his Bible diligently. He was saved and became a preacher.

When we read our Bibles, let us remember always that it is a gift to us from God, "The Author!"

"He Has Spoken"

One day, a missionary in Africa saw an unknown native coming toward her. The native was dressed in skins. He was leading a goat. He carried in one hand a spear. The native tied the goat to a nearby tree. Then he put down his spear and came to the missionary. He asked, "White Lady, has God's Book arrived in our country?" "Do you know about God's Book?" she asked.

Oh, yes," replied the native, "my son brought me pieces of paper. On them are some of God's Words. He has been teaching me some of the words: 'God *so* loved the world, that He gave His only begotten Son, that whosoever believeth in Him should not perish, but have everlasting life.' Lady, I love God's Word. I heard that God's Book has arrived. I have walked for five days. I have brought this goat to buy God's Book!"

The missionary showed the native a copy of the Bible. It was printed in the native's own language. She showed him the place where the words he had quoted were printed. "Give me that Book," he begged, "you may keep the goat!" The missionary gave him the Book. The native pressed the Bible against his heart. He walked back and forth saying over and over again, "God's Book! God's Book! He has spoken to us! Oh, how I love God's Book!"

The Square

A boy went to the barn one day. He took his father's tools and some boards and set to work making a kennel for his dog. He sawed and nailed and in a few hours had the kennel almost completed. Then his older brother came in from the field. He reproved the boy for getting the tools down in the dirt. He said they would be broken and lost. He told the boy he was wasting the lumber and nails, and then he asked what he was trying to make. The boy told him that he was making a kennel for the dog. The older brother said, "That thing will fall down before night." Then he picked up the square from the dust

and placed it on the corners of the kennel. Instantly the boy saw that his work was very imperfect. None of the corners was square. The boy suddenly knew that if he had used the square when he was building the knennel, it would have been straight and true.

Many of us look upon our lives and think we are good. But if we would measure our lives by the Bible, the true square, we would see how crooked our ways are. As we build the house of life day by day, let us measure our lives by the Word of God. Let us build according to the Word of God and then our lives will be true and straight and beautiful.

A Good Test

A Mohammedan trader in India asked a European if he could buy a Bible from him. "Why?" asked the European. "Oh," said the Mohammedan, "I have found out that the people who read the Bible are honest. They can be trusted. When a ship brings a trader who is unknown to me and who wishes to trade with me, I will put the Bible near him and watch him. If he opens it and reads it, then I will know that I can trust him. If he throws it aside with a sneer or a curse, I will know that I cannot trust him and will have nothing to do with him."

Her Life Changed

In Guatemala, there lived a woman named Mercides. She ran a saloon. One day, she was going through a bunch of old papers. She found a page her son had torn out of a Gospel song book some years before. She read it, and liked the words of the hymn. She asked her son about it, and he said,

"Mother, that page is from a Gospel song book. It tells about believers in Jesus." "Are they in Heaven?" she asked. "No, they are right here on earth." "Well," said Mercides, "I will believe in Jesus. I want joy like that. Is there any one in our village who can tell me more about Jesus?" The son told her about a woman in the village who had a Bible.

That very day, Mercides found the woman, and borrowed her Bible. She sat up all night, reading the Bible. She found Jesus, the Saviour, as she read. Then and there, her life was changed. The next day, when customers came to the saloon for drinks, she said, "You can't get any more drink here. The woman who used to sell it is not here. Today, a Jesus-believer lives here!" She poured out the barrels of liquor.

Now, Mercides keeps a little store, where she sells buttons, needles, thread, and dress goods. Every one who comes into her shop receives a tract or a Gospel. Mercides has led many of her friends and neighbors to Jesus, the Saviour. How mighty is the Word of God!

The Highwayman

Once John Wesley was traveling in the country. A highwayman stopped him. He demanded Wesley's money or his life. Wesley gave the man his money. Then he said, "Let me speak one word to you: The time may come when you will be sorry for the life you are living. You may be sorry for your sins. When that time comes, remember God's Word. God's Word says, 'The Blood of Jesus Christ His Son cleanseth us from all sin.'" Years later, John Wesley came out of a church where he had been preaching. A stranger stepped up. He asked Mr. Wesley if he remembered about the time he was robbed on the highway. Mr. Wesley remembered it. "I am the man who robbed you," said the stranger. "The verse you quoted from God's Word that night changed my life completely. I became a Christian. I gave up the sinful way. I have long been attending God's house and studying His Word!"

The Bible says, "For the Word of God is quick, and powerful, and sharper than any two-edged sword" (Heb. 4:12 f. c.); "For I not ashamed of the Gospel of Christ: for it is the power of God unto salvation to every one that believeth" (Rom. 1:16).

"It Kicks Me"

A missionary in India gave a Testament to a Brahman priest, who promised to read it faithfully. The priest read it for a month. Then he came back to the missionary and said, "I wish you to take the Book back. When I read it, it kicks me!" The Bible convicts of sin.

In a Cake Shop

A lady went into a cake shop in Japan to purchase some cakes. While waiting for the cakes, she saw that the walls were papered with leaves from the Bible. This was so strange that she asked the old lady who ran the shop about it. The old lady said that one day when she was passing by a bookshop, she saw a pile of paper which had been discarded. She had taken the paper home and pasted it on her wall, which needed papering.

One evening, the old lady's grandson came in and began reading aloud from the paper on the wall. The old woman became greatly interested. She listened to all that her grandson read. After that, she got all who would, to read from the paper to her.

One day, a young man came in. He asked her if she understood the words on the paper, and whether she was a Christian. She told him how much she enjoyed hearing the words read, but that she did not understand much. The young man took her to church the next day. There, for the first time, she heard the Gospel story. She attended the church regularly, and became an earnest Christian. After that, she kept a stock of tracts in the cake shop, and into *every bag* of little cakes, she placed a Gospel tract!

More Precious Than Gems

A diamond merchant in England was picking some gems to send to a trader in India. He wrapped each diamond with great care. When he came to the last one, which was the largest of all, he wrapped it with some soft paper from the wastebasket in his office. It was paper which had been torn from an old Bible. On the paper were written the first three chapters of John. When the trader in India received the precious gems, he removed the paper from them. As he took the wrapping from the largest diamond, he read these words, "For God so loved the world, that He gave His only begotten Son, that whosoever believeth in Him should not perish, but have everlasting life" *(John 3:16).*

The Indian trader was astonished. He read the words over and over. He asked, "Why did I not know about this before?" God's Word grew in his heart. Finally, the trader said, "Surely, this message is for me. Surely God's salvation is for me!" He believed in God's Word. He told others the Good News of the Gospel.

Some time later, a missionary went to that place in India. He expected to find only heathen. Instead, he found a large gathering of Christian Indians.

Undiscovered Riches

Some years ago, a poor old man, living in New Jersey, discovered about five thousand dollars in an old family Bible in his possession. The bills were scattered throughout the Bible. Many years before, the aunt of this man had died. In her will, she had left to him her family Bible. The will read, "To my beloved nephew, Stephen Marsh, I will and bequeath my family Bible and all it contains!" The nephew took the Bible to his home, and laid it on his table. Days, months, years passed by. Often his eyes rested on the Bible. Sometimes, his hand touched the old Bible, but not once did he open it. Through these years, the nephew lived in poverty. At last, when he was an old man, one day he began to pack his trunk, getting ready to move to his son's home. There he intended to spend his few remaining years. When he picked up the old Bible, he opened it. To his amazement, he saw a twenty dollar bill. He turned a few leaves, and found another bank bill. Then, he looked throughout the Bible, and discovered many bank bills. For thirty-five years, he had lived in poverty while there were great riches within his reach in *the old family Bible.*

Hidden in Her Heart

In Armenia, a whole village of sixty families became Mohammedans. They did so under threats of torture and death. One woman, who was one hundred and ten years old, refused. Holding her Bible close to her heart, she said, "I am too old to deny my Lord!" The fierce Turks snatched the Bible from her. They tore it up and burned it. Calmly, she said, "You can do that, but you cannot tear the promises out of my heart!" Through the years, the woman had loved and read and meditated upon God's Word. Many of the promises of His Word were hidden in her heart. How true it was that no one could snatch those promises out of her heart!

> "Thy Word is like a garden, Lord,
>   With flowers bright and fair;
> And every one who seeks may pluck,
>   A lovely cluster there!
>
> "Thy Word is like a deep, deep mine
>   And jewels rich and rare
> Are hidden in its mighty depths,
>   For every searcher there."

The Proof

An unbeliever once asked an educated and cultured Christian woman how she could prove the Bible is the Word of God. She said to him, "How can you prove there is a sun in the sky?" "Why," he replied, "because it warms me, and I can see its light." "And so it is with me," she said; "I *know* the Bible is the Word of God, because it warms my soul, and gives light to my pathway!"

The Pocket Testament League

Some years ago, a young school girl in Birmingham, England, accepted Christ in a Gospel meeting. The moment she found the Saviour, she had a great longing to win others to Him. Several years later, when she was in high school, she tried to bring her classmates to the Saviour. Some times she would speak to a girl during recess. Then she would run upstairs to get her Bible, but when she would return, the girl would be gone, and the opportunity would be lost. So the girl decided to quote verses from the Bible, but found she would become confused. Finally, she decided to carry a Testament always in her pocket, so she could show the other girls the way of life, right from God's Word, anywhere, anytime. She told a Christian friend about what she was doing, and she, too, began to carry a Testament with her, and another, and another, began to carry Testaments with them. That was the beginning of the Pocket Testament League, a movement which has girdled the world! It began because a young high school girl wanted to be a *ready* and a *faithful* witness for Jesus!

It Will Light Us Home

A minister had to return home late one night from a meeting in a distant backwoods settlement. It was a dark night, and a woodsman provided him with a torch of pitch pine wood. The minister said, "It will soon burn out." The woodsman said, "It will light you home." The minister said, "The wind may blow it out." The woodsman said, "It will light you home." The minister said, "It may rain," and the woodsman again replied, "It will light you home." In spite of the minister's fears, the torch did light him home. The Word of God is the Light unto our pathway which God has given us. It will light us home!

In Love with the Author

Some years ago, a young lady was reading a book. She found it very dull and uninteresting. In disgust, she threw the book on the shelf in the closet. There it lay forgotten for some months. One evening, she met a young man. She liked the young man, and became greatly interested in him. When he told her his complete name, she exclaimed, "Why, I have a book whose author's name and initials are exactly the same as yours!" And she mentioned the title of the book which she had thrown on the closet shelf. The young man said, "Why, I wrote that book. It is mine!" That night, the young lady sat up until the early hours of the morning reading the book. The once dull book was now filled with interest, because she *knew* and *loved* the author.

How often people think the Bible dull and uninteresting, because they do not know its Author. When they know and love God, the Author of the Bible, then the Bible is a living, wonderful Book.

Undiscovered Treasure

In one of the Western states some years ago, men and women were engaged in picking up tiny gold nuggets out of the sand of a small stream. They did not know that, with a little more effort, they could have uncovered a rich vein of the precious metal in a near-by mountain side! How many of us are satisfied to gather a few bits of truth by reading here and there in God's Word, when great treasures could be unearthed by reading God's Word carefully and diligently. We are to *"search* the Scriptures." We are not to read them casually and carelessly. Rich rewards await those who will study God's Word *diligently,* and who will delight in the law of the Lord!

A Wise Choice

An aged gentleman in London invited his servants to come into the house and receive presents from him on his birthday. When the groom appeared, he asked, "Which will you have? This Bible, or a five pound note?" The groom replied, "I cannot read, so I think I will take the money. It will do me more good." He asked the gardener, "Which will you take? This Bible or a five pound note?" The gardener replied, "My wife is ill. So I will take the money, which I badly need." He asked the cook, "Will you take the Bible, or a five pound note?" The cook replied, "I can read, but I never get time to look in a book. So, I will take the money and buy a fine dress." He asked the chambermaid the same question, and she took the money. Finally, the errand boy came. "My lad," he asked, "will you take these five pounds, and buy a new suit to replace your shabby clothes, or will you take this Bible?" The errand boy replied, "My dear mother always told me that the Law of the Lord is *better* than thousands of gold and silver. I will take the good Book, if you please!" The old man beamed! "God bless you, my boy," he said, "and may your wise choice bring riches and honor and long life to you!" The lad received the Bible. As he opened it, a bright gold piece rolled to the floor. Quickly turning its pages, he found them interleaved with many bank notes! He had made a *wise choice*!

A Bible Bookworm

One time, Mr. Spurgeon, the great evangelist, was in Scotland. He came across a very old and much-worn Bible. He held it in his hand reverently. He turned it this way and that. Then, he saw a small hole where a worm had eaten its way from one cover to the other. "Lord, make me a bookworm like that," the preacher exclaimed. "It has gone clear through the Bible from Genesis to Revelation!"

The Mirror

A missionary carried a few mirrors, or looking glasses, to Africa. The natives had never seen their own faces, except in the water of some lake or some stream. Soon news of this wonderful instrument, which showed people their own features, was spread abroad. The missionary was invited to visit tribe after tribe. Away in the interior, there was a princess in one of the tribes who had been told that she was the most beautiful woman in the tribe. When she heard of the wonderful looking glass, she sent for the missionary, telling him to bring one of the mirrors.

The princess was not a beautiful woman. She was the least attractive woman in the tribe. When she got the mirror, she went into her hut alone to take a long look at her "beauty." She held up the glass, and saw how ugly she really was. With great anger, she dashed the looking glass to pieces, banished the missionary, and made a law that no looking glass should ever be brought into the tribe.

Why did the princess hate the looking glass? She hated it, because it told her the truth about herself. That is the reason many people hate the Bible. The Bible tells us the truth about ourselves. It tells us that we are lost sinners. It tells us that we need a Saviour.

The Bible for Everyone

A group of shepherds gathered to hear a missionary read the Bible. It was in the mountains of Asia Minor. It was a chilly night, and the rugged men were seated around a log fire. The minister read from the 10th chapter of John these words, "Verily, verily, I say unto you, I am the Door of the sheep. All that ever came before Me are thieves and robbers: but the sheep did not hear them. . . . I am the good Shepherd: the good Shepherd giveth His life for the sheep. . . . I am the good Shepherd, and *know* My sheep, and am *known* of Mine. . . . And I lay down My life for the sheep" *(John 10:7-15)*. A voice interrupted the minister. "Sir, is that the Gospel?" "Yes," replied the minister, "it is the Gospel of Jesus Christ." The face of the rugged shepherd glowed with pleasure, as he said, "Oh, I didn't know that it was a Sheep Book. I understand that."

"My Words Shall Not Pass Away"

A woman, whose husband was a drunkard, bought a Bible one day. She found comfort in reading it. She soon loved it, and treasured it *above* everything else. One day, her husband came home drunk. He found her reading her Bible. He snatched the Bible from her, and threw it into the stove. "Now we shall see what will be left of your new religion," he said angerily. The next day, he opened the door of the stove. He was about to stir up the cinders when his eye fell upon a page left from the burned Bible. He read these words: "Heaven and earth shall pass away; but My Words shall *not* pass away"! The man stood still. He was filled with sorrow because he had tried to destroy

God's Word. Soon afterward, he was converted.

Good Ground

A man in Kwonghsi, China, was given a Bible. He began to read it. He read it to his whole family. The Word was received in good ground. The family and the man believed the Word of God. They became followers of Jesus. The man wrote a sign and hung it over the door of his house. The sign said, "This household belongs to the living God!" When a missionary came to that village, she was surprised to find this man and his family believing in Jesus, and following Him.

From the Dump

Someone placed Bibles in all the rooms in a hotel in Western Canada. The owner of the hotel was angry. He gathered all the Bibles and threw them out on the dump heap. A poor girl came to the dump, hoping to find something useful. She noticed the Bibles. She picked up one and took it home. She began to read it. She received God's Word into her heart. There, it fell on good ground and began to grow and bear fruit. Soon, the girl found Christ as her Saviour. Her life was changed. She became good and kind and helpful. She began to tell others of her Saviour.

God's Word Protected

When Dr. Judson, the missionary, was in Burma, he translated the New Testament into the language of the Burmese people. He had just finished the work when he was thrown into prison. His wife took the precious pages, and buried them in the ground. But, they could not be left there. They would soon decay, and if any one found them, they would surely be destroyed. What should she do?

Mrs. Judson made a pillow from a roll of cotton. Inside the pillow, she placed the New Testament, written in the language of the Burmese. She carried the pillow to the prison for her husband to sleep on. It was a hard and poor pillow, but for seven months, Dr. Judson slept on it. He knew that within the pillow was God's precious Word. That Word must be protected and kept.

Some time after that, Dr. Judson was hurried off to another prison. His old pillow was thrown into the prison yard to be trodden under foot. The keeper of the prison thought that it was worthless cotton, and a hard pillow. Some native Christians saw the pillow, and rescued it from the prison yard. They took it home, and treasured it, because it was Dr. Judson's pillow. Long afterward, the New Testament manuscript was found within the pillow! It was complete. It was uninjured. God had again worked a miracle to save His Word. In a few years, the Burmese were reading the Bible in their native tongue!

The Best Medicine

A lady one day went to a famous physician about her health. She had a nervous ailment, being easily worried and excited. She told the doctor about her troubles, and asked him what to do. He said, "Madam, go home and read your Bible more!" "But, Doctor," she asked, "don't I need some medicine?" The great doctor said, "Go home, and read your Bible an hour a day. Then come back to me in a month!"

At first, the lady was angry. Then she began to think that it would not cost her anything to do what the doctor ordered. And then she remembered that it had been a long time since she had read her Bible regularly. She was a Christian, but she had allowed worldly cares to crowd out her Bible study and her prayer time. So, she decided to do what the doctor said.

In a month, the lady went back to the doctor's office. When the doctor looked into her face, he said, "I see that you have been an obedient patient. You have obeyed my order faithfully! Do you feel now that you need other medicines?" "No, Doctor," said the lady, "I feel like a different person. I am no longer nervous and easily upset. How did you know just what I needed?" The famous doctor turned to his desk where lay his worn Bible. "Madam," he said, "if I should omit my daily reading of this Book, I would loose my greatest source of strength and skill!"

THE CALL OF GOD

He Answered the Call

A little Scotch boy was lying in the heather beside a mountain stream. He was watching the fleecy clouds in the sky. Soon, he fell asleep, and had a dream. He dreamed that he saw above him a beautiful light. From it came a golden chariot, drawn by horses of fire. Down the sky it came, faster and faster, and then it stopped suddenly at his feet! He saw no one, but he heard a sweet voice saying to him, "Come up hither, I have work for thee to do!" The lad arose to follow the golden chariot. When he stood to his feet, he awoke and knew that it was a dream. The boy never forgot that dream. He never forgot the voice which said, "Come . . . . I have work for thee to do!" One day, he answered the call. In his room, he knelt and prayed, "Oh, Lord, I have no silver and gold to give to the missionary cause. But what I have I give unto Thee. I offer MYSELF to Thee. I want to do Thy work! Wilt Thou accept the gift?" God did accept the gift. Alexander Duff, the Scotch lad, who had heard the voice calling from the golden chariot, became a mighty preacher of the Gospel in the great land of India.

The Call to Preach

When Ralph was just a little boy, he felt God's call to preach. A visitor once asked him, "Ralph, when you grow up to be a man, what are you going to do?" Ralph replied, "I am a preacher now, but I can't preach!"

One day, Ralph was playing "Indian" with his brother Robert. Ralph said, "I want to be an Indian chief." They had fun playing for awhile. Then Ralph came into the house crying. His mother asked, "Ralph, what is the trouble?" Ralph replied, "Robert and I were playing 'Indian,' and I said that I wanted to be an Indian chief. Now, Robert says I can't take it back. He says I must be an Indian chief all of my life, and I want to be a preacher!"

The mother patted Ralph on his head, saying, "Ralph, you were just playing. You don't have to be an Indian chief.

God wants you to be a preacher. So, you can be a preacher if God calls you to be a preacher." Today, Ralph is a preacher of the Gospel!

The Voice of God Is Calling

A missionary, home on furlough from India, was asked, "Do you expect to return to India again?" The missionary replied, "I dislike India with its dirt, and filth, its fevers and dreadful diseases. I dislike the perpetual fight with mosquitoes, the snakes in our bathroom, the scorpions in our shoes. I dislike its poverty and its hardships, its demon-possessed priests, its sin and shame, its anxieties and discouragements. But the Voice of God is calling, day and night, calling me back to India. I can be happy *only* in the *center* of God's will, and His place for me is over in hot, dusty India, telling the simple message of God's love to a multitude of dark-skinned people, whose souls I love with my *whole* being."

A Faithful Messenger

How glad we are that nothing can stop God's true messengers who are called and *sent by Him*! Dr. Hinson of Portland, Oregon, underwent a serious operation. He was warned by the physician that he *must not preach* any more. "Why not?" he asked. "Because your physical condition will not permit it," said the physician. "Do you mean that if I preach I shall die?" "Yes, that is precisely what will happen," said the doctor. "But how long will I live if I stop preaching?" asked Dr. Hinson. "Why, you might live for many years,"

said the doctor. "How long will I live if I preach?" "You will probably die very soon." "Well," said Dr. Hinson, "I will *preach and die!*"

Nothing should stop God's messengers from doing what God has called them to do. Jeremiah, the Prophet, said, "I will not make mention of Him, nor speak any more in His Name. But His Word was in mine heart as a burning fire shut up in my bones, and I was weary with forebearing, and *I could not stay*" (*Jer. 20:9*).

A Heart of Stone

A minister was talking to the boys and girls in a Sunday School. He said: "How sad it is to know that each time you say, 'No' to the Lord Jesus, your heart gets a little harder. If you keep on saying 'No' to Jesus, your heart gets harder and harder. By and by, you will have what God calls, a heart of stone. Then you will die in your sins." The minister told the boys and girls to give their hearts to Jesus while they were young.

One dear little girl, five years old, heard what the minister said. She kept thinking about her father. He never went to church. He never listened to the Word of God. He never read the Word of God. When she got home that day, she ran into her father's arms, and said, "Daddy, Daddy, feel your heart. Is it getting like stone?" The father asked, "What are you talking about?" She said, "The man at Sunday School said 'If you keep saying, "No" to Jesus, your heart will get like stone.' O Daddy, I hope your heart is not like stone. I want you to be saved."

The father was angry. He asked the mother, who had taken the little girl to Sunday School, "What have they been telling this child?" The mother explained to him. She said, "God loves you. God is calling you to come to Him. He wants to save you from your sins. If you keep saying, 'No' to His voice, your heart will get harder and harder, until it is like the hardest stone. Then you will die in your sin."

The father saw tears in the mother's eyes. He felt the arms of his little girl about his neck. He heard her say, "O Daddy, don't keep on saying, 'No' to Jesus!" Then the father said, "I won't keep saying, 'No' to Jesus. I will settle this thing *right now!*" He got down on his knees, and gave his heart and life to the Lord Jesus!

Called to Be a Missionary

Some years ago, a little boy named Tinsley Smith came to his mother, and said, "Mother, I love the Lord Jesus. I want to always follow Him. Jesus wants me to be a missionary to Africa. He wants me to tell the poor people of Africa about Him. Mother, I am going to be a missionary to Africa when I grow up." The mother placed her hand on Tinsley's head and said, "Son, if Jesus wants you to be a missionary for Him in Africa, you must study hard and prepare for the work."

Throughout the years, Tinsley kept his face set toward Africa, the place Jesus wanted him to go. He studied hard in school for many years. Finally, he became a doctor. Then, he told his mother, "Good-by," and he left for Africa. Now, for many years, he has been in Africa. He is a missionary doctor. He helps the poor, sick Africans, and tells them about the Saviour.

The Beckoning Hand

Dr. Thomas Lambie was a missionary with the Sudan Interior Mission. When he returned to America, he was urged by his brother-in-law to remain in America, and share in the brother-in-law's large medical practice, which would soon be turned over to him. Dr. Lambie attended a missionary conference. The meetings were long, and tiring.

One night when Dr. Lambie was very tired, he either dozed off and had a dream, or he had a vision while he was awake. He never knew which. But at that midnight hour, he saw a map of Africa. From the center of the map came a hand and an arm. It was stretched toward him, pleading and beckoning. It was the hideous hand of a leper. Dr. Lambie hesitated. He did not want to grasp that hand, but he could not evade it. And at last he took the hand in his. To his surprise, he found that it was not the hand of a leper, but the hand of Christ, with the print of the nails in the palm!

After that dream or vision, Dr. Lambie knew that he could not remain in America. He must return to Africa and continue to give the Gospel to the lost. He must do the work to which Christ had called him.

CARE OF GOD

Needed: A Cow

Charles Haddon Spurgeon, the great preacher, used to tell an incident about his grandfather. His grandfather had a large family, and a very small income. He loved his Lord, and he would not have given up his preaching of the Gospel for anything. He looked for his reward, not on earth, but in Heaven.

The grandfather had a little farm, and one cow, which furnished milk for his many children. One day, the cow died suddenly. Grandmother said, "James, how will God provide for the dear children now? What shall we do for milk?"

"Mother," replied Grandfather, "God has promised to supply *all* our needs. I believe that God can send us fifty cows if He pleases!"

On that *very day*, a group of Christian men were meeting in London. They were a committee for the distribution of money to poor ministers. Grandfather had never asked that committee for any money. He presented *all* of his petitions to the Lord. After the committee had distributed the money to various needy ministers, there were five pounds left over. They considered what to do with this balance.

"Well," said one, "there is a Mr. Spurgeon down in Essex who is a poor minister. He could use five pounds."

"Oh," said another, "don't send him five pounds. I know him. He is a worthy man. I will add five pounds to the amount!"

"No," said another, "don't send him ten pounds. I will give another five pounds if somebody will put a fourth five pounds with it!" So twenty pounds, about one hundred dollars in our money, were sent to Mr. Spurgeon.

The next morning, a letter came to Grandfather. When he opened it, and saw twenty pounds, he exclaimed, "Now, Mother can't you trust God about an old cow?"

The Old Couple

An old man and his wife lived in a little cottage. Times were hard. They needed money. They borrowed money. They used the little cottage as security for the debt. The time came when they had to pay back the money. But they had no money.

One day, a lawyer came to the cottage to tell the old people that they must move out. The cottage was to be sold to pay the debt. The lawyer entered the little hall. He heard the voice of the old woman say, "Come, Father. I am ready to begin our prayers." Down on his knees went the old white-haired man. He began to pray. He reminded God that they were His children. He told how hard it would be for them to be without a home in their old age. He quoted several promises from the Bible, telling how safe are God's children when they put their *trust* in God. Last of all, he prayed for God's blessings on those who wanted to take their little home away.

The lawyer heard the prayer. He turned away from the door. He left the little cottage quietly. He went to the man who had sent him to tell the old couple to move out. He said, "I couldn't do anything after I heard that prayer. My mother had faith in God. She trusted Him for everything!" "Well," said the man; "my mother trusted God, too. You go in the morning and tell the old man and woman that the cottage is theirs! It will be their home as long as they live!"

Held by God

One day, little Maisie was very tired and fretful. Mother stopped her work. She took Maisie up in her arms, and held her close. In a little while, Maisie was rested.

Mother herself was tired and weary. A great t r o u b l e had come to her. Maisie's father had recently died. Now, Maisie's mother was filled with sorrow. She sighed as she held Maisie in her arms. Little Maisie asked, "Mother, don't you want to be 'holded'?"

Tears came to the eyes of Mother. Little Maisie patted her cheeks, and then she whispered, "Mother, God will hold you, won't He?" Maisie's words brought comfort to Mother's heart. Mother knew God and loved Him. God held her and comforted her heart.

"He Will Keep Me"

One day, little Charles was greatly frightened. A big fierce dog ran into the yard, and started toward the little boy.

Quickly, he turned and ran to his father, crying for help. The father picked Charles up in his arms. Then Charles looked down at the dog and said, "You can't hurt me. My daddy is holding me, and he will keep me!"

The Fawn

A man, who was very fond of hunting, lived in a section of the country where the woods were filled with wild deer. One morning, he was walking across his field. He heard the sound of his hounds in the distance! Looking through the cracks of his high fence, he saw a little fawn running before the hounds. The fawn looked very weary. Its tongue was hanging out. Its sides were covered with foam. The little fawn had just strength enough to leap over the fence. It ran and fell down at the feet of the hunter. Looking up, with its great liquid eyes, in a pleading manner, it seemed to say, "Oh, sir, please help me!"

The hunter came to the rescue of the helpless creature. He stood there and fought away the hounds. He said afterwards, "I felt that all the dogs in the countryside could not capture the little fawn after it, in its weakness, had appealed to me for help!"

If a hunter would come to the deliverance of one of God's little creatures, surely the great God will deliver His children who come to Him for help in time of trouble and danger.

David Brainerd

David Brainerd resolved to carry the Gospel to a savage tribe of Indians in the forest. His friends said they would never see him alive again. He carried with him a little tent under which he slept. After weary days of traveling, he came near an Indian tribe. After a night's sleep, he tarried in the tent for awhile in the morning to pray. He pleaded with God to help him as he gave the Gospel to the savage Indians. He thought that no eye but God's rested on him. But some Indians had watched as he pitched his tent. Then they had hastened and told the Indian chief of the approaching white man. A council was held, and it was decided that the white man must die. Then a group of Indians went back to the little tent, and hid in a sheltered place, waiting for the missionary to come out.

Brainerd continued long in prayer. Finally, the Indians became impatient. Silently, they drew near the tent, and looked in the inside. They saw Brainerd on his knees. Then, they noticed a great rattlesnake push its ugly head under the tent, and crawl toward Brainerd. When the snake reached Brainerd's feet, it reared itself as if to strike its fangs into the back of the missionary's neck. Suddenly, it drew back! Then, it glided out of the tent.

The watching Indians were amazed. Surely, some unseen hand had kept that snake from injuring the white man! They went back to their village and told the chief what had happened. They decided that the white man was under the protection of the Great Spirit, and concluded that they must not harm him, but sue for peace.

Presently, Brainerd finished his prayer. He took his Bible and went toward the Indian village. To his surprise, the *whole* tribe went out to greet him. They treated him with great respect. They listened to his preaching when he told them of Christ. They obeyed his in-

struction to trust in Christ *alone* for salvation. Had he not been sent to them by the Great Spirit?

Delivered from Lions

A little boy in Africa was sent on a lonely path to deliver a message for a missionary. The path went through the jungle where there were many wild beasts. The little boy was frightened, but he said to himself, "Heavenly Father has sent me on this journey! He will care for me!"

Suddenly, as the little boy followed a turn in the path, he saw two huge lions! They were crouching by the side of the path waiting for him! What was he to do? If he ran back, the lions would come running after him. If he went forward, they would spring on him. What did he do? He knelt in the path right where he was, and prayed to God. He asked God to take care of him. Then he said, "I must forget my doubts, and deliver this letter to the missionary!" He got up and walked straight down the path past the lions. The lions never made one attempt to harm him.

The God who delivered Daniel from the lions delivered the little black boy from the lions. Won't you trust such a wonderful God to keep you day by day?

Not Alone

In the course of his work, a pioneer preacher incurred the ill will of a leader of a gang of horse thieves and bandits. The leader made a boast that he would surely "get the preacher."

One afternoon, a man in the lumber camp was hurt by a falling tree. The preacher was sent for. To reach the lumber camp, he had to pass through some rough "cut" land. It was evening as he entered it, and all at once he was overcome with fear. He got off his horse, and prayed to God for deliverance, asking for His care. He got back on his horse, and went on his errand, unmolested and unharmed.

The next day, the leader of the bandits was shot. He called for the preacher to come to his deathbed. The leader confessed that on the previous night he had lain in wait for the preacher in the bad land, intending to kill him. Then, the leader asked, "Who were those men who rode with you?" The preacher said, "I was alone." The leader of the bandits screamed, "You were not! There were two men with you, one on either side, and I never in my life saw such horses as they rode on! *Who were they?*"

The Bible says, "The angel of the Lord encampeth round about them that fear Him, and delivereth them."

Blessing from a Bomb

A farmer in England sent some money during the war to the Scripture Gift Mission. He asked the members of the mission to pray for the safety of his place from the German bombs, and for water to help his crops. The Mission prayed, asking God to watch over the farmer, and to do His will in the matter.

Not long afterwards, during an air raid, a bomb crashed down on the farmer's place. It broke every window in his house, but it did not hurt man or beast. It went so deeply into the ground that it set free a new spring of water. There was so much water the farmer had enough for his own farm, and was able to help water the farms of his neighbors.

After the next harvest, which was very bountiful, the farmer sent two hundred dollars as a thank offering to the Scripture Gift Mission.

How wonderfully does God care for His children when they place themselves in His keeping!

Room for All

When Gypsy Smith was a little boy, he was left alone with his younger sister for six weeks while his daddy was away. When Daddy returned, he took the little sister on his knee, and smothered her with kisses. Gypsy Smith waited his turn. In a gypsy family, the youngest always receives the first kisses. Then, the father turned and held out his arms for the boy. Gypsy Smith ran into his father's arms. He cried to his little sister, "You get me out of my father's arms if you can!" Then the father said, "There is room for both of you in Daddy's arms," and he held them both securely in his arms! All of God's children may find shelter in God's arms.

"Said the Robin"

"Said the Robin to the Sparrow,
 'I should really like to know
Why these anxious human beings
Rush about and worry so?'

"Said the Sparrow to the Robin,
 'Friend, I think that it must be
That they have no heavenly Father
Such as cares for you and me.'"
—Selected

God's Watchmen

When missionary Von Asselt, a Rhenish missionary, first went to Sumatra in 1826 he found the natives near the coast savage and cruel. Twenty years before, two missionaries who had come to them with the gospel had been killed and eaten. Missionary Von Asselt and his wife were very lonely at first. They could not understand the language of the natives, but they did understand their hostile looks and gestures. They felt that they were surrounded by the power of darkness. Often in the night they had to get up and read the Word of God and pray to find relief from their fears. After two years they moved several hours journey inland to a tribe which was somewhat civilized and more friendly. There they built a little house and life became a little more easy and cheerful. They had been in the new place a few months when a man from the hostile district came to talk to them. After he had chatted for a while with the missionaries, the man asked, "Teacher, I have a request. I want to have a look at your watchmen close at hand."

"What watchmen do you mean? I do not have any," said the missionary.

"I mean the watchmen whom you put around your house at night to protect you."

"But, I have no watchmen," the missionary said again. "I only have a boy and a cook who help me. They would make poor watchmen."

The man from the hostile tribe looked at the missionary unbelievingly. He said, "Do not try to make me believe otherwise, for I know better. May I look through your house to see if they are hidden there?"

"Certainly," said the missionary. "Look through it, but you will not find any watchmen."

So the man went in and searched every corner of the little house. Then he came out, very much disappointed.

"Now," said the missionary, "I have a request. I want you to tell me about the watchmen around my house."

Then the native from the hostile tribe told this story. "When you first came to us, we were very angry with you. We did not want you to live among us. We did not trust you. We decided to kill you and your wife. Night after night we went to your house to kill you, but when we came near the house there always stood close around it a double row of watchmen with shining weapons. We did not dare to attack them to get into your house. We were not willing to give up our plan to kill you. So, we hired an assassin to do it for us. He laughed at us and said 'I fear no God or devil. I will get through those watchmen easily.' So one evening he marched ahead of us, swinging his weapon over his head. When we neared your house, we let him go on alone while we remained behind. Soon he came running back and said, 'I dare not risk going through alone. There are two rows of big strong men standing close together and their weapons shine like fire.' Then we gave up the plan to kill you. Tell me, where are these watchmen?"

The missionary told the native that neither he nor his wife had ever seen the watchmen. Then he got his Bible. Holding it open before the native, he said, "This book is the Word of our great God. In this book He promises to guard and defend us. We believe this Book. We do not have to see the watchmen which God places around us. We know He is protecting us. But God has shown you the watchmen in order that you may learn to believe that He is the great and true God Who watches over and protects His children."

Delivered from a Flood

A few years ago, there was a flood in the State of Colorado. A railroad coach turned over in the flood. A mother and her little girl were among those trapped in the coach. They could not get out. The water began to rise in the coach. Soon, it came up to the mother's arms. She was holding her little girl in her arms. The little girl was frightened. She said, "Mother, what shall we do?" Mother said, "Pray, dear." The mother cried unto God in her heart. The little girl prayed out loud, "Jesus, I trust you. Jesus, I trust you." She said this many times. From that moment, the waters began to go down! They went lower and lower. The lives of the people in the coach were saved!

God Never Fails

Locusts came to a Chinese village. The locusts began to eat all of the rice in the fields. They began to eat all of the leaves off the trees. The people in the village placed little flags around their fields. They prayed and asked their locust-god to destroy the locusts. But nothing happened.

In the village was one Christian. He refused to pray to the locust-god. He said, "The locust-god cannot hear prayer. He will not answer prayer. But my God can hear. I am going to ask Him to save my field." The Christian began to pray earnestly. He asked the Lord to save his field from the locusts. And the Lord heard and answered his prayers. The Lord delivered him in the time of trouble. The locusts destroyed every green thing around the little village. They never touched the field of the Chinese Christian!

The Proper Remedy

A missionary, living in China among a heathen people, found herself without money and without food. In her distress, she claimed the promise of God that He would supply her *needs*. She was also in poor health. A few hours later a gift from a business man in another part of China arrived. He had sent her several large boxes of Scotch oatmeal. She had a few cans of condensed milk on hand. No other supplies came. So, for four long weeks, she lived on oatmeal and condensed milk. As the days passed by, she found that she was feeling better. By the end of the four weeks, she was in excellent health.

Some time later, the missionary told of her experience to a company of people. A physician was present and heard her story. He asked her about the nature of her former illness. She explained her case to him. Then the physician said, "The Lord supplied your need more truly than you realize. For the sickness from which you were suffering, we physicians prescribe a four-weeks' diet of nothing but oatmeal gruel for our patients! The Lord knew your needs. He prescribed for you, and saw to it that you took the proper remedy!"

The Great Provider

A little boy was bringing home a loaf of bread. A man asked, "What have you there?"

"A loaf of bread."

"Where did you get it?"

"From the baker," the boy replied.

"Where did the baker get it?"

"He made it from flour."

"Where did the flour come from?"

"The flour came from wheat which the farmer grew."

"Who made the wheat to grow?"

"God!"

"Well, then, from whom did you get that loaf of bread?"

"Oh," said the little boy, *"I got it from God!"*

Our Helper

A theological seminary was in great need of money. Three of its managers met to talk over the situation. One asked, "Is there no one to help us?" The second replied, "No one." The third was a man of great faith in God. He had been in earnest prayer before the meeting. He said, "Gentlemen, you have said you can do nothing. I know I can do nothing. So, we are just three ciphers. But the Lord Jesus is certainly *one*. Now, if we will put Him before the three ciphers, we become a thousand, do we not? I propose that we put the Lord Jesus *first*. Let us get down on our knees and ask Him to show the way."

The suggestion was followed. New courage came to the hearts of the three men. Help came from God for the Bible school, and the difficulty was met!

God Was Their Keeper

When America was young, our brave, God-fearing ancestors had to battle with cold, hunger, wild beasts, and unfriendly Indians. At the edge of a little settlement stood a cabin where an aged Quaker and his wife lived. The whole settlement was disturbed, because the Indians were on the "warpath." One night, the Quaker and his wife read the 91st Psalm, which tells of God's care. After they read the Psalm, they prayed, and went to bed. The Quaker asked, "Mother, did you leave the latchstring on the *inside* tonight?" "Yes, Father, I did," she replied. "Well, Mother, I think we should leave the latchstring on the *outside!* We are not to be 'afraid for the terror by night; nor for the arrow that flieth by day.'" The aged Quaker got out of bed and put the latchstring on the *outside* of the door, saying, "Mother, God will take care of thee and me!"

Toward midnight, the door opened. An Indian chief, with his braves, entered. They whispered for a few minutes. Then, they quietly went out and closed the door. The next morning, the Quaker and his wife found the little village in *ruin*. Theirs was the *only cabin* left standing!

When the Indian chief and the braves had come to their cabin, and had found the latchstring dangling on the outside, they decided that the people in that cabin had *trust* and *friendship*. The aged couple said, "It was God who delivered His weak and helpless children!"

Held by God

Two brothers were discussing the safety of God's children. One said, "I tell you a child of God is safe as long as he stays in the lifeboat, but if he jumps out, he is lost."

The other replied, "You remind me of something that happened in my own life. I took my little son with me in a boat. He was so small that he did not know the danger if he would fall, or jump, into the water. So, I sat with him all the time. I held him fast, so he could neither fall out or jump out of the boat."

"But," said the other brother, "suppose he had wriggled out of his coat, and got away in spite of you?"

"Oh," said the other, "you misunderstand me if you suppose that I was just holding his coat. *I was holding him in my arms!"*

How glad we are that God, our Father, is holding and supporting us with His strong arm and hand. He has said, "I will strengthen thee; yea, I will help thee; yea, I will *uphold* thee with the right hand of My righteousness" (*Is. 41:10*).

Helpless Sparrows

A sparrow once built its nest in a freight car, while the car was in the shop for repair. When the car was in order, it was started again into service. Inside was a nest full of young sparrows. The trainmen noticed the nest with the baby sparrows, and the mother sparrow hovering in a frightened manner nearby. The trainmen notified the division superintendent. He ordered the car out of commission until the little birds were large enough to go out into the world and care for themselves. If a great railroad system can be ordered to protect helpless sparrows, is it hard for us to believe that the great Superintendent of the universe can and does order things for the good of His children?

Saved by Bad News

A missionary left his wife and child on a mission boat. He was going to a far-away village to preach the Gospel. He had not gone far when a messenger ran after him. He told the missionary that his baby was ill, that he must return to the boat quickly. Some savages were waiting in the bushes to murder the missionary. When the messenger arrived, he was almost to the bushes where the savages were hiding. God delivered the missionary from death.

Asleep During the Storm

A wild storm was raging around a prairie home. The mother, grandmother, and three children sat in a dark room. They were fearful that at any moment the home would be swept away. Little Walter whispered with his grandmother a few moments and then he disappeared. The mother hunted for him in the darkness, and found him in his room fast asleep. The next morning she asked him how he could go to sleep when they were all in such great danger. He replied, "Why, Grandma told me God would take care of us, and I thought I might as well go to bed again!"

He Could Not Sink

A visitor, walking on the shore of the Dead Sea, lost his balance and fell into the water. He could not swim. Greatly afraid lest he sink and drown, he flung his arms about. At last, he was exhausted and could do no more. Then he found, to his surprise, that the water *bore him up! He could not sink!* The water of the Dead Sea is so heavy with salt that, when he lay still, he floated to the surface. He could not sink!

There is a Power beneath us and around us waiting to bear us up. If we will cease from *all* our strivings, flounderings, and *useless* efforts, then the power of God will bear us up.

A Fact

A minister once paid a visit to an old Scotch lady. He wanted to give her a Bible verse to help and comfort her. Before he left, he said, "My friend, what a beautiful promise is this: 'My God shall supply *all* your *need.*'" The old Scotch lady replied, "Hoot man, that's not a promise; that's a *fact*. Each day, He supplies my need."

"Fear Ye Not"

One winter day, a minister was sitting on the veranda of a Southern hotel, enjoying the sunshine. Suddenly there came a dull thud, as of something falling. Before his eyes, not ten feet away, he saw the body of a little sparrow crumple as it hit the floor. The sparrow turned upon its back, with its little claws stretched toward the sky. A shiver passed through the body, and then the tiny eyelids closed. The sparrow gave a quick, short gasp, and all was over! A spot of crimson on the breast gave the story of the tragedy. His swift flight through the air had brought him into collision with some pole, or other object, and his life had been the price!

The death of this tiny sparrow was not noticed by any one but the minister. But, like a flash, there came to his mind, the words of Jesus: "Are not two sparrows sold for a farthing? and one of them shall not fall on the ground without your Father"; "Fear ye not therefore, ye are of more value than many sparrows" *(Matt. 10:29, 31)*.

Heaven's Riches at Our Disposal

One day, there came to Dr. Chapman's study a millionaire, who said, "I know that you need some money. I will not tell you how I know it, and I will not inquire the amount. But I ask if it would be a comfort to you to know that my fortune is behind you." Before Dr. Chapman could answer, his visitor drew from his pocket a checkbook. Handing it to Dr. Chapman, he said, "The checks are all signed with my name. You may fill them in for whatever amount you need!"

Orphans Fed by God

One morning, George Mueller sat down at the breakfast table with several hundred orphan children. As he bowed his head to give thanks for the food, a little boy asked, "But, Mr. Mueller, where is the food?" Mr. Mueller replied, "My son, we have placed ourselves in God's care. God will order and pay for what we need!" They all bowed their heads while thanks were given to God.

When the prayer was finished, there was a knock at the door. A baker brought in enough bread for breakfast. When the bread was placed on the tables, there was another knock at the door and the milkman brought in enough milk for every child! That is how God fed some of His little ones!

CHILDREN, FAMOUS

Sold for a Roll of Tobacco

A group of slaves were sold by auction in the market place in Nigeria, Africa. One poor little boy was placed on the auction block who had such a miserable appearance that the slave buyers laughed. They did not even want to bid for him. Finally, he was bought for a roll of tobacco. The little boy was forced to walk to the coast with a gang of other slaves. He was put on a ship bound for America. But the ship was captured by the British. They took the slaves to Freetown, and set them at liberty. The little boy was put in charge of some missionaries. Many years later, he was consecrated as the first bishop of Nigeria. The ceremony took place in St. Paul's Cathedral, London, in the presence of church officials, statesmen, and noblemen! He did wonderful work for God in Nigeria. His name was Bishop Samuel Crowther!

A Little Factory Girl

Mary went to work in a factory when she was eleven years old. She had to help supply the needs of her younger brothers and sisters, because her father was a drunkard. She was not tall, or strong. She was not well educated. How could such a sorrowful little girl ever grow up to be a useful and blessed woman? But a poor old woman warned Mary to escape the fire that shall never be quenched. Mary gave heed, and came to the children's Saviour. That little girl was MARY SLESSOR, who brought such great blessing in Calabar, West Africa!

A Shilling a Week

When William was five years old, he stood barefooted and cold and hungry in a street in Glasgow. He wondered why no one gave him food when he had had nothing to eat for a day and a half. When William was six and one-half years old, he went to work in a factory, putting heads on pins for twelve hours a day. He earned a shilling a week. When William was seventeen, he heard the Gospel for the first time. He believed it and received the Saviour. William is now in heaven, but he left behind him his "monument." It is the

Orphan Homes of Scotland which he founded. For William was none other than William Quarrier!

A Sickly Boy

Little Hudson Taylor had a good home. He had a Christian father and mother. He had plenty of books, and food, and clothing. He had careful training and much love. But he lacked one earthly blessing — good health. He was always ailing. Often he failed to go to school, because of sickness. When he was eleven, he dropped out of school. When he was fifteen, he became a bank clerk. He had to quit that job, because of inflamation of his eyes. Then Hudson was converted. He loved Christ, but how could such a frail fellow be of much use in His service? When he was twenty-one, Hudson sailed for China on a cargo boat. He went out as a missionary to carry God's message of salvation to the millions in that vast land. Before he died of old age, God had used him to found the China Inland Mission

A Dull Year

It had been a dull year in the little church. The deacons finally said to the old pastor, "We love you, but don't you think you had better resign? There hasn't been a convert this year." Sadly, the pastor answered, "It has been a dull year. Yet, one did come. That was wee Bobby Moffat. But he is so small I suppose it is not right to count him."

A few years later Bobby Moffat asked the pastor, "Do you think I could ever learn to preach? I feel within me that I ought to. If I could just lead souls to Christ, I would be so happy!" The pastor answered, "Well, Bobby, you might preach. Who knows? At least, you can try." Bobby did try, and years later, when Robert Moffat came back from his wonderful missionary work in Africa, the King of England rose and Parliament stood as a mark of respect!

The Most Unpromising Boy

Some years ago, in a manufacturing town of Scotland, a young lady asked for a Sunday school class. She was given a class of boys. The boys were very poor. The superintendent offered to give each one of them a new suit of clothes to wear to Sunday school. The worst and most unpromising boy in the class was a lad named Bob. Two or three Sundays after he received his new suit of clothes, he was missing. The teacher hunted him up. She found that his new clothes were torn and dirty. She invited him to come back to Sunday school, and he came. The superintendent gave him a second suit. After attending a few more times, Bob again was absent. Once more. the teacher sought him out, only to find that the second suit was ruined.

"I am utterly discouraged about Bob," said the teacher, when she reported the case to the superintendent. "I guess I must give him up!"

"Please don't do that," the superintendent answered; "I hope there is something good in Bob. Try him one more time. I will give him a third suit if he will promise to attend regularly!"

Bob did promise. He received his third new suit. He attended Sunday school regularly after that. He came to Jesus, the Saviour. He joined the church. He was made a teacher. He studied for the ministry. That forlorn, ragged, runaway Bob became REV. ROBERT MORRISON, the great missionary to China who translated the Bible into the Chinese language!

CHOICE

Which Way Will You Go?

Two trains used to leave the La Salle station in Chicago at the same time. For seven miles they ran side by side. Then their tracks turned and went in opposite directions. One train went west and made its way to the Pacific coast. The other went east and went to New York City. The trains ran side by side at first, but ended their run with a continent separating them.

Two boys began life side by side. They lived next door to each other. They played together. They went to school together. They joined the same Scout troop. After a few years, one became a Christian. The other did not. One followed the pathway of the righteous, leading to Heaven. The other followed the pathway of sin and destruction. One will land in Heaven, by the grace of God. The other will land in Hell.

How careful we should be to choose the Right Way. Let us today choose Jesus, the Way to Heaven.

The End of the Way

A man was visiting a friend in the country. One morning he started for a walk, taking his host's little boy with him. The man saw an inviting path which led through the pastures. The path was fringed with clover and buttercups. He started to go along the path but the little boy held back. "Why don't you want to come along this path" the man asked. "That path was made by the pigs," the boy replied, "before you get very far you'll get into the awfullest patch of mud and weeds that you ever saw."

When we are choosing the path of our life we must find out what the end of the path will be. The beginning may be pleasant, but what about the end?

A Disastrous Choice

When Aaron Burr was about nineteen years old, he felt that he must make a choice between God and the world. He was deeply troubled about his decision. He went into the country for a week where he could be alone to consider the matter. At the end of that time, he made his choice. He chose the world and not God! From that time, Aaron Burr threw himself recklessly into sin, sinking lower and lower. How different his life's story would have been if he had chosen God!

The Wrong Choice

In a prison in the United States of America, there was a man serving a sentence for crime. This man had a good mother who not only prayed for him, but who did everything she could to get him to choose Christ. Many of his friends, including ministers of the Gospel, likewise pled with him to turn from his evil, downward way to Christ and the Heavenly way. The man's heart was hardened against all the pleadings of others.

At last, his mother went to the governor of the state, asking him to pardon her son. The governor, a Christian, went to the man's cell. He spent a long time with him, pleading with him to turn from his evil way, accept Christ as his Saviour, and begin a new life. Not knowing that he was talking with the governor of the state, the man did as he had done before. He turned a deaf ear to all the pleadings.

Later, the warden asked the man if he knew whom he had been talking to. He said, "No." When he was told that he had been talking to the governor, he said, "Oh, he wanted to help me, but I would not let him!"

Boys and girls, God loves you. He wants to help you. Will you choose to let Him, or will you refuse to heed His voice?

The Two Choices

Every day, two little girls played together. They went to the same school. They had the same friends, and the same teachers. One of them chose to trust in the Lord Jesus as her Saviour. She chose to follow God. The other little girl would not accept Jesus as her Saviour. She chose not to follow God.

As the years passed, the girls' lives grew farther and farther apart. One girl followed the Lord. She loved the Bible. She loved the church. She had Christian friends. The other girl followed the world. She loved the things of the world. She had ungodly friends. When death came, the Christian lady went to Heaven, to be with Jesus. But the wicked, sinful woman passed out into eternity, unsaved, *lost*, without hope, and without God, and went to hell.

He Chose the Way of Sin

One day, a minister preached in a penitentiary. He saw a familiar face in the audience. At the close of the sermon, he went to the convict. The prisoner said, "I remember you very well. We were boys in the same neighborhood. We went to the same school. We sat beside each other in the same room. My prospects were as bright as yours. But at the age of fourteen, you made the choice to become a Christian, and enter God's service. I refused to come to Christ. I made the choice to go into the ways of sin. Now you are a happy and honored minister of the Gospel. I am a *wretched outcast*! I have served ten years in this penitentiary, and am to be a prisoner here for *life*!"

May *you* say,

> "I have made my choice forever,
> I will walk with Christ, my Lord,
> Nought from Him my soul shall sever,
> While I'm trusting in His Word."

Hide-and-go-seek

One day, a little girl was playing with some friends. They were playing, "Hide-and-go-seek." One of the little girls would hide, and the other little girls would seek her. How carefully they searched for her. They looked behind the doors, under the table, in the corners, up the stairs, and down the stairs.

God wants us to seek Him. He wants us to seek Him diligently. He has promised that when we seek Him, we will find Him. How easy it is for us to find the Lord. While we are seeking Him, He is seeking us. It does not take long for a seeking Lord and a seeking sinner to meet.

The Bible says, "Seek ye the Lord while He may be found, call ye upon Him while He is near" *(Is. 55:6)*; "Seek ye the Lord, and His strength: seek His face evermore" *(Ps. 105:4)*; "But if from thence thou shalt seek the Lord thy God, thou shalt find Him, if thou seek Him with *all* thy heart, and with *all* thy soul" *(Deut. 4:29)*.

Seeking Lost Treasures

Some little boys, playing near a river bank, found a treasure. They dug up a pot containing three hundred dollars in silver coins! The coins were very old. Some of them had come from other countries. The pot of coins was found near an historic building. The building had stood there on the river bank for many years. When men heard what the little boys had found, they rushed to the river bank, and began to dig. They were hunting for more lost treasure. Although many men searched for many days, only thirty-five dollars in coins were found.

Men seek diligently for treasures hidden in the ground. They should seek *more* diligently for God. If they will seek God with the whole heart, they will surely find Him.

Thirsting for God

One day, some dogs chased a little deer. For hours the little creature ran this way and that way, trying to escape from the dogs. Finally, the dogs became discouraged and went away. Then, the little deer stood still, trembling! He was tired, and, oh, so thirsty! How he longed for some of the water from the little brook. Timidly, he made his way to the brook. There, he drank his fill of the cool water.

Long ago, David wrote, "As the hart [deer] panteth after the water brooks, so panteth my soul after Thee, O God. My soul thirsteth for God, for the living God" *(Ps. 42:1, 2 f. c.)*. David loved God. David longed for God. He thirsted for God. Do *you* long for God? Do you thirst after God? Jesus said, "Blessed are they which do hunger and *thirst* after righteousness!"

He Found the Way

Once there came to a missionary in Arabia a true son of the desert. He was wild and unkempt. His brain was dulled by drugs and drink. Yet he was a seeker after God. He said to the missionary, "There is only *one God*. There is only *one* way. I *must* find the *one* way. For years, I have been seeking that way. I have asked my Moslem teachers to help me. I have asked others to help me. But no one has. Will you help me to find the *one way*?"

Day after day, the missionary told the young Mohammedan of Christ, the Way. But the man's mind was dark and unbelieving. Then, one day, the light broke! He joyfully said, "I *do* believe in the Son of God. He is the Way! I have sought Him with my *whole* heart, and I have found Him!"

Finding Important

A Christian once said to an elderly woman, "Now, you have promised to seek the Lord. Only remember, the seeking will not save you. But if you seek, you will *surely* find, and the finding will save you!" It is the finding of Christ, the Saviour, that saves us.

CHRISTIAN LIVING

Like Christ

One time, Dr. Samuel W. Zwemer spoke very simply about the Lord Jesus Christ to the people in the waiting room of a mission hospital in Arabia. A Bedouin, who had come five hundred miles to be treated by him, said, "I understand all you have told us. I have seen that sort of man myself!" Then he told this story: "He was a strange man. He looked after the sick, the prisoners, and those in trouble. He treated the Negro slave boys kindly. When people hurt him, he did not hurt them back. He took long trips in the broiling sun to help people. He was just what you said!"

Dr. Zwemer had been telling about the great love of Christ, how He lived for others and helped them, and how He finally died upon the Cross. The Bedouin had seen Dr. Zwemer's brother,

Peter Zwemer, who had opened Christion work at Muscat many years before, and had not lived many years to see the results of his work. Peter Zwemer had lived and loved like Christ, His Saviour!

"I Have Watched You"

Two rival merchants attended a revival meeting being held in their city. These men knew the troubles and testings which daily arise in business life. After some nights, one of them went forward to confess his faith in Christ, the Saviour. The other was under conviction, but unyielding. When he saw his business competitor go forward, he said to himself, "I will watch him. If he believes what he says and really lives it one year, then I will know that there is really something in this Gospel, and I will become a Christian myself."

For one year, the merchant watched the other man. He saw a complete change in his business life, his social life, and his everyday life. At the end of the year, the watcher sought and found God, and the forgiveness of his sin through Christ. He then went to the merchant, whose life he had watched so closely, and said, "For one whole year, I have watched you. Your life convinced me that there is something real in your Christian faith!"

"We Knew Him Well"

A missionary, arriving in a strange land, began at once to tell the people of Jesus. He told them of the love, compassion, tenderness, and healing *power of Christ.* As he spoke, he was pleased to see how interested his listeners were. He noticed the nods and smiles of his audience, as he told how Jesus went about doing good. Finally, he stopped, and asked how many of them had ever heard of this Man before. It seemed they all knew Him. He questioned further, and found that they were thinking of a Christian doctor who had lived for a few years among them, and had ministered to their needs. "Yes," they said, "we knew him well!" Oh, that we may live such Christlike lives that others will see Jesus in us!

Remember to Whom You Belong

One day, two little boys started to go to a birthday party. The mother called the little boys to her and said, "Now, boys, remember to whom you belong!" The little boys went to the party. They knew what their mother wanted them to do. They were kind and gentle and polite. They did nothing that would bring shame to their father and mother.

We belong to Jesus. We have His Name upon us. We are called Chris-

tians. We must always remember to whom we belong. We must never do anything that will bring shame to Christ. We must live in such a way as to bring honor to Him. Let us remember the words of Jesus, "Let your light so shine before men, that they may see your good works, and glorify your Father which is in Heaven" *(Matt. 5:16).*

Little Mary

Once there lived a little girl named Mary. She was a Christian. She was always gentle and kind and good. Mary became sick and went home to be with Jesus. On her tombstone, they wrote the words, "It was easy to be good when Mary was with us!" Is it easy for others to be good when you are with them?

"Press Those Questions"

Dr. J. M. Buckley conducted a meeting one day at a Negro church in the South. A woman rose to tell her experience. She told of the preciousness of her religion, and how it brought light and comfort to her. "That's good, sister," commented Dr. Buckley, "but how about the *practical* side? Does your religion, your experience, make you a better wife? Do you prepare *better* meals for your husband? Are you kind and gentle in the *home?*" Just then, Dr. Buckley heard the Negro preacher whisper ardently into his ear, "Press those questions, Doctor, press those questions! That's *my wife!*"

Why Their Attitude Changed

Two missionary brothers, who had spent some years on the mission field in French Equatorial Africa, were sailing for the United States. Aboard the same ship there were many soldiers and a number of prisoners of war. Each morning, Gospel services were held on the deck for the benefit of the soldiers. Some were saved. They requested that one of the missionaries help them in the further study of God's Word.

At the end of the voyage, the soldiers told the missionaries how they had disliked them at first, but, as they watched and saw the way they *lived*, they came to love the missionaries, and longed to know Christ. How important it is for God's children to live Christian lives before others.

Like Jesus

A young Buddhist studied the life of Christ. He said, "Your Christ is wonderful, so wonderful! But you Christians are not like Him." God wants us to be like Jesus. He wants our lives to be filled with love and kindness. Can others see Jesus in you?

A Christian Chinaman

A Chinaman applied for the position of cook in an American family. The family belonged to a fashionable church. The lady asked the Chinaman, "Do you drink whisky?" "No, I Clistian man!" "Do you play cards and gamble?" "No, I Clistian man!"

The Chinaman was hired. He was found to be honest and dependable. A few weeks later, the lady gave a party. During the party, the ladies played cards for prizes, and wine flowed in abundance. The new cook did his part acceptably. But the next morning, he appeared before his employer. He said, "I quit now." "Why, what is the matter?" "I Clistian man. I told you so

before. I no work for heathen American!"

The Beautiful Life

A Japanese came to a preacher's study in Boston and said, "Sir, I am in search of the beautiful life. Can you tell me where it is found?" Said the minister, "I see you want to talk about religion." "Oh, no," said the Japanese. "I don't want to talk about that. My country is *full* of religion. I want something else. You see, at the boarding house where I live in Cambridge, there lives also a carpenter. To me his life is beautiful. He never thinks of himself. He is always thinking of others. When we pass the dishes at the table, he will not take anything until all the rest have been helped. He never thinks of himself for a second. To me, his life is beautiful!"

The minister handed the Japanese a New Testament and said, "Take this and read it. If you find the Life which this Book tells about, then you will know the life beautiful!" Two years later, the Japanese returned to the minister. He said, "I have read the Book. I have found the beautiful life. I have found Christ, the Saviour!"

Serving Jesus Every Day

Last June Alice graduated from high school. Throughout her high school days, she had tried to live for the Lord Jesus, and honor Him. She had spoken to her schoolmates and teachers for Him. She had bravely *refused* to take part in the worldly amusements in the high school. She had spoken of her faith in the Bible, when the Bible was ridiculed in her science classes. When Alice graduated, God brought her into honor. She was chosen as one of the "Ten Star Seniors" by the teachers of her high school. She was the *one* senior, out of a class of 375, who received the citizenship award, a gold wrist watch, given because of her loyalty, friendship, courtesy, scholarship, dependability, *etc*. Alice said to her mother, "I never dreamed I would receive any award. I didn't work for awards. I just tried to serve Jesus the *best* I could every day!"

A Translator

A friend said to a young man, "I hear you are connected with a Bible society." "Oh," said George, "I am a translator!" "What?" asked the friend. "Are you a translator?" "Yes," said George, "I am busy translating the New Testament into my *daily life!*" Boys and girls, we hope that you will daily seek to live beautiful, clean, holy lives that will show forth Jesus to those around you. The Bible says, "Be ye holy; for I am holy" *(I Peter 1:16 l. c.)*; "Follow peace with *all* men, and holiness, without which no man shall see the Lord" *(Heb. 12:14)*.

Playing Like a Christian

A little boy and girl often played together. They both learned to love Jesus, the Saviour. One day the little boy said to his mother, "Mother, I know that Emma is a Christian." "What makes you think so?" asked the mother. "Because she plays like a Christian," said the boy. "Plays like a Christian," said the mother; "why what do you mean?" "You see," said the little boy; "Emma used to be selfish and get angry at every little thing. Now, Emma is not selfish. And she does not get angry, even if you take everything she has!"

An Out-and-out Christian

Gypsy Smith once asked a man, "Are you a Christian?" "Yes," answered the man. "How long have you been a Christian?" "Twenty-eight years, off and on," replied the man. "More *off* than *on*," replied Gypsy Smith. Then, Smith added, "I would rather be an out-and-out Christian, one always living for the Lord, than an off-and-on Christian!"

A Stumbling Block

A blind man went about carrying a lantern on his arm. Someone asked him why he carried a lantern when he could not see. He replied, "To keep others from stumbling over me!" How careful we should be to keep our lives pure and clean and shining for Jesus, so others will not stumble into hell because of us! The Psalmist said: "Blessed is the man that . . . nor standeth in the way of sinners" *(Ps. 1:1)*.

Easier to Live With

Two sisters were separated for a time, living in different cities. While away from home, one of them became a Christian. They came home on a visit. After a few days, the other girl said to the Christian, "I don't know what has happened, but you are a great deal easier to live with than you used to be." That is the way it should be with *every* Christian.

Acting Like Christians

Two little boys lived next door to each other. One day they were playing together. The little boys were from Christian homes. While they played, they began to quarrel. The quarrel was long.

The quarrel was hot. Suddenly, little Edward said, "I think it's time one of us acted like a Christian. How about you acting like one?" It was really time that *both* of the little boys acted like Christians.

"I Wanted Your Saviour Too"

A lady who was a Christian had an unsaved husband. For many years, she went to church alone. The husband drove her to church. Then, he left her and went back home. The wife prayed for a long time that her husband would be saved.

One Sunday morning, the invitation to accept the Lord Jesus as Saviour was given. How surprised the lady was to see her husband go up to the front of the church and kneel. He gave his heart to the Lord Jesus.

Afterward, the husband said, "Wife, I have been watching you for a long time now. Your *life* is clean and beautiful. You were always kind. I knew that you had something I didn't have. This morning, after you left me, the singing in the church drew me into the church. I took a back seat. When the minister asked if there were any who wanted to give their hearts to Jesus, I decided that I wanted your Saviour, too!"

Bringing Glory to Jesus

Leonardo da Vinci was painting the picture of the Last Supper. A friend saw the picture. He said, "The most striking thing about the picture is the cup which the Master holds in His hand!" The great artist was disappointed. He said, "Nothing in my picture must take the attention away from the face of my Master!" So the great

artist took a brush and changed the picture.

Nothing in our lives, boys and girls, should take the attention from the Lord Jesus. If we sing, we must sing in such a way that the people will think of Jesus, and not of us. Whatever we do, it *must* bring glory to Jesus, and not to ourselves. He must receive all praise and all worship.

"I Have Seen the Gospel"

A traveler in China asked a native if he had ever read the Gospel. "No," he replied, "but I have *seen* it. I have seen a man who was the terror of his neighborhood, with his curses and violent temper. He was an opium smoker, a criminal, and was as dangerous as a wild beast. But the Lord Jesus made him *gentle* and *good*, and he has left off opium. No, I have not read the Gospel, but I have *seen* it, and it is *good!*"

"I Just Lived the Gospel"

A missionary in New Guinea returned after several years of service. A friend asked, "What did you find at your station in New Guinea?"

The missionary replied, "I found something that was more hopeless than if I had been sent to the jungles to a lot of tigers. Why, those people were so degraded that they seemed to have no moral sense. They were worse than beasts. If a baby cried and annoyed his mother, she would throw him into the ditch and leave him there to die. If a man saw his father break his leg, he would leave him on the roadside to die. They had no compassion, no love, no pity for others!"

"Well, what did you do for such people? Did you preach to them?"

"No," replied the missionary, "preaching would do no good. *I just lived the Gospel.* When I saw a baby crying, I picked it up and comforted it. When I saw a man with a broken leg, I mended it. When I saw people in distress, I pitied them. I took them into my home. I cared for them. I lived that way, day by day. Finally, the people began to come to me and say, 'What does this mean? What are you doing this for?' Then it was that I had *my chance to preach the Gospel.* They *knew* what I meant!"

The friend asked, "Well, what happened? Did you succeed?"

The missionary replied, "When I left, *I left a church!*"

"Has some one seen Christ in *you* today?
 Christian, look into your life, I pray,
 The *little* things you've done or said,
 Did they accord with the way you prayed?
 Have your thoughts been pure, your words
   been kind?
 Have *you* sought to have the Saviour's mind?
 The world with a criticizing view
 Has watched; did it see Christ in you?"

A Vile Temper

A woman went to a minister saying, "I wish you would go and talk to my husband. He is getting so he doesn't stay home at night, and he sets the children such a bad example. If I talk to him, he slams the door and goes off!"

The minister knew something about that home. He said to the woman, "Before we pray for your husband, I want to talk to you about something: What about your vile temper? Will you say to God: "O, God, I come to Thee confessing my vile temper. My bad temper is driving my husband from home. It is harming my children. It is bringing dishonor to the Name of the Lord. Deliver me from my bad temper, so I may present the kindness of Christ to my husband and children, and so help them!"?

The woman did not take the golden advice to heart. She jumped to her feet, and ran away from the minister in another fit of temper! How each one of us needs to pray daily that God will help us live unto Him in our homes!

CHRISTMAS

The Birthday of Her Dearest Friend

A gentleman visited a friend whom he had not seen for a long time. He had not been seated long when the little daughter brought out her birthday book. He turned the leaves of the book and read the names of many of her friends written by the day of their birth. When he came to December 25, he found only ONE NAME. It was carefully written,

"Dear Lord Jesus"! The gentleman said, "Mary, I thought this book was for the names of your friends!" The little girl looked up to him with her face flushing with joy. She said, "The Lord Jesus is my BEST and DEAREST Friend, and His birthday is the nicest birthday of all the year!"

A Christmas Eve In No Man's Land

It was Christmas Eve in "No Man's Land." It was during World War I.

A most unusual thing happened. Battle-weary men in one trench began to sing:

"Silent night, holy night,
All is calm, all is bright!"

Enemies, in the opposite trench, answered by singing:

"O little town of Bethlehem,
How still we see thee lie!"

All firing ceased. The spirit of Christ brought peace as foes became friends for awhile!

A King Is Born

At six o'clock in the morning of March 20, 1811, all Paris was aroused. The artillery was booming. It was announcing the birth of a prince! The cannon shot forth one hundred volleys to proclaim the fact that the great Napoleon had a son! Soon, the city was filled with laughter and shouting as the people celebrated the birth of a prince.

How different was the world's reception of Heaven's Royal Child on the first Christmas Day! The little town of Bethlehem made no demonstration of welcome. The world offered Him nothing better than a barn; yet, the Lord Jesus, one day, will be "King of kings and Lord of lords!"

Christmas Day in a Barn

It was Christmas Day, 1944, in cold and foggy Belgium. The Americans had been advancing, driving the Germans before them. The kitchen of one American battery was located in an old Belgium barn. The men were brought back from the front line in groups to enjoy a warm dinner. As their mess kits were filled with food, they searched for a dry corner or a warm place in which to eat it. Some of the men burrowed down into the musty hay to find additional warmth. A chaplain and a soldier happened to find a place together in the old manger of a horse stall. While the two were eating, the soldier said to the chaplain, "Isn't it odd that we should be in this manger on Christmas Day?" The chaplain answered, "I reckon if Jesus could be born and laid in a manger, we can eat in one." As the two thought upon this fact, a special warmth and happiness came to them.

"Everywhere Christmas!"

Everywhere, everywhere, Christmas tonight!
Christmas in lands of the fir tree and pine,
Christmas in lands of the palm tree and vine,
Christmas where snow-peaks stand solemn and white,
Christmas where cornfields lie sunny and bright,
Everywhere, everywhere, Christmas tonight!

Christmas where children are hopeful and gay,
Christmas where old men are patient and gray,
Christmas where peace, like a dove in its flight,
Broods over brave men, in the thick of the fight!
Everywhere, everywhere Christmas tonight!
— Phillip Brooks

Do You Think of Jesus?

A teacher once asked his class, of forty pupils, to write on a sheet of paper the word, "Christmas." "Now," said the teacher, "write after the word, 'Christmas' the first thing you think of." When the papers were returned to him, the teacher read the answers. The answers given were: "tree"; "holly"; "mistletoe"; "presents"; "turkey"; "holiday"; "carols'; "Santa Claus." Not *one person* had written, *"Jesus"!* How sad it is that so few think about the Lord Jesus on His birthday, Christmas!

God Among Men

In the Palace Rospigliosi in Rome, Italy, is a famous painting by Reni, called "The Aurora." This painting is on a high ceiling. Visitors to the palace often stand and look up at the painting until their necks get stiff and their heads grow dizzy. To relieve the strain, they lower their heads and eyes. To their surprise, in a broad mirror near the floor, they can see the picture, "The Aurora." The visitors can sit down and in comfort study the picture reflected in the mirror.

For many centuries, the people of the Old Testament days searched to find out what God is like. Then, one day, the people suddenly discovered that God was in their midst! Jesus Christ, the Son of God, revealed God to the people. When they saw Him, healing the sick, feeding the hungry, raising the dead, casting out demons, stilling the tempest, comforting the sorrowing, forgiving the sinners, they *saw* what God is like!

A Prince Is Born

Recently, in England, a baby prince was born. He was born in a beautiful palace. He was placed in a beautiful bed. How different it was with the Baby Jesus, who was the King of kings, and the Lord of lords.

> "Out of the ivory palaces,
>   Into a world of woe,
>   Only His great, eternal love,
>   Made my Saviour go!"

"If Christ Had Not Been Born!"

If Christ had not been born,
Hearts burdened and forlorn,
Must seek in vain,
Peace to attain,
If Christ had not been born!

But now both hope and cheer,
God gives to us each year,
To seeking hearts,
His grace imparts,
His love, for Christ has come!

The Joy of Christmas

Some years ago, in Korea, a small prince climbed on the wall which separated the royal palace from the mission compound. He called down to the missionary lady, and asked if she would not give him a "Jesus birthday." He meant he wanted a Christmas celebration. He was not allowed to attend the usual program in the little mission church. The missionary lady promised him that she would remember him. She and her helpers decorated a lovely little tree for him. When he appeared on the wall, they carried the little tree to him. They told him what the Bible says about the coming of Jesus, the Saviour. Then, they sang a few beautiful Christmas songs and prayed. Afterward, they gave the little prince the decorations from the tree, and the small red song book which contained the words of the Christmas songs.

Later in the day the missionary lady heard a terrible noise over the wall. On investigation, it was found that the small prince had his fat gentlemen-in-waiting lined up and was demanding that they sing the beautiful joyful songs in the little red book. Said the little prince, "I know the joyful noise is in that book, and you have got to get it out!"

The coming of Jesus brought great joy to this earth. Wherever the missionaries go with the good news of salvation, hearts are made joyful and lives are changed. It is said that the heathen sing sad and mournful songs in minor keys, but when the missionaries come with the Good News of salvation, they sing happy songs in bright major keys! How *glad* we are that Jesus came to our needy world!

Christmas Dinner Provided

It was the day before Christmas. A little lad in a Gypsy van asked his father, "What do we have for Christmas dinner?" The little lad's mother was dead. The father of little Gypsy Smith answered, "I do not know, my dear." Then, he called his children to him. He said, "Let us sing." Together, they sang this beautiful song:

"In some way or other,
 The Lord will provide:
 It may not be my way,
 It may not be thy way;
 And yet in His own way,
 The Lord will provide!

"Then we will trust in the Lord,
 And He will provide;
 Yes, we will trust in the Lord,
 And He will provide!"

The father had once made money by playing a fiddle in saloons. Now, he was a Christian. He no longer played in the saloons. He trusted the Lord.

Suddenly, a knock came on the door of the van. The knock stopped the singing. A man said, "God is good, is He not? I have come to tell you how the Lord will provide. In town, at the little shop, there are mutton and groceries waiting for you!" Immediately, the father took a wheelbarrow, and brought the supplies home. Gypsy Smith and his brothers and his father had a fine Christmas dinner. God had provided for His trustful children!

If Jesus Had Not Come

It was Christmas Eve. Before bedtime, Daddy read the Christmas story to Bobby. Then he told Bobby how much the coming of Jesus meant to the world. He told Bobby how sad this world would be if Jesus had not come.

Bobby went to bed and was soon fast asleep! He dreamed that he awoke on Christmas morning, and there were no holly wreaths in the window, and no stockings hanging by the chimney. He went for a walk. He found that the factories were busy at work. When he passed the place where the orphanage stood, the lot was vacant! When he reached his church, he found the doors nailed fast, and a big sign in front saying, "For Sale." He went to find the hospital, but there was only an empty lot. He ran home as fast as he could and picked up his Bible. All of the last part of the Book had blank pages. Then Bobby awoke and, lo, it was all a dream! Slipping down on his knees, Bobby prayed, "Oh, dear Jesus, I am so glad that You did come! We need Christmas! We need the holly wreaths and cheer. We need the orphanage and the church and the hospital. I am *so glad* that you did come! Help me to tell others about you."

Lighting Up the World

A little boy was telling the Christmas story to his mother. He told about the shepherds and the angel of the Lord and the Heavenly glory that shone round about them. He said, "Mother, the shepherds were very much afraid, but the angel said to them, 'Don't be afraid, shepherds. They are only lighting up.'"

How true it was that the Heavenly host were "lighting up" this world! They were telling of the joy and peace that was coming because of the birth of the Saviour.

The Peace-Bringer

During World War I, a day dawned on the battlefield in northern France. The fog was so thick that no one could see more than a few yards from the trenches. As the fog lifted, it was seen that the Germans had drawn their lines back a little, and the French had gone forward a little. Between the two lines stood a lonely farmhouse. As the sun rose, heavy guns began to boom.

Suddenly, on both sides the firing ceased. A strange silence came. There, in the green meadow by the farmhouse, was a little baby, crawling on its hands and knees. It appeared perfectly happy and contented. It laughed as it plucked the dandelions. Not a shot was fired.

The coming of the Baby Jesus brought peace into the world — Peace to tired and troubled hearts, Peace to every sin-stricken soul who would trust in Him as the Saviour.

CHURCH

No Christians — No Tigers

A colonel in the Army was on board a steamer going to Bombay. One day he said at the dinner table, "I have been in India for many a year and I have never seen a native Christian during the whole time."

Several days later the colonel was telling of some of his hunting experiences. He said that he had killed thirty tigers with his rifle in India.

"Did I understand you to say thirty?" asked a missionary at the table.

"Yes sir, thirty," replied the officer.

"Well now, that's strange," said the missionary. "I have been in India and I have never seen a live, wild tiger dur-ing all that time."

"Very likely not," said the colonel, "but that is because you didn't know where to look for them."

"Perhaps you're right," admitted the missionary. Then after a moment or two of thought the missionary said, "Perhaps, colonel, the reason you have never seen a native convert in India, as you affirmed the other evening at this table, is because you didn't know where to look for them. Perhaps you never went to any of the churches."

Bones in the Church

There are six different kinds of bones in the average Church. There are the

WISHBONES. They are always wishing for better things, but they never get down to work for them and pray for them. Then there are the JAWBONES. They do altogether too much talking. They gossip and make trouble for everyone. Then there are the FUNNYBONES. These are like the crazy bone in your elbow and are always getting hurt. They are too touchy. Their feelings get hurt too easily. Then there are the DRY BONES, or FOSSILS. They are dead and cold. They show no signs of Christian life whatever. Then there are the TAILBONES. They are always behind — behind in their donations and behind in their work for the Lord. Then, the last kind are the BACKBONES. They are the spiritual life and support of the Church. They know what is right, and they stand for the right, and work for the right. There are too few back bones in the Church. Are you one?

The Wrong Orders

A passenger train was running toward New York City. Suddenly there was a head-on collision. Fifty were killed. The engineer was pinned under his engine. Blood was pouring from his nostrils and tears were running down his cheeks. In his dying moments he held out a piece of yellow paper and said, "Take this. This will show you that someone gave me the wrong orders."

When lost men and women stand before God's throne of judgment some of them will point to unbelieving preachers and say, "Someone gave me the wrong orders." How careful preachers should be to preach Christ. He is the only way to Heaven and life everlasting.

Lost in the Church

Some stereopticon pictures were being shown in a little church one evening.

The church was crowded and in darkness. A knock at the door summoned an usher. Presently he made his way to the front and announced, "Little Mary Jones is lost. Her family and friends are searching everywhere for her. If anyone knows her whereabouts please go to the door and tell the friend who is inquiring for her." No one moved so the lecturer went on with his address and the pictures.

At the close of the lecture, the lights were turned on. Immediately a lady noticed Mary Jones on the front seat. Going to her she asked, "Why, Mary, didn't you hear them inquiring for you? Why didn't you let them know you were here?" Mary replied, "But I'm not lost. I knew where I was. They must have meant some other Mary Jones."

How often people in the church are lost and don't know it. They are in the church but they have never felt their need of Christ, and have never believed the gospel.

A Small Church

A missionary in China visited a Chinese Christian who lived alone in a hut in the midst of his cornfields. He did not live in the nearby village, because the village was very wicked and evil. No one in the village was a Christian. The Chinese Christian gave the missionary a simple meal. After the meal, he invited the missionary to come "into the church." The missionary followed the Chinaman out of the house and through some tall grass. They came to a little clearing and there was the smallest church the missionary had ever seen. It was four feet high. The two crawled inside, and sat down. With a shining face, the Chinaman said to the missionary, "I had to build this house for God. My heart wasn't at peace until I did it. Every evening and every morning, I come here, and meet with God. I talk to Him, and He talks to my heart. Now, teacher, will you pray to Him?" The missionary could hardly pray for the "lump" in his throat. He *knew* that God was meeting in that little church with *one* who loved Him.

Something Fresh Every Time

Someone asked Old John why he loved to go to the village church. Old John *never* missed a meeting in the little church. John said, "I often see you go down to the pond to fish. You fish in the same pond, in the same water day after day, don't you?"

"Yes," said the other.

Then Old John smiled, and said, "No, you don't. The water you fished in yesterday has gone to the sea. Every day you fish in fresh water. Now you wonder why I like to go to the little village church week after week, and see the same folks, and sing the same old hymns. But, friend, I want to tell you that every time I go to the church, there I meet with the Lord, and He always has something fresh and new for my heart!"

A Peculiar Family

In a certain home, the father had not missed church or Sunday School for twenty-three years. The mother had a perfect record for eleven years; the son had not missed for twelve years; the daughter had not missed for eight years.

Someone asked, "What is the matter with that family? Don't they ever have company on Sunday to keep them away

from God's House? Are they never tired Sunday morning? Don't they ever go on week-end trips? Don't they ever go on Sunday picnics? Don't they ever get their sermon over the radio? What's the matter with them? They always seem so happy and cheerful!"

You know what was the matter with that family: They loved the Lord Jesus; they loved His House. They always put God *first* in their lives. No wonder they were happy and cheerful! We hope that you can say with David, the Psalmist, "I was glad when they said unto me, Let us go into the House of the Lord" (*Ps. 122:1*).

"The Great Physician Is There"

A poor Korean woman, living outside of town, heard that some wonderful things were happening at a mission hall where Jesus was preached. This old woman walked into town to attend the mission. She did not know the name of the mission. So she asked someone to show her the way to the place where they cured broken hearts. She was directed to the little mission hall. If any one walked into your town today, and asked to be directed to the place where they cured broken hearts, would the people on your street say, "I know the place you mean. It is the church over yonder! The Healer of men, the Great Physician, is always there!" If this can be said of *your* church, it is bringing much help and happiness to a sad world.

Is Our Worship Better?

A missionary tells us that in one of the great temples of Japan, the devotion of the worshiper consists in his running around the sacred building one hundred times, and dropping a piece of wood into a box at each round. After this wearisome exertion, the worshiper goes home tired, but happy at the thought of having done such worthy service to his god.

We may think this worship is unspeakably silly. Yet, how much difference is there between running around a temple a certain number of times, and just "going to church," and sitting through a service while our hearts and minds are far away from God, and then going home? Unless we worship God with a definite purpose, reverently and obediently heeding His voice, and listening to His Word, how is our worship better than that of millions of others who know not the *true and living God?*

The Jesus Mark

A little girl in the West was baptized one Lord's Day. The next day at school, her friends asked her why she was baptized. She said, "I was a little maverick out on the prairie." (A "maverick," boys and girls, is a young calf which has not been branded. No one knows who owns it.) "When I was baptized, the Jesus mark was put on me, and now everyone knows that I belong to Jesus!"

Like Hell

A young lawyer once boasted that he was going west to live where there were no churches, no Sunday Schools, no Bibles. He was an infidel. Before a year was over, however, he wrote to a college classmate, a young minister. He begged him to come out where he was and start a Sunday School and church. He closed his letter with these words: "Be *sure* to bring *plenty of Bibles.* I have become convinced that a place without Christians and S u n d a y s and Bibles and

churches is too much like *hell* for any man to live in!"

Why They Attended Church

A Christian man once said, "When I was a small child, I wondered at the interest shown by my father and mother in going to church. Every service, including the *prayer meeting,* seemed equally important. More than once, I have heard my mother say, 'Oh, I can hardly wait until I get to church.' And though we were living on a farm, it was the *custom* on Wednesday afternoon, even in the harvest season, for my father to stop the work of the day a half hour, or an hour, earlier than on other days, to get to prayer meeting *on time!*

What was there at the little country church which meant so much to my parents? As I watched, it became evident to me that church attendance meant more to them than the performance of duty. The toils and trials of the week wore on them physically and spiritually. When they went to God's House everything earthly was thrown off and cast aside. They met with God, and felt His touch on their bodies as well as their souls. The inspiration they received at the services helped them to get through the trials and toils of everyday life victoriously. Where was there room for 'a prayer meeting night headache,' or a 'Sunday morning sickness?' "

Ring It Again

A father once took his son with him to visit the country church he attended when a boy. He told his son how he often rang the bell to call the people to God's House to worship. When they reached the church, they found it locked and deserted. Looking through a window, they saw the long bell rope. The father borrowed a key and o p e n e d the door. The little boy eagerly said, "Father, ring the bell! Ring it again!" So, the father rang the old church bell.

The bell had been silent for a long while. The people no longer came to the little church to worship God. When the father rang the bell, all the people far and near heard it. They came to the church to see what was the matter. The father told them how much he loved the little church. He told them how much the church had meant to him when he was a boy. He said that he was so sorry to see the church closed and neglected. With the father's help, the old church was put in order, and was opened again for worship and service.

How glad the father and the little boy were that they could help open again God's House!

"The Lord Is Here"

There is an old lady, very deaf, whose eyes are bad, who is *always* at church. She cannot hear a word of the service, but she looks up and reads the hymns and the Scriptures, and she sits there and looks at the preacher and prays. She says, "The Lord is in His holy temple, and I come here to meet the Lord!"

The Empty Place

Several hundred years ago, in a little village in Southern Europe, there lived a duke who had ten beautiful daughters whom he loved much. When they were young, he liked to watch them play. When they grew up, he liked to sit in the garden with them, and listen to them sing as they did their needle work, or watch them as they picked the flowers. Gradually, the daughters married, but each year they gathered at the father's table to eat Christmas dinner. Then, a daughter married a prince from a far country. She thought the journey was too far to go home for the Christmas dinner. How sad the father was each year when he saw his daughter's empty place at the table.

Before his death, the old duke built a beautiful church in the little village. The church was complete except there were no lamps in it. One of his daughters asked, "Father, where are the lamps?" The duke answered, "My daughter, each worshiper will carry his own lamp! I have provided small, bronze lamps, one for each person in the village. The worshipers will bring these lamps with them. If one fails to come, and his place is left empty, then that corner of the church will be dark and lonely. I hope that all of God's sons and daughters will *come* at the *appointed time* to worship Him, and that no place will be empty; no corner dark!"

Four hundred years have passed since the duke built the little church. The bronze lamps have been handed down from father to son, and carefully treasured. When the bell of the little church rings, the people wend their way up the hill, each carrying his own lamp, for no one wishes his corner to be dark and gloomy.

Do *you* fill your "corner" in God's House *every* Lord's day, or do you leave your corner empty and lonely?

Where He Went

Lord Faraday loved God. He served Him faithfully. He was pleasing to God, and God blessed him. He became a great scientist. Many people praised him, and applauded him. He never forgot God. He never failed to give honor to God. He never forgot to serve God faithfully. One night, Lord Faraday gave a lecture before a great crowd of people. He explained some hard things in science. At the end of the lecture, the people rose and clapped and cheered. Then the king of England arose, and praised Lord Faraday. The people expected Lord Faraday to make a reply. But, when the clapping had died down, Lord Faraday could not be found! Where was Lord Faraday? He had slipped away to attend the prayer service of the little church to which he belonged. It was *prayer meeting* night, and he *never* failed to attend the place of prayer!

COMING TO JESUS

"Am I Too Little?"

A minister preached on the love of Christ. He urged his hearers to come to Jesus. After the meeting, a little girl came to him and asked, "Am I too little?" "Too little for what, my dear?" the minister kindly asked. The little girl answered, "Am I to little to come to Jesus?"

The minister took the little girl up into his arms. He said, "No, my dear, you are not too little. It was to the little ones that Jesus said, 'Suffer little children to come unto Me, and forbid them not, for of such is the kingdom of heaven.' "

The dear little girl wiped her tears and went to her mother. She told her mother that she had come to Jesus and that she was saved! How glad mother was to hear her little girl confess her faith in Jesus! Next day, the little girl brought another little girl to the meeting, saying, "She wants to be saved, too!"

Dear children, you are welcome to come to Jesus. He longs to have you come to Him. He will make you happy in His love. Then you, too, can tell others about Him.

Come to Jesus Now

The great Matthew Henry was saved from sin when he was eleven years old. Dr. Watts was saved at nine. Jonathan Edwards, at eight. Richard Baxter at six. All of these children became great Christians, and lived long, useful lives in the service of the Lord Jesus.

> "Come to Jesus, little ones,
> Come to Jesus, *now!*"

Come with Your Sins

A poor man went to a druggist. He asked, "Mister, have you got anything for a bad cold?" The druggist asked, "have you brought a prescription with you?" The man answered, "No, but I brought *my cold with me!*" When we come to God with our sins, we do not need to bring a prescription with us. All we need to bring is our sinful selves. He will cleanse us from sin. He will forgive us.

Believe God's Invitation

During a revival in a factory town, the foreman in the factory became concerned about his soul's salvation. But he could not find peace. His boss was a true follower of Jesus Christ.

One morning, the boss sent a note to the foreman requesting him to call upon him at 6 P.M. Promptly at 6 P.M., the foreman arrived. "I see," said the boss, "that you believed the words of the letter which I wrote you. You came just as I requested you to come. Now, here is another letter for you."

The boss handed his foreman a piece of paper on which were written the words, "Come unto Me, all ye that labour and are heavy laden, and I will give you rest"; "Him that cometh to Me I will in no wise cast out." As the foreman read these wondrous words, his lips quivered. His eyes filled with tears of joy, and he said, "I see it! I see it all! It is faith that does it. I believed the letter you wrote me, and came to you. Now I believe the words of the Bible, and come to Jesus, the Saviour!"

"Come, Ye Sinners!"

When the great Vanderbilt lay dying, he knew that he could not face God "dressed in his own righteousness." He knew that he needed the righteousness of Jesus. He requested that the following hymn be sung:

"Come ye sinners, poor and needy,
    Weak and wounded, sick and sore;
Jesus ready stands to save you,
    Full of mercy, love, and pow'r.

"Let not conscience make you linger,
    Nor of fitness fondly dream;
All the fitness He requireth,
    Is to feel your need of Him!"

At the conclusion of the hymn, Vanderbilt, the multimillionnaire, said, "I am a poor and needy sinner!" Remember, boys and girls, when you come to the Lord Jesus, you must not come with any goodness of your own. You *must* come as a poor, lost sinner, and He will receive you. He will forgive your sins, and remember them no more.

"Just as I Am"

An aged minister once spoke to a beautiful young lady about her sin and need of the Saviour. He urged her to come to Christ, the *only* Saviour from sin. The young lady, Charlotte Elliot, became angry. But she could not forget the plea of the minister. Finally, she came to the Saviour. She wrote these beautiful words:

"Just as I am! without one plea,
    But that Thy Blood was shed for *me*,
    And that Thou bidd'st me come to Thee,
    O Lamb of God, I come! I come!"

She Brought Herself

A little girl had been listening to a sermon, in which the minister urged people to bring others to Jesus. "I think I will bring somebody to Jesus," said the little girl." "Whom will you bring?" asked her father. "I think I will bring MYSELF," she answered.

Don't Try to Stop Us

One day, a little girl stood on a platform. She was going to recite the verse, "Suffer the little children to come unto Me, and forbid them not . . . ." It was her first time to try to say a verse in public. She said, "Suffer," and then she stopped. She tried a second time. She said, "Suffer," and again she became frightened, and stopped. Finally, she said, "Jesus wants all of the little children to come to Him, and don't any of you big folk try to stop us!"

Not Too Young

Rose Mary was six years old. She attended Sunday School. One day, the teacher asked all who wished to accept Christ to come to the front. Rose Mary left her seat. The teacher said, "Rose Mary, you are too young. You had better go back to your seat." Rose Mary went back. She began to cry. The teacher asked her why. Rose Mary sobbed, "My father and mother don't want me to be a Christian. Now, you don't want me to be a Christian either." Then teacher told Rose Mary that if she really wanted to come to Jesus, she could come to Him. Rose Mary came to Jesus. He saved her from her sin. After that Rose Mary lived for Jesus day by day.

Come As You Are

A Chaplain tried to point a young soldier to Christ. But the soldier did not seem to understand how to be saved. Before the Chaplain left, he gave the soldier a hymn book. When next they met, the soldier said, "Chaplain, everything is all right now. When I opened the little hymn book I read,

" 'Just as I am! and waiting not
To rid my soul of one dark blot;
To Thee, whose Blood can cleanse each spot,
O Lamb of God, I come!' "

"Chaplain, when I read these words, it was all clear to me. I came to Jesus *just as I was,* and His Blood cleansed away my sins!"

God's Invitation

When the caravans are crossing the Sahara Desert, they often send a rider on a camel ahead to find water. As soon as he finds water, before he stoops to drink, he shouts aloud, "Come!" Across the desert, there is echoed the glad word, "Come!" How good it is to hear the glad invitation, "Come!" when one is thirsty. Today, we hear God's invitation to us. He is saying, "Come and take of the Water of Life freely!" Will you not come to the Lord Jesus today?

Come Now

How important it is that we come to the Lord Jesus *now* while we hear His call. Tomorrow may be eternally *too late!* A meeting was held in a mining district of England. A strong miner was deeply burdened. At the close of the meeting, he walked up to the preacher to inquire what he must do to be saved. The preacher showed him the way of salvation. From the Scriptures, he showed him that Christ came into the world, seeking to save that which is lost; how He gave His life a ransom for us, dying on the Cross for the sin of the world; how *all* we need to do is to come to Him, believing in His finished work on the Cross. The miner was so burdened with his sins that he could not see the light. Hours passed by, while the preacher urged him to turn from self and sin, and "behold the Lamb of God, which taketh away the sin of the world!"

No peace came to the miner. At eleven o'clock, the preacher suggested that the miner go home and return to the chapel the following evening, and then make peace with God. The miner replied, "No, I will not leave. It *must* be settled tonight or never!" The two remained together, talking and praying. Hours passed. As the clock struck three, the light of the glorious Gospel suddenly burst upon the miner. He saw and believed the glorious *fact* that the work of Christ on the Cross took away *his sin* and brought him peace and joy! Rising from his feet, he exclaimed, "It's all settled now! The Lord Jesus Christ is *mine!*" He thanked the servant of God who had been so patient with him.

A few hours later, the miner went to his work in the mine, happy and rejoicing because he was a saved man! Suddenly, a crash was heard! Part of the roofing of the mine had fallen in, burying a number of men beneath it. Willing hands set to work, digging out the earth and debris to rescue those who were underneath. After awhile, they reached the converted miner. Life was not quite gone, and he was speaking. Eagerly, they listened and caught these words, "Thank God, it was settled last night!" Those were the last words he said.

In the Depth of the Ocean

A professional diver was at the bottom of the sea. He saw an oyster on a rock. A paper was fastened to the oyster. He detached the paper and began to read it through the glasses of his helmet. To his surprise it was a part of a tract. As he read it, his heart was touched. He had rejected many Gospel invitations to come to the Saviour, but here was another and an unexpected appeal. Said the diver, "I could hold out no longer. God's mercy had followed me to the bottom of the sea. Right there, where I was in the depth of the ocean, I repented and accepted Christ as my Saviour."

His Alone

An influential Chinaman, who held a high office in the educational life of China, accepted Christ. He was a man of high station and great wealth. Great opportunities lay ahead of him. It was the study of the New Testament which brought to him the conviction that Jesus Christ was the Saviour of men and his Saviour. He seriously weighed the matter of confessing Christ publicly. He "counted the cost!" Then he determined to confess Christ before men. His dearest friend pleaded with him earnestly not to do such a rash thing. He urged the new believer to be a *secret* follower of Christ. He said, "Bow down before the tablet of Confucious. It will only be an empty form. In your heart, you may believe what you like!" The believer replied, "A few days ago, One came to dwell within my heart. He has changed all life for me. I dare not bow before any other, lest He depart! I am His *alone!*"

A Brave Captain

A captain in the army was wonderfully saved. The next morning, he bought a large Bible, and laid it open on his table. He said, "I want the Bible to speak to others for me, I am afraid that I am not strong enough to speak for myself!" Many of his companions laughed at his faith, but he *stood* true to Christ, without trembling. Soon, he not only had the open Bible on the table, but he was also speaking to others for the Lord Jesus! His daily prayer was this: "Enable me, Lord, not only to please my commanding officer, but also to please Thee!"

The Boys Will Laugh

When Dr. Harry A. Ironside was a little boy, his mother urged him to trust the Lord Jesus Christ as his Saviour.

He said, "Well, Mother, I would like to do it, but the boys will all laugh at me!" Mother replied, "Harry, remember, they may laugh you into hell, but they can never laugh you out of it!" Those words gave Harry the courage to confess Christ as his Saviour.

The Lifted Hands

One Sunday night, the head nurse in a children's hospital was reading Bible stories to the little ones. Afterwards, they sang hymns. One little girl asked, "Nurse, may I sing a song, too? I learned it at Sunday School." The nurse said, "Yes." The little girl sweetly sang: "I am Jesus' little friend." When she came to the words, "Jesus' friend, little friend, on His mercy, I depend," she held up her hand. When the nurse looked around the room, she saw many other little hands uplifted. The little children wanted to show that they, too, wanted to be a little friend of Jesus, that they, too, wanted to love Him. Surely, the heart of Jesus was touched when He saw these little hands reaching up to Him!

The Fatal Delay

One day, a minister's phone rang. A lady asked the minister to come and visit her husband who was very, very sick, and unsaved. The minister went and told the unsaved husband about the Lord Jesus, the Saviour. The man said, "If the Lord will restore me, I will forsake my sin. And when I get well, I will come to the church and confess Him publicly as my Saviour, and be baptized!"

God restored the man. Soon, he was well again. One day, the minister called and found him sitting out on the wood- pile, watching his chickens. The minister said, "Soon you will be ready to keep your promise to the Lord." The man replied, "I am going to keep my promise. I will be at church a week from next Sunday. I will confess the Lord publicly and be baptized.

The man did not keep his promise. He did not forsake his sin. He did not confess Christ as *his* Saviour. He did not go to church. The Bible says, "He, that being often reproved hardeneth his neck, shall suddenly be destroyed, and that without remedy" (*Prov. 29:1*).

One day, the minister's phone rang, and the man's wife said, "Oh, come quickly! My husband is dead! He was at a banquet at a hotel. Suddenly he fell over dead." That man's funeral was very sad. He had been warned but had refused to change his ways.

Little Abigail

When little Abigail was five years old, her mother was very sick. Abigail prayed for God to spare her mother's life until she had confessed Jesus as her Saviour. God answered her prayer. Her mother got well. Then Satan tempted Abigail not to tell her mother that she was saved. Satan said, "If you confess Christ, your mother will die. You asked God to spare her life *until* you confess Jesus as your Saviour."

For two years, little Abigail kept her mouth shut about Jesus. She was very unhappy because she did not tell her mother that Jesus was her Saviour. One day, Abigail heard a little girl singing: "I do believe that Jesus died for me!" Little Abigail ran home, and told her mother about her faith in Jesus. She could no longer keep still. As soon as she confessed Jesus, how happy she became. The joy bells rang in her heart.

The Two Martins

What miserable failures are the silent Christians who never confess the Lord Jesus before others. Long ago, during the time of the Reformation, two Martins believed in the Lord Jesus. One was Martin of Basel. He was afraid to make a public confession of Jesus. He wrote on a leaf of parchment these words, "O most merciful Christ, I know that I can be saved only by the merit of Thy Blood. Holy Jesus, I acknowledge Thy sufferings for me. I love Thee. I love thee." Then, he removed a stone from the wall of his chamber. He hid the piece of parchment behind a stone. It was not discovered until more than a hundred years had passed.

The other Martin was Martin Luther. He found the Lord Jesus to be a wonderful Saviour. He said, "My Lord has confessed me before men. He died for me. I will not shrink from confessing Him, even before kings!" Boldly and fearlessly, Martin Luther confessed Christ before men.

Today, we revere the memory of Martin Luther. But who cares for Martin of Basel? How many of you ever heard of him before? Let us always gladly confess the Lord Jesus, remembering His promise, "Whosoever therefore shall confess Me before men, him will I confess also before My Father which is in Heaven."

"Jesus, It's Me"

A timid little girl went to a minister before meeting began, and asked, "Will you please pray for me in the meeting?" I want to be a Christian, but please do not mention my name." In the meeting which followed, when every head was bowed and there was perfect silence, the minister prayed for the little girl. He said, "O Lord, there is a little girl here who does not want her name known. But You know who she is. Save her precious soul!"

There was silence for a moment. Then the little girl arose, and said in a pleading voice, "Please, it's me, Jesus! It's me!" Her heart was so hungry for forgiveness of sin that she was not ashamed to say, "Jesus, it's me!" As soon as she prayed her little prayer, she felt God's peace in her heart. She knew that the Lord had heard and answered her prayer. She knew that Jesus was her Saviour.

CONSECRATION

The Gift of Self

An evangelist held a service in a little town. At the close of the service, a little girl came up to him and presented him a bouquet of flowers. They were the first spring flowers, and she had gathered them herself. The evangelist asked, "Why do you give me these flowers?" She answered, "Because I love you." "Do you give the Lord Jesus such gifts of your love?" "Oh," replied the little girl, "I give MYSELF to HIM!"

One String and Paganini

Paganini was a great violinist. It was announced that he was going to play at the Royal Opera House in Paris. The rich, cultured people of France gathered to hear him. When he appeared on the stage, the audience was almost breathless with excitement. He commenced to tune his violin and a string broke! The audience was annoyed. As he continued to tune the violin, a second string snapped. A moment later, third string gave way. The people groaned at the seeming delay. Paganini paused for just a second. Then he said, "One string and Paganini!" He lifted his violin and placed it 'neath his chin, and then, from that single string, he played music that seemed almost divine.

When Saladin saw the sword which Richard Coeur de Lion had fought with so bravely, he marveled that so common a blade should have performed such mighty deeds. Then some one said to him, "It was not the sword which wrought the mighty deeds. It was the arm of Richard!"

We may be small, poor, or obscure. We may be worth nothing in ourselves. But when we are in the mighty hands of God, great deeds can be performed. The Bible says, "But God hath chosen the foolish things of the world to confound the wise; and God hath chosen the weak things of the world to confound the things which are mighty; And base things of the world, and things which are despised, hath God chosen, yea, and things which are not, to bring to nought things that are: That no flesh should glory in His presence" (*I Cor. 1:27-29*).

The Gift of an Indian Chief

In the far west, a missionary was speaking to a group of Indians in a tent. He was telling them about the Lord Jesus Christ. As he was speaking, an old Indian chief arose. He walked forward and laid his tomahawk at the missionary's feet. He said, "Indian chief give his tomahawk to Jesus Christ." Then he sat down. The missionary continued to speak, telling of the love of God in Christ Jesus. Rising from his seat the second time, the old Indian chief walked forward. He took his blanket from his shoulders, and laid it at the missionary's feet. He said, "Indian chief give his blanket to Jesus Christ." Again he sat down. The missionary spoke on as he told how God had given the choicest of heaven's gifts when He sent Jesus Christ to the world to redeem lost men. Presently, the Indian chief disappeared from the meeting place. By and by, he came back, leading his pony to the tent door. He tied the pony to a stake just outside the tent. Then he walked up to the missionary and said, "Indian chief give his pony to Jesus Christ." Once more, he took his seat. He had given to Jesus all the THINGS he had! Now, the missionary was telling of the death of the Lord Jesus Christ on the Cross. The old chief had no peace in his heart. Tears began to stream down his bronzed cheek. He stumbled toward the front once more. Kneeling before the missionary, he said with trembling lips, "Indian chief give HIMSELF to Jesus Christ!" Then, glorious peace and happiness flooded his soul!

Of the early Christians in Corinth, Paul wrote, "And this they did, . . . (they) first gave their OWN SELVES to the Lord" (*II Cor. 8:5*). Have YOU given YOURSELF to the Lord Jesus Christ?

"Oh, Mother, I Want You!"

A young girl had been an invalid for several years. She was a shut-in. Her mother was a pleasure-loving woman.

She did not like the idea of being shut in with her daughter. She hired a nurse to care for her invalid daughter. She traveled abroad. From time to time, she sent gifts to her daughter. Sometimes she sent books. Sometimes, pictures. Sometimes, jewelry. One birthday, the mother sent her a rare and beautiful Italian vase. The trained nurse brought it to the girl. She looked at it, and then she said to the nurse, "Take it away! Take it away! Oh, mother, do not send me anything more. I want no books, no pictures, no vases. Oh, mother, I want YOU!"

The Lord Jesus Christ wants YOU more than He wants anything else. He says to you, "My son, my daughter, give Me thy heart!"

The Best for God

A missionary in India saw a woman hurrying toward the Ganges River. In her arms she carried a sickly, whining child. By her side there walked a beautiful, strong, healthy child. The mother hurried to the bank of the river. The missionary, seeing that the mother was in deep distress, tried to help her. The mother said that she wanted to make an offering to her god. The missionary told her of the Lord Jesus. She told how Jesus had died on the Cross for her. She tried to pursuade her to trust in Jesus. But the mother was firm. She would not believe in Jesus.

The missionary was called away to attend to some other duties. In a little while, she hastened back to the river, hoping to find the woman again, and tell her more of the love of Jesus, and of His willingness to save her. Soon, she saw the woman in the distance. She had the sickly child in her arms. But the beautiful child who had walked by her side was GONE! Then, the missionary knew what had happened. The woman had thrown her beautiful child into the river! That was her gift to her god. "Why did you do it?" asked the missionary. The woman replied, "I had to make an offering to my god. Maybe, he will hear me now!" "But," asked the missionary, "why did you give your beautiful boy? Why did you not give the sickly child?" The woman stood erect. Proudly she said, "We give our gods our BEST!"

Surely, those who know the true and living God should give their BEST to Him. He wants our love. He wants our service day by day. Will you give Him your BEST?

Consecration of Self

The collection basket was being passed in a little church in Texas. When it reached the poor Indian, he said to the usher, "Please put it down a little lower." When it was lowered, he said, "Still lower, please." When it reached the floor, he stepped into it. That was his way of saying that he wanted to give HIMSELF to Jesus Christ.

"All for Jesus, all for Jesus,
All my being's ransomed powers;
All my thoughts, and words, and doings,
All my days and all my hours."

His Slave Forever

Many years ago in the southland, a beautiful slave girl was placed upon the auction block. She was to be sold to the highest bidder. The bids rose higher and higher, for one man who stood near the edge of the crowd kept raising the bid. Finally, the girl was sold to him. When he went to get the girl, she kept her eyes lowered to the ground. She was filled with shame and embarassment. He said to her, "My girl, I have purchased you in order to give you your freedom! Here are the papers that set you FREE. You are no longer a slave. You may go wherever you want to go!" The girl looked up with unbelieving eyes. She saw the man's kind, honest face. She asked, "Is it true? Did you really buy me to set me free?" The man replied, "I did." With a rush, the girl fell at his feet. She bathed his shoes with her tears, as she said, "Sir, I will be your slave forever!"

The Lord Jesus has purchased us with His precious Blood. We are redeemed not with silver and gold, but with the Blood of Jesus. He has purchased us and He sets us free from sin and Satan. Our hearts should be so filled with love for Him that we, too, will exclaim, "I will be your slave forever!"

All for Jesus

A young man was a candidate for the foreign mission field. The Bishop, who was examining him, asked, "Have you considered that you will have to go away from home and friends to a strange land?" "I have," replied the young man. "Have you considered that you must leave your loved ones and, perhaps, you may never see them again?" "I have," replied the young man. "Have you considered that your health may fail and you may be laid low with fevers?" "I have, sir, and if I had a thousand lives I would give them ALL to Jesus! Oh, Bishop, please don't ask me any more questions, but SEND ME, SEND ME!"

What Is Your Gift to God?

A missionary in Japan watched a native woman, who was offering rice to the image of her god. The missionary asked, "Do you have to feed your god?" The woman turned and looked at the shelf where all of her gods were placed. There were rice and other good things placed there. She said, "Oh, yes, I feed my gods every day." Then she asked the missionary, "Don't you feed yours?" The missionary answered, "Oh, no. Our God feeds us. Day by day, He feeds His children!" With great surprise, the native woman asked, "Well, what do you give to your God?" The missionary replied, "I give Him my heart, my love, my LIFE!"

Which Was the Greater Gift?

Two men stood on a pier in New York City Harbour. They were watching a great ocean liner leave for Africa. One man said, "That ocean liner is carrying a gift from me for a mission station in Africa. I am sending all the supplies needed to equip a mission hospital." The other man said, "That liner carries a gift from me also. It carries my only daughter. I have given her to the Lord. She is to be a missionary in Africa." The first man looked at the second man and said, "Friend, your gift far surpasses my gift!"

How wonderful it is to give ALL we have to Jesus! We should give Him our lives, our loved ones, our possessions, our ALL.

"I knelt in tears at the feet of Christ,
    In the hush of the twilight dim;
And all that I was, or hoped, or sought,
    I surrendered unto Him!"

"Count On Me!"

A college student was persuaded by his mother to visit an art gallery. She wanted him to see the painting of "The Man of Galilee." The student viewed the wondrous painting from every angle. An attendant noticed how earnestly he studied the picture. Coming quietly to him, he said, "Great picture, isn't it?" The student replied, "Yes, it is a great picture!" Then, forgetting the presence of the attendant, the student stepped thoughtfully closer to the painting, and said, "Oh Man of Galilee, if I can in any way help You to do Your work in the world You may count on me!"

Jesus First

An old Negro woman in Africa came to a missionary and said "I want to learn how to read and, Missus, I want you to teach me to read 'Jesus' first." The missionary asked 'Why do you want to read the word 'Jesus' first?" "Because, Missus, if I learn to read 'Jesus' first, everything else will come easier." She was right. When we put Jesus first, everything else comes easy.

The Hindered Christ

"The Lord Jesus wanted a tongue one day,
  To speak a message of cheer,
To a heart that was weary, worn, and sad,
  And weighted with doubt and fear.
He asked me for mine, but 'twas busy quite
  With my own affairs from morn till night.

"The Lord Christ wanted a hand one day
  To do a loving deed;
He wanted two feet, on an errand for Him
  To run with gladsome speed.
But I had need of my own that day;
  To His gentle beseeching I answered, 'Nay.'

"And the dear Lord Christ — was His work
    undone
  For the lack of a willing heart?
It is through men that He speaks to men,
  And men must do their part.

He may have used another that day,
  But I wish I had let Him have His way."
      — Selected

Everything for Jesus

Suppose a mother gave her child a beautiful plant covered with flowers and asked her to carry it to a sick friend. The child takes the plant away but when she reaches the friend's door, she decides to keep the plant for herself. She plucks off one leaf and gives that to the friend. A week later she plucks off another leaf and takes that to the friend. The following week she takes another leaf to the friend.

Has the child obeyed her mother? No, indeed. Only giving the whole plant to the friend would be obedience.

God has asked us to give to Him our whole life — our heart, soul, mind, and strength. Should we pluck off a little leaf of love now and then for Him, and keep for ourselves our life? Let us give Him all.

"Crown Him Lord of All!"

Friends had gathered at the bedside of a noble and aged missionary. It had been hours since the missionary had moved or spoken. Then, they noticed her lips moving. Bending low, they caught the faint word, "Bring!" They asked, "Bring what? Do you want your medicine?" She shook her head. Again, she whispered, "Bring!" "Bring what?" they asked. With a smile on her face, and with her last breath, the missionary said, "Bring forth the royal diadem, and crown Him Lord of all!"

The Master's Touch

One day, Ole Bull, the famous violinist, was making his way through a great forest. He came upon a hermit's hut.

Ole Bull asked the hermit to allow him to spend the night in the hut. That evening, by the light of the fireplace, the old hermit entertained his guest. He played for him on a violin the few simple pieces he knew. When he had finished, Ole Bull asked, "Do you suppose I could play that violin?" "It isn't very likely that you can play, but you may try," said the hermit. The great violinist took the instrument. He drew the bow across the strings. Instantly, the hut was filled with beautiful music! He played the songs that the hermit's mother had sung to him in his childhood: "Jesus Lover of My Soul"; "Rock of Ages"; "Abide with Me." Soon, the hermit wept like a child. He had left his home and loved ones, because he had been disappointed in business, and had become bitter toward all men. As Ole Bull played the violin, a new harmony entered his heart. That night, he became a changed man! He went back to dwell among his fellowmen.

How filled with harmony and peace our lives will be if we will place our lives in the hand of the Master. His touch will change us.

The Meaning of Consecration

A young girl asked a minister, "Will you please tell me what you mean by consecration?"

The minister replied, "It is to sign your name at the bottom of a blank sheet of paper and let God fill in the paper as He wills."

"My King, My Life, My ALL"

David Livingstone honored God, and God honored Livingstone. Livingstone is called, "The Pathfinder." He went to Africa, and there blazed a trail for the Lord Jesus. His body was laid at rest in Westminster Abbey with the remains of other famous people. Showing how much he loved and honored God, Livingstone wrote in his diary these words, "March 19, my birthday. My Jesus, my King, my Life, my *all*, I again dedicate my *whole* self to Thee. Accept me, and grant, O gracious Father, that I may finish . . . my work for Thee. In Jesus' Name, I ask it. Amen."

General William Booth

Years ago, a minister fell in love with the world's unlovely ones, because Jesus' love was in his heart. He went to the East End of London to help the poor, lost sinners, which were there in great multitudes. For days, he stood in the streets among the poor, lost men and women. He loved them because he loved souls of men. One night, he went home and said to his wife, "Darling, I have given *myself*, I have given you and the children, to work for God among those sick souls." The wife smiled and took his hand, and the two knelt and prayed. That was the beginning of the *Salvation Army*, and of the great work of William Booth.

Some years later, someone asked, "General Booth, tell me what has been the secret of your success?" General Booth hesitated a moment, and the tears trickled down his cheeks. Then, he said, "I will tell you the secret: God has had *all there was of me to have!* There have been greater men, and men with greater opportunities; but from the day I got the poor of London on my heart, and a vision of what Jesus Christ would do for them, I made up my mind that God would have *all* there was of William Booth. God has had *all* the adoration of my heart, all the power of my will, and all the influence of my life!"

In the Master's Hands

Mendelssohn, the great musician, went one day to see the great Freiburg organ. At first, the old custodian of the organ refused to give him permission to put his fingers on the keyboard. He did not know who the visitor was. Finally, the old man agreed to let him play a few notes. Then, most wonderful music came forth from the organ. The old custodian was spellbound! When the great musician had finished playing, the old man asked his name. When he heard that his visitor was Mendelssohn, he was filled with humiliation. He exclaimed, "And to think I refused at first to give you permission to play on my organ!"

If we will place our lives into the hands of the great Master, the Lord Jesus, what wonderful music will come from them!

Unseen Stones

A brilliant Oxford student went to Africa as a missionary. He died after a year's work there. Before he went to Africa, he said, "With African missions, it is as with the building of a great bridge. Many stones have to be buried in the earth for a foundation. If God wants me to be one of the *unseen* stones, lying in an African grave, I am content!"

"Indian Lay Down Indian"

Many years ago, there lived in the Selkirk mountains a lonely Indian. He made his living by hunting and trapping. All of his family had been killed by white men. He grew up a wild savage.

There came to the mountain another trapper. This man was kind, and pa-tient. The Indian came to trust and love him. Then the white man began to teach him about Jesus.

Months passed by. One moonlight night, on top of a mountain peak, the young Indian came to his white friend. He was dressed in all of his finery. He took the white man's hand. He kneeled and prayed silently, and then he made this confession of faith, as he put his words into action: "Indian lay down blanket; Indian lay down pipe; Indian lay down tomahawk; Indian lay down Indian!" That was the Indian's way of saying that he believed in Jesus, and was giving his heart and life wholly to Him.

All for Jesus

"I washed my hands this morning,
  So very clean and white,
And lent them both to Jesus
  To work for Him till night.

"I gave my feet to Jesus
  To walk with Him all day,
Go anywhere for Jesus,
  And never let me stray.

"I gave my tongue to Jesus
  To speak for Him all day,
To say a word of kindness,
  To sing of Him and pray.

"I told my ears to listen
  Quite closely all day through,
For any word from Jesus
  To tell me what to do.

"My eyes are set to watch Him
  About my work and play,
To keep me out of mischief
  For Jesus' sake all day.

"I gave my heart to Jesus,
  To love Him all day through,
To think of all His goodness,
  To please Him and be true!"

Counting the Cost

Two young soldiers were one day talking about the service of Christ. One of them said, "I cannot tell you all that the Lord Jesus is to me, or all that He has done for me. I do wish that you would enlist in His army and become His follower."

The other young man said, "I have been thinking about it, but if I follow Jesus, there are certain things in my life, sinful things, which I *must give up.* In fact, I am counting the cost."

A Christian officer passing by heard the last remark. He stopped and placed his hand on the shoulder of the young soldier and said, "Young man, you talk of counting the cost of following the Christ. Have you ever counted the cost of *not* following Him?"

How poor will we be in this life without Christ! How lost we would be in the life beyond without Christ!

A Jewish Boy

One day, in a Sunday School, a Jewish boy arose and said, "Jesus, I my cross have taken, all to leave and follow Thee!" The eyes of many filled with tears, for they *knew* what this would mean to the young Jew. His father had told him that he must either leave the Sunday School and give up Christ, or leave home forever. The words he spoke showed that he had given up *all* of this world to follow Christ. Christian friends determined to help him. They secured for him a position by which he could earn his living. During the years that followed, the young man's life showed forth his love and devotion for the Lord Jesus.

Even Unto Death

A missionary from India visited a college, seeking volunteers for the mis-

sion field in India. He said the work was not difficult, that they would have good homes, and enjoy the services of plenty of servants. *Not one volunteered!* Later, another missionary came to the college, seeking volunteers for the Congo. The missionary said bluntly to the students, "It will most likely mean certain death to some of you, too!" *Immediately,* six men volunteered for service.

She Refused

The beautiful daughter of a minister entered a large university. Many attentions were showered upon her. When she was asked to attend dances, she graciously *refused.* When she was asked to take Sunday morning rides or hikes, she replied, "Why, I can't. I always go to Sunday School and church on the Lord's Day." When she was asked to play cards, she said, with real distress, "Oh, I can't possibly do that. I am a Christian. Please excuse me!"

The young men and women of the college begged, teased, and reasoned with her. Finally, they ridiculed her and began to call her narrow, and prudish! But the young woman remained true to her Christian convictions and to her Lord. She continued to follow the Lord God with all her heart. That is what God wants you boys and girls to do always.

No Sacrifice

David Livingstone, the great missionary to Africa, said, "People talk of the sacrifice I have made for God. Can that be called a sacrifice which simply pays back, in a small part, the great debt we owe God and others? Is that a sacrifice which brings peace of mind and a bright hope of a glorious hereafter? It is no sacrifice. It is a privilege! Anxiety, sickness, suffering, and danger may cause the spirit to waver, but only for a moment. These are nothing compared with the glory which shall be revealed for us hereafter. How can we talk of sacrifice when we remember the great sacrifice which Christ made who gave Himself for us?"

Zigzagging

One day, a farmer drove into town. When he stopped at the little store, his dog, tired out, followed him in. The dog had followed the farmer's wagon all the way into town. Someone in the store blamed the farmer for tiring his dog by permitting him to follow him. The farmer said, "That dog is not tired from following me. He is tired out by his zigzagging. There was not an open gate, or a hole in the fence that he did not run in and explore. It was his zigzagging that tuckered him out!"

Garibaldi's Challenge

One day, Garibaldi, the great Italian reformer, made a speech before thousands of Italy's young men. He urged them to fight for the freedom of their home land. One timid fellow approached him asking, "If I fight, sir, what will be my reward?" Like a flash came the answer, "Wounds, scars, and, perhaps,

death. But remember that through your scars, Italy will be free!" "Then," said the young man, "I will follow to the death!"

Are *we* willing to follow Jesus, even unto death? Many men forsake all for their country. Many men die for their country. How sad it is that more Christians are not willing to forsake *all* to fully follow Christ, the King of Glory. How sad it is that we are not willing to die, if need be, for Him.

The Finished Task

David Livingstone, the famous missionary to Africa, followed the Lord fully. He spent his years giving the Gospel to the people in a land of darkness. Stanley found Livingstone in the heart of Africa after a long search. Stanley wanted Livingstone to return to England. He was to be "knighted" by the Queen, and welcomed by thousands of admirers.

There seemed to be every human reason why Livingstone should return to England. The weight of years was pressing upon him. The shortest marches bothered him. He was often compelled to rest for days. But Livingstone said to Stanley, "No, I can't go back to England. It is impossible. I *must* finish the task which God has given me to do!" Livingstone remained in Africa, faithfully following the Lord to the end of his earthly journey.

CONVERSION

At the Darkest Hour

Dr. R. A. Torrey was a famous evangelist. He was used of God to bring many lost souls to the Saviour. When Dr. Torrey was a young man, he was

deep in sin. He had no faith in God, the Bible, Heaven, or hell. His mother was an earnest Christian. She pleaded with him to turn to God for forgiveness. She prayed for him. Finally, he said to his mother, "I'm tired of it all. I'm going to leave home and not bother you anymore! You will not see me anymore." The mother followed him to the door, and to the gate, pleading, praying, loving, and weeping. At the gate she said, "Son, when you come to the darkest hour of all, when everything seems lost and gone, if you will earnestly call on your mother's God and seek Him, you will get help."

After he left home, Dr. Torrey went deeper and deeper into the ways of sin. Finally, one night in a hotel room, he was unable to sleep. He was wearied with his sins, and weary of life. At last, unable to sleep, he said, "I will get out of this bed. I will take the gun over there on the dresser, and end my life!" As he got out of his bed to do that awful thing, his mother's words came back to him, "Son, when the darkest hour of all comes and everything seems lost, if you will *earnestly* call on your mother's God, you will get help!"

Young Torrey fell on his knees beside his bed. He cried out, "Oh, God of my mother, if there be such a Being, I want help. I want light. If you will give it to me, I will follow You!" In a moment, his dark soul was filled with light. He *knew* that God was his Helper. He knew that Christ was his Saviour! He hastened back to his home. When his mother saw him, she exclaimed, "Oh, my boy, I *knew* you were coming back! You have found the Lord! God has told me so!"

A New Man in Christ Jesus

Charles G. Finney was a great preacher, who lived many years ago. One night, when Mr. Finney was preaching, a bad-looking man came in the church. After the service, the bad man said, "Mr. Finney, I want you to come with me." Some men warned Mr. Finney not to go. They said, "That man is a criminal. He is a murderer." Mr. Finney said, "That man wants me to go with him, and I am going. You pray for me!"

Mr. Finney went with the man through the streets, and then through dark, winding alleys. Finally, the man opened a door into a dark room. He lighted a candle. Then, he shut the door and locked it. Mr. Finney saw several guns, and a revolver on a table in the room. The man said, "Mr. Finney, I am a criminal. But tonight, I heard you preach about the Lord Jesus Christ. You said that He can save us from sin. Now, I want to know your honest opinion: Do you think that a man like me can be saved?" Mr. Finney said, "If you will confess and forsake your sins; if you will believe in Christ, the Saviour, then your sins will be forgiven."

The man said, "Mr. Finney, I am not only a criminal, but I am a gambler. I am not only a gambler, but I am a murderer. Do you believe that God will forgive me?" Mr. Finney answered, "I am compelled by the Lord to preach His Gospel. I do not care what your sins are. If you will confess and forsake your sins; if you will trust in Jesus Christ, the Son of God, He will cleanse you by His Blood from *all* sins!"

Then, Mr. Finney quoted some verses from the Bible: "And the Blood of Jesus Christ His Son cleanseth us from *all* sin"; "Come *now*, and let us reason together, said the Lord: though your sins be as scarlet, they shall be as white as snow; though they be red like crimson, they shall be as wool". Said Mr. Finney, "My man, if you will confess and *for-*

sake your sins, I believe God will have mercy upon you!"

Mr. Finney left the man. For a few moments, the man sat by the table. Then, he took his cards and threw them in the fire. He took his whisky bottles and emptied them in the gutter. He buried his guns and revolver. Then, he confessed his sins to God, and cried unto Him for forgiveness.

About daybreak, the man went home. He could not sleep. Presently, it was breakfast time. His little girl called him to breakfast. Kindly, he answered, "Darling, tell Mamma that Papa does not want breakfast." The little girl could not believe her ears. He had never called her "darling" before. She ran and told her mother about it. The mother and the little girl came in. The father placed one arm around mother, and the other arm around his little girl. He told them that he had confessed his sins and forsaken them, and that he had believed in the Lord Jesus. Now, he was a *saved* man; a *new* man in Christ Jesus! How happy they were as they had their first prayer meeting together!

How wonderful it is that the Lord Jesus can make *new* creatures of us!

Seams That Never Rip

A young girl worked in a sewing factory. The Lord Jesus saved her. How different her life became. She said, "Many times I used to sew seams that would not hold. They were sure to rip. But since the Lord Jesus has saved me, I sew seams that will never rip!"

A Better Servant

We heard of a servant girl who did the house cleaning carelessly. She never swept under the rugs. One day, the girl attended special meetings at the church. She trusted Jesus, and was saved. She was a different girl in the *home*. She did her work cheerfully and well. Said the lady for whom she worked, "She is surely a Christian now, for now she sweeps beneath the rugs, too!"

A Different Life

In a large factory in Dayton, Ohio, there was a foreman who often got drunk. He would work a good part of the time. Then he would get drunk and stay away from his work for two or three days. Then, one day, everyone noticed a change in the foreman. He looked different. He attended to his business. He did not get drunk. Some of the men in the factory began to tease him. They said he had been saved in the noonday shop meeting. The manager came by, and asked, "Is it true? Have you been converted in the noon shop meetings?" The foreman stood straight. He looked the manager in the face, and replied, "Yes, sir; I have been saved. My life is *different* now. I have turned the corner!"

Saved in Prison

Mr. Moody preached one night on the story of the Philippian jailer. When Mr. Moody preached this sermon, a newspaper wrote the story. They called the story, "How the Jailer Got Caught."

In a jail in St. Louis was a burglar named Booth. Someone gave him a copy of the newspaper. He read the story that Mr. Moody had told. His heart was touched. He trusted Jesus as his Saviour. God gave this thief a new heart, and a new nature.

Soon, the keeper of the jail saw a change in Booth. He was no longer rough and mean. Finally Booth was sent out of the prison a free man. He went out to preach the Gospel to others. He told how God can save even a wicked man and give him a new heart and a new nature.

Both Became Christians

Over in England, there once lived two great men who were unbelievers. They were Gilbert West, a famous English jurist, and Lord Littleton, a light in the literary world. These men agreed to destroy Christianity. They thought that two things were necessary to do this: They must prove that the resurrection of Jesus was fiction, and not *fact;* and they *must* explain away the conversion of Saul. West assumed the task of "getting rid" of the resurrection. Littleton took the task of disposing of the conversion of Saul on the Damascus Road.

After a year, or more, the two men came together to compare notes. They had had ample time to work on their respective tasks. When they met, *both were Christians!* Each confessed he had been converted as a result of his own research. The resurrection had withstood the test of unfriendly investigation. Saul's conversion had also held up under investigation, and could not be explained away.

The Way of Life

A little girl asked her father: "Do you ever pray?" He replied, "Your mother or your aunt has put you up to this." "Oh, no," said the child, "but the preacher said that all good men pray." The father answered, "You and your mother and your aunt can go your way. I will go mine!" Then the little girl asked, "Which way are you going,

Father?" Suddenly, it flashed upon the father that he had chosen the way of *death.* He began to pray for mercy. God saved him, and he left the way of death to walk in the way of life. Which way have you chosen? Which way are you going?

The Old Colonel

One night there wandered into Water Street Mission, New York, a man known as "the old colonel." He was tall, being over six feet. He was old, being over sixty years old, but he looked older. He had a long, dirty gray beard. His gray hair was dirty and uncut, hanging way down his back. His eyes were bleary. His face was rugged and dirty. His ragged overcoat was fastened with a nail. His trousers were filled with holes. Instead of shoes, he had on his feet rags tied with strings.

Sin and whiskey had brought the old colonel to this pitiable condition. One never would have thought that he was a college graduate; that he had studied law in the office of President Lincoln's great law secretary, Stanton!

That night, down in the Water Street Mission, the old colonel heard the message of the Lord Jesus. He was told how Jesus loved him; how Jesus had died to save him from sin and ruin. The old colonel cried out, "O Lord, if it is not *too late,* forgive this poor old sinner!" For seven nights, the old colonel returned to the mission. On the last night, he said, "Brother Hadley, I believe that the Lord Jesus can save me. I trust Him *now!*"

From that moment, the old colonel was a changed man. He was truly born again. He never touched another drop of whisky. God was good to him. He restored his intellect. His powers to do good returned to him. He even became younger looking in appearance. He was a dignified, Christian gentleman, faithful to the Lord Jesus to the day of his death.

How we thank God for the new birth! How we thank God that the Lord Jesus can give us a *new* heart, a *new* nature, a *new* life! "Hallelujah, what a Saviour!"

The Human Tiger

A French explorer in Africa came to the region of the Barotsi people. He heard many stories about the native king, known as "The Human Tiger." This king's greatest delight had been to torture to death those who offended him. One day, the explorer came to a missionary station. The pastor, who was himself a Frenchman, invited him to attend services on Sunday. The French explorer knew nothing of God. He went to church to be polite, and sat through the service.

After the service, the explorer asked the pastor, "Who was that remarkable looking man, sitting next to me, who listened so carefully to all you said?" The pastor replied, "That was King Lewanika, 'The Human Tiger.' He has been saved. He is a loyal and a faithful member of my church!" "Oh," said the explorer, "if that is what Christ can do, *I mean to be His!*"

Christ Made Him Different

An Italian woman, whose husband had accepted the Gospel, and became a Christian, was asked, "Is it true that your husband has changed his religion?" "No," she replied, "but his religion has changed him! Now he has

Christ, and Christ has certainly changed him! You must have noticed yourself that he doesn't get drunk any more, and that he does not swear and scold like he used to."

Saved Under Water

A man, who was a great sinner, was helping load freight on a big steamer. As he was going up the gangplank, someone pushed him, and he fell into the water. He gave a horrible oath as he disappeared into the water. His comrades rescued him from the water. He seemed to be drowned; but they worked hard to revive him. Finally, they were successful. Color came back to the man's face, and he began to breathe deeply. His first words were, "Praise God! I'm saved." Someone said, "Yes, you were nearly gone." He replied, "I don't mean being saved from drowning. I mean that the Lord has saved me from sin. He has forgiven me. He has taken my sins away."

Then the rescued man told what had happened: When he found himself in the water under the boat, he thought the end had surely come. In a flash, he saw himself kneeling at his mother's side as he had in his boyhood days. He heard his mother praying for him. He saw his sin as high as a mountain. He cried to God to save him for Jesus' sake. In that moment, he *knew* that God had forgiven him; that his sins were cleansed in the Blood of Jesus! That was why he praised God.

Has God forgiven *your* sins? If so, you, too, can praise God!

Christ Made Him Whole

A preacher was telling how Jesus can save a sinner and make him *whole*.

"Jesus can save you, He can forgive your sins and give you a new heart and a new life," the preacher said.

A man stood up and said, "Preacher, that's it! For years, I was a hard drinker. I lost my job. I sobered up, and got another job. And again I failed. For years, I tried to patch up, but the patches would fall off. My wife and children had to leave me. One cold, wet, windy night, I sat in the doorway of an empty house, half asleep. A Bible woman asked me to come into a nearby mission. There, I heard of the Lord Jesus. They told me how He died on the Cross for me. I came to Him, and He didn't patch me up. He made me whole! He gave me a new heart and a new nature. Now my wife and children are with me, and we all are happy together!"

A New Stomach?

Sam Hadley was a drunkard. One day, the Lord Jesus saved him. Jesus took away *all* his desire for strong drink. One day, Sam Hadley was praising the Lord for taking away his desire for strong drink. A doctor said, "Man, you would have to have a new stomach to have the desire for drink removed." "Praise God," said Sam Haadley, "I knew I had a new heart, but this is the first time I knew I had a *new stomach!*"

Sam Hadley did not have a new stomach; but when Jesus saved him, Jesus gave him a new heart and a new nature. Sam Hadley was a new man inside. He no longer loved sin. He no longer desired strong drink.

What Jesus Christ Can Do

Some years ago, a man was in prison in Japan. He had been in prison for twenty-five years. He was a murderer. One day, this man was sitting in his cell. He was planning to make trouble among the other prisoners. He wanted to cause a riot. A Book on a shelf above his head fell and struck him. He picked it up, and read on the open page, "Come unto Me, all ye that labour and are heavy laden, and I will give you rest."

The Book was a New Testament. It had been placed in the prison cell by the governor who was a Christian. The murderer, whose name was Miyamoto, began to read the New Testament. He read about the Lord Jesus. He read how Jesus could save lost sinners from their sin. He was wonderfully saved. His whole heart and life were changed.

Not long afterward, he was set free from prison. He returned to his own village and family. Everyone noticed the great change which had come into his life. He planned to move away from his village, but his neighbors begged him to remain. They said, "Your life is a good example to our boys. Your life shows us what Jesus Christ can do. We want the Jesus religion, too!" Soon, the people in the little village were asking for copies of the New Testament which would tell them about Jesus, the Saviour. They wanted to be a Christian like Miyamoto.

From Liquor to Paint

A Salvation Army girl often visited a saloon in the City of Cleveland. She went into the saloon to give out tracts, and tell the poor lost people about Jesus. The keeper of the saloon refused to hear about Jesus. But one Saturday night, he listened to what the girl said. The next day, he attended a mission service, and there gave his heart to the Lord Jesus. How greatly did he love the Lord Jesus! His heart and life were changed. He went to his saloon, and poured all the liquor out in the street. Instead of running a saloon, he began to sell wallpaper and paint. Each day, he told those around him "how great things" Jesus had done for him.

COOPERATION

Two Agreed

Wonderful things often happen when God's dear children work together, and pray together for the salvation of the lost.

One Sunday morning, a young preacher read his text. It was this: "If *two of you shall agree* on earth as touching any thing that they shall ask, it shall be done for them of My Father which is in Heaven" *(Matt. 18:19)*. A little lady stood to her feet and asked, "Young man, do you believe that promise? Are you willing to agree with me and pray with me for the salvation of my *lost* husband?"

The preacher was silent a moment. He was thinking deeply. A blacksmith arose and said, "I will agree with you. I will pray with you for the salvation of your husband!"

That afternoon, the little old lady and the blacksmith prayed *earnestly* for the salvation of the husband. The husband had been a rough sinner all of his life. He had had no room for Jesus in his heart. That night, God answered the *united* prayers of the *two* who *agreed*! The husband was wonderfully saved!

The Fourth Man Won

Some years ago, four Christian men were burdened for an unsaved doctor. They wanted the doctor to be saved. They decided to pray *together* and work *together* for his salvation. After they had prayed, one by one, the men went to the doctor's office. There, they pled with the doctor to become a Christian. The doctor would not listen to the first man. He listened to the second and third men, but he would not yield. When the *fourth man* came to the office to talk to him, the doctor could hold out no longer. He gave his heart and his life to Jesus!

Joining Hands Too Late

One evening, in the Province of Alberta, Canada, a happy father and mother went for a stroll through a nearby wheat field with their little boy. As they wandered through the field, each thought the other one held the hand of their child. All at once, they realized that the boy was not with them. They called and called, but there was no answer. Soon, they became terrified. They hunted in the tall wheat without results.

Finally, the father went back to the village and got a searching party together. Many willing helpers searched all night. When it was nearly dawn, some one suggested that they all join hands and cover the entire wheat field, in a last effort to find the lost child. They joined hands, and soon they came across the lifeless body of the child! A hush spread over them, for they had found the child too late! They gathered about the body, and as they stood there in silence with bowed heads, some one whispered, "Oh, if we had only joined hands before it was TOO LATE!"

Let us join hands in rescuing the perishing ones before it is too late.

The Best Horse

Two boys stood in a barn discussing the merits of a team of beautiful black horses. One was a city lad who had come to visit his friend on the farm. As the boys talked, they petted the horses. The city lad, knowing little about the marks of a good work horse, said, "I would rather have this one. There is not a blemish on him."

The farmer boy replied, "Boy, you wouldn't rather have him if you had to work with him. He's the best looking, but this other horse is the best horse on the farm. He will pull with any other horse. He will pull so hard that he is almost stretched out flat. His collar doesn't fit too well, but he pulls anyway. That's why he's got scars on his shoulders. The horse you like won't even come up against the collar when the pulling gets tough. He lets the other horse do all the hard work. You see, looks don't count for much when there is hard work to be done."

Pulling Together

Two tough old mules — say, get this dope —
Were tied together with a piece of rope;
Said one to the other, "You come MY way,
While I take a nibble of that new mown hay."
"I won't," said the other, "You come with ME,
I have some hay, over this way, you see."
So they got nowhere, just pawed up the dirt,
Pulling each way, how that rope did hurt.
Then faced they about, those stubborn mules,
And said, "WE'RE ACTING JUST LIKE HUMAN FOOLS!"
"Let's pull together, I'll go your way,
Then you come with me and we'll BOTH EAT HAY."
So they ate their hay and LIKED it too,
And said, "Let's be comrades, good and true!"
As the sun went down they were heard to bray,
"Ah, this is the end of a perfect day!"

The Fanner Bees

One midsummer evening, a man went into a bee garden with his friend, the bee keeper. They stopped near a bee-hive. From the hive came a sound like that of sea waves, advancing and retreating. The old bee keeper said, "They are the fanner bees. It's their job to keep the air in the hive sweet and fresh. They stand near the center of the hive with their heads lowered. Their wings move so rapidly that if you saw them, you would think you were looking at a gray mist. The movement of their wings drives out the bad air through one entrance, and sucks in the pure air at the other side." The old bee keeper lighted a candle, and held it near the entrance to the hive. Instantly, the light was put out by the strong current of evening air.

As they stood together there in the garden, the man said to the bee keeper, "Isn't that how God wants His children to act? Are not we to work together, each doing his part to drive out the bad, and to let in the sweet and pure?"

COURAGE

Brave Scotch Bairns

Years ago, the Scotch Covenanters were being persecuted. King Charles sent out his soldiers to round up the Covenanters. One day, King Charles' soldiers came to a certain village. They could find no Covenanters. So they rounded up a number of children and commanded them to tell where their parents were hidden. They threatened to shoot the children if they would not betray the secret. In spite of the cruel threat, not one lad or lassie would tell. The officer was a rough man. He said, "If you do not tell me quickly, you will be shot!" The little children huddled closer together, but remained silent. Then the officer said, "Make them kneel down." All knelt down, except one lad who said, "I have done nothing wrong. I'll not kneel down. I'll die standing up!" The officer said, as the children were crying pitifully, "You have not prayed!"

Suddenly, a little girl said, "Please, sir, my mother taught me a song. We will sing that!" All the children stood, and, as the tears ran down the soldiers' faces, their little voices rang out: "The Lord, my Shepherd, I'll not want!" The officer himself had learned that song at his mother's knee. His heart, too, was touched. Before the song was finished, he and the other soldiers had disappeared, leaving the little children in peace!

"They Fell Facing the Enemy!"

During World War I, a battle was won by the Americans at terrific cost of life. After the battle, a general walked over the battlefield. It was strewn with American dead. The general observed that ALL the heroic dead had fallen with their faces toward the enemy!

May God help each Christian soldier to face, unafraid, the enemy of souls, Satan! May we go forward under the banner of our Captain, Jesus, always with our faces against the enemy.

Daniel's Backbone

A class of boys in Sunday school was studying the story of Daniel. The teacher had different boys read verses aloud. Presently, he asked one boy to read Daniel 3:6. This verse reads, "Because an excellent spirit was in him." By mistake, the boy read, "Because an excellent SPINE was in him!" It was bad reading, but it was the truth, for Daniel was a man with a REAL BACKBONE! He was always strong and courageous.

"We Don't Have to Come Back"

Some years ago, an ocean vessel was wrecked on a reef near the American coast. A lifeboat crew was preparing to go out to the scene of the wreck. Some of the young men in the crew were untrained. One of these young men turned with a white face to the old sailor, who was captain of the lifeboat, and said, "The wind is blowing toward the sea. The tide is running out. We can never come back against the wind and the tide. What's the use of going?"

The old sailor looked at the young man and said, "Launch the boat! We have to go out, but WE DON'T HAVE TO COME BACK!"

A Fearless Lawyer

One day, a stranger came into Abraham Lincoln's law office. "State your case," said Lincoln. The stranger told Lincoln about his case. When he had finished, Lincoln said, "I cannot serve you. You are WRONG and the other party is RIGHT!" The stranger replied, "That is none of your business. I will hire you and pay you for taking the case!" Lincoln exclaimed, "My business is NEVER to defend wrong. I never take a case that is wrong!" The stranger asked, "Not for any amount of pay?" "Not for all you are worth," replied Lincoln.

He Refused

Harry Shepler was a sergeant in the Army. One morning, he was told to report for work at the canteen. There he was to serve *beer* to the soldiers. Shepler was a Christian. He *knew* it was *wrong* to serve beer. *He refused* to go to the canteen, and work. He was reported to a major. The major sent for him. He asked, "Are you the young man who disobeyed orders this morning?" "Yes, sir," he replied, "I am." "Why did you do it?" asked the major. Shepler replied, "I do not believe it is *right* to do what I was asked to do. I am a Christian. I entered the Army to be a soldier, and not a *bartender!*" The major arose and held out his hand. He said, "Shepler, you are the kind of man we want; the kind we need. I am glad to see a fellow who will refuse to do wrong. You need not report for duty at the canteen!"

Always be brave. Always stand for what is right. Always *refuse* to do what is wrong.

Little Pedro

A missionary was preaching to some Mexicans. A little boy came walking down the aisle on little fat, brown legs. With serious eyes, he looked up at the missionary and said, "You ask what I would have done if I had been in the crowd when Jesus fell, carrying His Cross. Please, sir, if I had been there, I would have helped Him carry it!"

The missionary said, "But, Pedro, if you had helped Jesus carry His Cross, the cruel Roman soldiers would have beaten your back with a whip until the blood ran down to your heels!"

With a look of courage, the little boy said, "I don't care. I would have helped Him carry it just the same!"

Two weeks later, little Pedro was at the mission again. The missionary patted him on his back. Pedro cried out, "Don't do that! My back is sore. My back hurts!" The missionary took the little boy into the cloak room. There, he looked at his back. It was covered with big, bloody welts. "Who did that?" the missionary asked.

"Mother did it. She whipped me because I loved Jesus. But I don't care. I will always love and serve Jesus!"

A Brave Indian

In Mexico are many villages of Indians. In one of these villages an Indian named Antonia Reyes became a Christian. He was eager to tell his neighbors and friends about his Saviour. One dark night, he was called before the council. He found several Indians armed with guns sitting by a judge. The judge told Antonia that he must give up his new religion, or leave the village. Then the judge told the Indians to shoot Antonia if he did not obey.

Antonia was not afraid. He told the judge and the Indians that he could not give up Jesus; for Jesus Christ was his Saviour. For the first time in his life, he had joy in his heart. He felt that he could not leave the village until many others knew Christ as their Saviour. So Antonia stayed. He told all of his friends, all of his neighbors, and even the strangers about Jesus Christ, the Saviour.

Today, in that village, there stands a little chapel built by believers in Jesus Christ. It is a monument to Antonia, the Indian who loved Christ more than he loved his own life.

COVETOUSNESS

A Window and A Mirror

A certain old rich man was very stingy. He never gave anything to help the poor and needy. One day, a rabbi visited him. He led the rich man to a window and said, "Look out there. What do you see?" The rich man replied, "I see men and women and little children on the street." The rabbi led him to a mirror and said, "Look in there. What do you see?" The rich man replied, "I see myself!" Then the rabbi said, "In the window is glass, and in the mirror is glass. But the glass of the mirror is covered with a little silver, and no sooner is the silver added than you cease to see others, and see only YOURSELF!"

The old rich man had ceased to see others and their needs, because of his grasping greed and love for silver!

A Life Lost for a Few Cents

A ship was slowly sinking. The last lifeboat was being put off into the sea. The mate was about to step into the boat. Then he started back, saying, "Oh, I have forgotten my purse!" The captain of the ship shouted to the mate, "Come away! Leave your purse!" But the mate called back, "I'll be only a minute." Then he dived into the water in the hold of the ship. Just as he disappeared, the vessel gave a lurch. Those in the lifeboat were compelled to push off. They were just in time. A moment later, the ship rolled over and sank like lead beneath the waters.

The next morning, the dead body of the mate washed up on the nearby shore. In his hand, he tightly held his purse. When it was opened, it was found that the purse held *eighteen* pence. That poor mate had lost his life for a few cents! Some lose even more than their lives for money: they lose their souls!

Not Covetous

A Christian miner worked very hard every day in the mines for a living. One day, the overseer said, "Thomas, I have got an easier job for you. There will not be so much hard work, and you will get better wages. Will you accept it?" *Most* men would have jumped at such an offer. But Thomas said, "Our poor brother Tregony has a sickly body. He is not able to do hard work. I am afraid his work will shorten his life, and then what will his poor family do? Won't you *please* give the *easier* job to him? I can go on working, as I have done!" The overseer was wonderfully pleased with Thomas' generous love for a friend.

God Hidden

A minister was troubled because a man in his church loved money so much. From early morning till late at night, the man toiled to make money. He piled up his money in lands and stocks and bonds. He did not have time to be kind to others. He did not have time to serve God.

One day, the minister went to see the man. He opened his Bible, and pointed to the word, "God!" "Can you see that word?" asked the minister. "Certainly," replied the man. Then the minister took a piece of money out of his pocket and placed it over the word "God." "Can you see it now?" asked the minister. The man replied, "No!" Money was hiding "God" from him. The minister spoke kindly to the man and said, "Brother, don't let money hide God from you. Don't let money shut out the face of your Heavenly Father!"

The man learned the needed lesson. From that day, he began to live for God. He began to serve God and others.

Never Enough

An old man one day asked a boy, "When is a man rich enough?" The lad replied, "When he has ten thousand dollars!" "No," said the man. "Twenty thousand?" "No." "An hundred thousand?" "No." "Five hundred thousand?" "No." The lad gave up. He confessed that he did not know when a man is rich enough. Gravely, the old man said, "A man is rich enough when he has a little more than he has, and that is *never!*"

The Two Eagles

Some years ago, a man in his backyard saw a speck in the sky. He watched the speck. It grew larger and larger. Then he discovered that two large bald eagles were in deadly combat in the sky. They were fighting over a fish. Presently, the fish was dropped to the ground, but the eagles continued their deadly struggle. Soon, they were bloody and exhausted. With a wild scream, they suddenly parted, and each took a fatal plunge to the earth! They fell to the ground, *dead*, within a few feet of the man. Covetousness, or greed, had destroyed them. Each eagle had been so interested in getting the fish that it had forgotten his own life. How often men are just like those eagles. In the struggle for earthly possessions, they forget their own lives and even their souls.

The Satisfied Farmer

A Quaker wanted to teach his neighbors a lesson. He put a sign on a vacant lot adjoining his house, which read, "I will give this lot to anyone who is fully satisfied!" A wealthy farmer rode by and read the sign. He stopped, as he said to himself, "Since my Quaker friend is going to give that lot away, I may as well have it as anyone else. I am rich. I have all I need. So, certainly I can qualify!" When the Quaker friend saw the wealthy farmer at the door, he asked, "Art thou fully satisfied?"

"I surely am," said the farmer; "I have all I need!"

"Friend," said the Quaker, "if thou art satisfied, why dost thou want my lot?"

The wealthy farmer searched his heart. He knew suddenly that he was not satisfied. He was always wanting more than he had. Covetousness was in his heart, and discontent in his soul.

CROSS

Hidden in the Cleft of the Rock

A missionary worker was riding across the prairie in a wagon with some Indian friends. Suddenly they saw a terrible storm approaching. The missionary said, "We are certainly going to get soaked." The driver replied, "I hope not. Just ahead of us is a great rock. If we can reach that rock, we will be sheltered." As they hurried on their way, they saw the storm break in the distance. The rain began to pour down and advanced rapidly toward them. Then they saw the great rock looming ahead of them. It rose up in the air about fifty feet and covered about an acre of ground. As they neared the rock, a great cave was seen in its side. Just as the storm reached them, they rode into the cave. There they stayed, safe and dry, while the storm beat with all its fury upon the rock. While the storm raged, the Indians sang,

> "Rock of Ages, cleft for me,
> Let me hide myself in thee!"

The Highland Mother

In Scotland, there lived a widow who had a baby boy whom she loved very much. Times were hard. Food was scarce. She wanted to go to the home of a relative who lived across the mountain, about ten miles away. One day, with her baby, she started the walk across the mountains. A terrible storm suddenly came upon the mountains. The mother's strength soon failed. She did not reach the relative's home that night. The next day, men found her frozen body! In a sheltered nook nearby was her baby, safe and well. She had wrapped most of her own clothes about the baby to keep him warm.

Years passed. One day, the son of the minister who had conducted the mother's funeral went to a church in Glasgow, Scotland, to preach his first sermon. Somehow, that day, he kept thinking of the story of the Highland mother. He had often heard his father relate the story. Instead of preaching the sermon he had prepared, he told the story of the Highland mother's love for her baby.

A few days later, the young minister was summoned to the bedside of a dying man. "You do not know me," said the man. "I have lived in Glasgow for many years, but have never attended a church here. The other day, I passed your church and heard the singing. I slipped into a back seat. There I heard you tell the story of the love a widow mother had for her infant son. I am that son! I have never forgotten my mother's love. But I never thought of the love God showed in giving Himself for me, until I heard you tell my mother's story. I know now that God loves me. My mother did not die in vain. She must have prayed that I would love Christ and would become a Christian. Her prayer is answered!"

The Fire of God's Judgment

Years ago, some pioneers were making their way across the plains. They were journeying to a distant place that had been opened up for homesteading. They were traveling in covered wagons, drawn by oxen. One day, they noticed a long line of smoke in the west. It stretched for miles across the prairie. Soon, it was evident that the dried grass was burning fiercely. The fire was coming toward them rapidly! They had crossed a river the day before, but they knew that it would be impossible to go back to that before the flames reached them.

One man knew what to do. He gave the command to set fire to the grass behind them. When the grass had burned and the fire had moved on behind them, he commanded that the whole company move backward upon the place where the fire had been.

As the flames from the west roared toward them, a little girl cried out, "We will all be burned up!" The leader replied, "My child, the flames cannot reach us here. We are standing where the fire *has* been!"

The fire of God's judgment of sin fell upon the Lord Jesus as He died upon His Cross. There, they burned themselves out. All who are "in Christ" today, all who trust in Him, are safe *forever*!

The Brave Mother Hen

Prairie fires had been sweeping through the Middle West. A rescue party rode out to see if anyone needed help. They came to a charred cottage. On the ground, near the roadway, they saw what appeared to be a black chicken. Going over to it, they found that it had evidently been a hen, but now was quite dead, the head and back being burned almost to a cinder. The hen sat with her wings partly spread out. One of the men gave her a kick with his foot, and *three little chicks ran out*! Bravely, the mother hen had covered them, and had sat still in the midst of the scorching flame! Choosing to be burned to death, rather than have one of her little chicks perish, she gave her life.

On the Cross the Lord Jesus died for *us*. He chose death rather than *one of*

us should perish! The Bible tells us how the Lord Jesus, on the Cross, bore the sins and paid the penalty for us: "So Christ was *once* offered to bear the sins of many" *(Heb. 9:28)*; "Who His own self bare *our* sins in His own body on the Tree, that we, being dead to sins, should live unto righteousness: by whose stripes [we] were healed" *(I Peter 2:24)*.

Greater Than a Mother's Love

One day, there was a cry, "Fire! Fire!" A crowded tenement building, in the city slums, was on fire. The fire engines came thundering down the street. From every doorway of the burning building, from every window, people tumbled out onto the pavement. The flames mounted higher and higher. Smoke was pouring out from the broken windows and open doors.

Suddenly, a little woman rushed toward the fire marshal. She said that her child was on the third story of the burning building. The marshal said, "It is impossible for anyone to go in there now. No fireman can attempt it!" Without a word, the little woman shot past the marshal. He tried to catch hold of her, but failed. She rushed toward the burning building and disappeared through the smoke-filled door. She never returned. Some hours later, they found her in the remains of the building! Her hand, burned to a crisp, was resting on the face of the child she had tried to save!

How great is the love of a mother for her child! There is a love, however, that is *greater* than a mother's love. It is the love which the Lord Jesus has for lost sinners. He gave His life for sinners.

The Blizzard

Some years ago, a terrible blizzard came to North Dakota. A little country school was dismissed early because of the blizzard. Hazel Miner started home with her two little brothers. The blizzard became so bad that they could go no further. Hazel arranged some shelter for the boys. She wrapped the small boys in her coat. Then she herself lay over them to help keep them warm. Many hours later, when they were rescued, the two little boys were healthy and well. But their sister, who was lying over them, had frozen to death! Hazel gave her life for her two little brothers. The Lord Jesus gave His life for us upon the Cross.

For All Mankind

The night was dark. The road was lonely. A man named Kline was lying in wait for his enemy. He had decided to kill his enemy. Suddenly, he was startled to hear the voices of some children singing, as they were returning home from church. What were they singing? It was the little song:

> "Jesus died for *all* mankind,
> And Jesus died for *me!*"

The guilty conscience of the man made him hear these words:

> "Jesus died for *old man Kline*,
> And Jesus died for *me!*"

His heart was filled with terror and remorse. He fled to his home. His heart found no peace until he, too, knew the Lord Jesus as a personal Saviour. Then he was able to sing with the children:

> "Jesus died for *all* mankind,
> And Jesus died for *me!*"

"For Me Two Have Died"

On a ship, an old sailor, who was a Christian, often talked to a wicked young sailor about Jesus. He asked the young sailor to receive Jesus as his Saviour. But the young sailor laughed and would not do it.

One day the ship was wrecked. When the life boats were let down, there was not room in them for all. The young sailor had to remain behind. He was very pale. He muttered, "I am lost, eternally lost!" There was a place for the old sailor in a life boat. But the old sailor picked up the young sailor, and threw him down in the boat, saying, "You are not ready to die. I am. I am willing to die for *you*, but mind that I see you in Heaven." The young sailor was saved. The old sailor went down with the sinking ship.

Not long after this, the young sailor received Jesus as his Saviour. He often said, "For me two have died." The old sailor gave his life for the young sailor, and the Lord Jesus gave His life on the Cross that the young sailor might be saved eternally.

We Have the Peace

A friend said to a young lady who was sick, "You suffer much, I fear." "Yes," she said. Then she pointed to her hand and said, "But there is no nail there. He had the nails; I have the peace." Then she lay her hand on her brow, and said, "There are no thorns here. He had the thorns; I have the peace." Then she touched her side and said, "There is no spear here. He had the spear. I have the peace!" How truly she spoke. For us He made peace with God through His death on the Cross.

The Storm Fell on Him

A young English minister took a walk one afternoon. He came to a limestone gorge about two and one-half miles long. He was enjoying the scenery as he passed through the gorge, and he did not notice the storm clouds gathering overhead. Finally, he looked up and saw the dark, overcast sky. He turned and hastened toward home. The storm, however, overtook him. The rain began to fall in torrents. The young minister found shelter in the cleft of a great limestone rock. As he stood there in the place of shelter, he watched the rain descend, heard the thunder roar, and saw the lightning flash. He was deeply impressed! He took a pencil and piece of paper from his pocket, and wrote these words:

"Rock of ages, cleft for me,
   Let me hide myself in Thee!"

This experience was the inspiration that led Augustus M. Toplady to write our great hymn of faith, hope, and love. How beautifully the hymn sets forth our trust in Christ, who once offered Himself so that we might take shelter in Him.

As we look upon the Cross of Christ, we say with Isaiah, "And a Man shall be as an hiding place from the wind, and a covert from the tempest; as rivers of water in a dry place, as the shadow of a great rock in a weary land" *(Is. 32:2).*

"I Belong There"

A missionary in Africa was telling the heathen about the wonderful love of the Lord Jesus. The people were gathered in a clearing in the forest on a beautiful moonlit night. The missionary told them of the Lord Jesus. He told of the wonderful miracles of Jesus. Finally, he told of the death of Jesus on the Cross. He said that Jesus died on the Cross to save us from sin. As the missionary was talking, the chief jumped to his feet and said, "Stop! Take Him down from the Cross. I belong there myself. I am the sinner. He did not deserve to die!"

Boys and girls, the Lord Jesus was without sin. He died for us. The Bible says, "Christ died for *our* sins." Have you ever thanked Him for dying for you?

The Farmer's Sacrifice

A farmer in North Carolina drove two horses into town one day. He stopped in front of a store, and was about to enter when the horses became frightened. He sprang in front of them, and seized the reins. The horses dashed down the street while the man clung to the bridles. On the maddened horses rushed! Then, with wild frenzy, they rose on their haunches, and, leaping, came down upon the man with an awful crash!

People ran to rescue the bleeding body of the man. As he lay dying, a friend, bending tenderly over him, asked, "Why did you sacrifice your life for the horses and wagon?" With his last breath, he gasped, "Go and look in the wagon!" In the wagon, they found the farmer's little boy asleep on the straw! The farmer had given his life to save his little boy.

When the Lord Jesus went to the Cross, He gave His life to save all who will trust in Him. He gave His life for *you* and me.

"He died for you: He died for me,
   His Blood hath atoned for our race;
   O wonderful love! He came from above,
   To suffer and die in *our* place!"

He Bore the Punishment

One time, a little boy made mud pies. When he was very dirty, he went into the house. He climbed up on Mother's clean bed. He got the bedspread very dirty. Mother had said that no one should get her bedspread dirty. The little boy disobeyed his mother. In a little while, Mother returned from the store. She saw what her bad boy had done. She said, "I must punish my boy. He disobeyed me."

Big brother heard the little boy crying. He came in, and saw the dirty bed. He knew that Mother was going to punish the little boy. He felt very sorry for the little boy. He said, "Mother, let me take my little brother's place. Let me bear his whipping." So Mother gave the punishment to big brother, and the little boy went free. How much the little boy loved his big brother. How he thanked his big brother for taking his punishment.

The Lord Jesus was punished for our sins on the Cross. How we love Him! How we thank him for "taking our punishment!"

The First Claim

In a little country village, there lived a family of four. There were father and mother and two small children. They lived in a little cottage. One night, the little cottage caught on fire! In a few seconds, the whole roof and sides of the cottage were blazing! There was no fire engine in the little village. People ran to the fire and stood there helpless.

Suddenly, a young man rushed up. "What," cried he, "can't something be done to rescue the family?" No one answered. The young man r u s h e d through the flames into the cottage. A moment later, he rushed out. Under each arm, he had a little child. They were unhurt, for Andy had hidden them under his coat. Andy, however, was terribly burned. Scarcely had he gotten out when the roof of the cottage fell in with a great crash! The parents of the little children were never seen again.

A kind old woman took Andy to her home. She nursed him carefully, and cared for his burns.

Some time later, the village had a discussion. People wanted to know what was to become of the two children. It was decided to have a meeting to decide the question.

When the day of the meeting arrived, there were two who claimed the little children. The first was the squire of the village. He had money, and a good position. He offered a fine home to the children. The second was Andy. When he was asked what right he had to the little ones, he never said a word. He just stood up and held out his hands before the crowd. They were burned and scarred! They had been burned and scarred in recuing the little ones from the fire. The little children went to Andy. He had first claim on them.

The Mother Bird

Some men one day were trimming trees along the street. Just before lunch time, the men cut off a big limb in which was a bird's nest with four baby birds in it. The little birds were killed in the fall! Soon, the mother bird came back. She flew over again and again, calling, calling, calling for her babies. The men were sitting on the grass near the tree eating their lunch. They noticed the little mother bird flying over their heads, and calling. Suddenly, something dropped at the feet of one of the men. He picked it up. It was the little broken-hearted mother bird, *dead!* The mother bird's heart was filled with *love* and yearning for her baby birds. The Lord Jesus loved us so much that He laid down His life for us.

"He Gave His Life"

A chaplain was talking to a wounded soldier. Said he, "You have been hurt." The soldier replied, "Yes sir, but I thank God that I am alive. I am going home without my right hand, but my mother will be glad to have what is left of me." "Sure," said the chaplain, "your mother will be glad to have you as you are. Shall I write her and tell her that you have lost your right hand?" "Oh," said the soldier, "I did not lose it. I gave it!"

The Lord Jesus did not lose His life. He gave His life for the sheep. He said, "I am the good Shepherd: the good Shepherd *giveth His life* for the sheep" (*John 10:11*).

Drawn to Him

A man visiting a steel mill in Pennsylvania saw a wonderful thing: Out in the yard, where the men walked back and forth, some one held up a great magnet. As this magnet was held up, little pieces of iron, which had been trampled down into the earth, rose up in the air, and clung to the magnet. No one touched the pieces of iron, but the power of the magnet drew them. The visitor thought of the words which Jesus spoke, "And I, if I be lifted up from the earth, will draw all men unto Me" (*John 12:32*).

Many years ago, the Lord Jesus was lifted up from the earth on His Cross. There He died for lost sinners. Since then, millions of men and women, boys and girls, have been drawn unto Him. His death upon the Cross draws us to Him.

"If He Had Moved"

A minister was boarding at a farm house. The farmer was not a Christian. His wife had been praying for him for a long time. The minister longed to show the farmer how Christ died for him on the Cross.

Early one morning, the farmer took the minister out to the chicken house. He wanted to show the minister something. There, on one of the nests, sat a hen, with a number of baby chicks peeping out from under her wings. "Touch her," said the farmer. When the minister put his hands on the hen, he found that she was cold! Then hen was dead. "Look at the wound in her head," said the farmer. "During the night a weasel came. The weasel sucked all the blood from the hen's body. She never moved once! She was afraid the weasel would get her baby chicks. The baby chicks were saved, but the mother hen died."

"Oh," said the minister, "that was like Christ. He endured all the suffering on the Cross that we might be saved. He could have moved and saved His own life, but He wouldn't. You and I were under His wings. If He had moved, we would have been lost!"

Beautiful Hands

Some years ago, the home of an English family was discovered on fire. Everybody was out but the baby. The mother rushed into the burning building, and saved the baby. For years, the mother went about the house with her hands covered to hide the unsightly scars she received in rescuing her baby from the fire. One day, the daughter came into the mother's room unexpectedly and saw her hands uncovered. They were badly torn, scarred and disfigured. The girl was startled at the sight.

Then the mother said, "It happened when the house was on fire and you were in your cradle. I fought my way through the flames to get you. I wrapped you in a blanket and dropped you through the window and somebody caught you. I could not go down the stairway; so, I climbed out of the window. My hands were burned. I slipped and caught on the trellis work. My hands were torn. The doctor did his best for me. But my hands had been so badly torn and scarred that I have covered them up for years. They were torn and scarred when I rescued you from the flames!"

The girl took her mother's hands into her own beautiful hands, and, as she looked at them, she said, "Mother, they are beautiful hands; they are beautiful hands!"

Wounded for Me

After the first World War, an aged minister met a wounded soldier on a London street. The soldier was walking with crutches. The minister stopped and earnestly said, "Thank you for being wounded for me!" The soldier was greatly surprised that some one had thanked him for the sacrifice he had made for his country. Then the minister continued, "I know some One who was wounded for you, and I wonder if you have ever t h a n k e d Him?" "Wounded for me, sir?" "Yes," replied the minister. Then he told the young soldier about the Lord Jesus Christ dying on the Cross of Calvary.

The Sting Is Gone

A little boy was playing before the door of a cottage. His mother was working inside. Suddenly, a bee came buzzing at the door. The little boy ran to his mother, followed by the bee! He hid behind her. The bee stung the mother on her bare arm. She turned and took her little boy up in her arms. She showed him the place where the bee had stung her. She showed him the bee which was slowly crawling up her arm. "You need not fear the bee now, Willie," she said; "it has no sting. It cannot hurt you. It's sting is here!" Then she showed the little boy the sting — a small black speck sticking in the wound.

Afterward the mother sat down with her little boy on her knee. She told him how sin and eternal destruction follow the sinner. There is *one* place the sinner can hide safely; that is, behind the Cross of Christ. Jesus, the One who died on that Cross, received the fatal sting from sin. On the Cross, He died for sinners. Then the mother asked the little boy if he would not come to Jesus, and ask Jesus to save him from sin, and eternal destruction. How glad the little boy was to receive Jesus, and believe in Him as His Saviour!

DEATH

With Jesus

A little girl, whose baby brother had just died, asked her mother where baby had gone. The mother replied, "He has gone to be with Jesus."

A few days later, the mother was talking with a friend. The little girl heard her mother say, "I am so grieved to have lost my baby." Remembering what her mother had told her, the little girl asked, "Mother, is something lost when you know where it is? You told me that baby brother had gone to be with Jesus!" Her mother never forgot what her little girl said. Her sorrow was lessened as she remembered that baby brother had gone to be with Jesus.

Moving Day

John Quincy Adams was over eighty years old. One day, he was walking down a street in Boston when a friend met him and asked, "How is John Quincy Adams today?"

Old Mr. Adams eyes twinkled. Then he said slowly, "John Quincy Adams is very well, thank you. His earthly house, however, is sadly dilapidated. It is tottering on its foundation. The walls are crumbling. The roof is worn. The building shakes in the wind. John Quincy Adams will soon have to move out, but he is very well, in spite of the condition of his house!"

Going to Heaven

Dr. William Anderson of Texas loved the Lord Jesus. He lived for Him many years, and preached the Gospel. Dr. Anderson became very ill. One day, his mother was sitting in his room with him. Gently, he called her, "Come over here a minute." As she approached his bed, he said, "I want to tell you something. *I am going to beat you to Heaven!*" And, with a smile, he shut his eyes, and was *gone!* "Absent from the body — at home with the Lord!"

Victory

An old Methodist minister was dying. He was not weeping. He was shouting praises to God. A friend said, "Dr. Sewall, do not shout. Whisper, Doctor!" The old preacher replied, "Let the angels whisper, but not me. I have been cleansed from sin by the Blood of Christ. I have been redeemed from death and hell. I am on the threshold of eternal glory! Oh, that I had a voice that could be heard from pole to pole, so all the world could hear: "Victory! Victory through Christ."

Hold My Hand

A little girl said to her mother one night, "Mother, stay with me while I go to sleep!" Mother was very busy, but she sat down by her little girl. She held her soft hand while she went to sleep. As Mother sat by the bed, she prayed, "Dear Lord, when I come to death's door, when the time comes for me to go to sleep, hold my hand! Then I can go to sleep without fear!"

Jesus, the Conqueror of death, has promised to be with us in the hour of death. He has said, "Lo, I am with you alway!" David said, "Yea, though I walk through the valley of the shadow of death, I will fear no evil: for Thou art with me."

Light, Life, and Hope

An old Indian chief was told of the Saviour. He said, "The Jesus road is good, but I have followed the old Indian road all my life, and I will follow it to the end." A year later, the Indian chief was on the border of death. He called for the missionary and said, "Can I turn to the Jesus road now? My road stops here!"

When we come to the valley of death without Christ, there is no light, no life, no hope; with Him, there is light, life, and hope!

A Living Guide

Said a Christian in Turkey, "When I reach the parting of the ways; when I come to the great divide between life and death, I want a guide. I want a *living* guide. That is why I want Christ, and not Mohammed!" Are *you* not glad that you have a *living* Guide to go with you and show you the way through the valley of death? David said, "Yea, though I walk through the valley of the shadow of death, I will fear no evil: for Thou art with me" (*Ps. 23:4*).

A Dead Bone?

A native Christian in South Africa said, "When a heathen is dying, the witch doctors put into his hand a dead bone as a passport into the world beyond. When a Christian dies, he does not grasp a dead bone, as he passes through the veil. He grasps the hand of the *living Lord!*"

The New House Is Better

An aged minister had a fear of death. Toward the end of his life, he moved to another house. When the furniture had all gone, the old preacher lingered in the home where his children had been reared, and where his sermons had been prepared. At last, his servant came to him and said, "Sir, everything is gone. The new house is *better* than this one. Come away."

Those words taught the aged minister a lesson he never forgot. He seemed to hear God say, "Everything is gone. The house in *Heaven is better* than your *earthly* house. Come away!" From that time on, fear of death left the old minister. He *longed* for the "house not made with hands, e t e r n a l in the heavens!"

"I Shall See Jesus"

A little Negro boy was very sick. A missionary visited his bedside. The little boy spoke of his desire to go and be with Jesus. Said he, "I am going to Heaven soon. Then I shall see Jesus, and be with Him forever!" The missionary said, "If Jesus were to leave Heaven, what would you do?" "I would follow Him," said the little boy. "Suppose," said the missionary, "Jesus went to hell, what would you do then?" With a smile, the little boy said, "Ah, Massa, there is no hell where Jesus is!"

"Where Jesus is, 'tis Heaven there!"

Resting on His Name

A minister called to see one who was dying from leprosy. She was unable to speak. The nurse said to the minister, "She will not hear you. She is unconscious." The minister leaned over the bed, and spoke one word: "*Jesus!*" The dying woman heard the word, and her eyes opened, and a smile lighted up her face! She nodded her head, and then

her spirit winged its way to the Heavenly Home! She went Home resting on
the Name of Jesus, that matchless Name
that lights the dark corridors of death.

She Could Not Sink

Those about the bedside of one of
God's saints said, "She's sinking!" With
a smile of confidence wreathing her
face, the dying saint said, "Ah, no!
How can one sink through a Rock?"

A Light Through the Grave

A little boy went to Sunday School.
There, on Easter Sunday, he heard the
beautiful story of the risen Christ. His
mother was not saved. She was afraid
of death. The little boy ran all the way
home. With a shining face, he rushed

into the house, and said, "Oh Mother,
you need not be afraid of dying any
more. Jesus went through the grave
and left a light behind Him!"

Living a Thousand Years from Now

A distinguished American statesman
went abroad, hoping to regain his
health. A friend said to him just before
he sailed, "I feel sure that your health
will be restored, and that you will be
living and at work ten years from now."
"Living ten years from now?" asked
the great statesman. Then he added,
"My friend, I shall be living a thousand
years from now!" That man had real
faith in Jesus, the Conqueror of death.
He died a few days later. His body
was buried. But, that man, through
faith in Jesus, had entered life eternal.

DELAY

The Danger of Delay

A man was walking along a beach in
Scotland where the high rocks came
near the sea. He was unmindful of the
fact that the tide was rising and would
soon cut off his way back to safety. A
man on top of the rocks shouted to him,
"Hello! The tide is rising and this is
the last place where you can make your
escape. You had better climb up now
on the rocks." The man laughed at the
warning and went on. The tide kept
rising. After a while the man thought
it was time to return to the place where
he could climb up on the rocks. He
turned back and found that his retreat
was cut off. He tried to climb the steep
cliff where he stood, but he could make
no progress. He got stuck after he had

gone up a few feet. The waves came to
his feet, then to his waist, then to his
chin. Finally with a wild shriek for
help, he perished.

The tides of eternity are slowly rising. Only those who get on the "Rock
of Ages," Jesus Christ, will be saved.
Do not delay until it is too late.

Faded Roses

One day, Mary's Sunday School
teacher talked to her and asked her if
she would not give her heart to the
Lord Jesus. Mary said, "Oh, I do not
want to become a Christian now. I am
young. I want to have a good time. I
want to enjoy the pleasures of this
world. When I get old, I will give my

heart to Jesus." How sad the teacher was. Several days later, Mary received a long box, filled with flowers from her Sunday School teacher. When she opened the box, she was surprised and disappointed. The roses were wilted! When she picked the roses up, the petals fell off.

Mary was angry. She said, "I don't think my teacher should send me old dead roses." Her cousin who heard what she said replied, "Oh, Mary, you know your teacher would not send you old roses. She probably told the boy to bring you that box of roses several days ago, and he forgot to do it. The roses wilted and died. He just remembered about them today and brought them!"

That afternoon, Mary's Sunday School teacher came to see her. She invited Mary to go for a ride with her. While they were riding, the teacher asked, "Mary, did you receive the roses I sent to you *today*?" Mary said, "You sent them *today*? Then you did send me old wilted roses!" "Yes," said the teacher, "I sent you old wilted roses. I thought that was the kind of gift you like." "No, I don't," said Mary, "I like fresh roses. What made you think such a thing?"

Gently, the teacher said, "Mary, when I asked you to give your heart to Jesus, you said you would not do it now while you are young, when the bloom is on your cheek. You said you would wait until you are old and faded, and then you would give your heart to Jesus!"

Mary was silent for a moment. Then she said, "Oh, teacher, I see it all now. It is wrong for me to wait until I am old and faded and then give my heart to Jesus. I will give my heart to Him right now, and I will live for Him all my days!"

Too Late

A physician once told a young man that he had only a short time to live. The young man was astonished. He had not expected death so soon. With despair on his face, he said, "I have missed it at last!"

"Missed what?" asked the doctor.

"I have missed the salvation of my soul! Some time ago, I felt that God was calling me to come to the Saviour. I knew I was a great sinner. But I dismissed the thought from my mind, thinking that some *other time*, I would think about my soul's salvation. Now it is *too late*! I am *lost forever*!"

The doctor, who was a Christian, tried to tell the young man that it was not too late, that he could still come to the Saviour. But the young man said, "I felt the call of the Spirit. I did not respond. I had my chance. Now it is *too late*!"

The Bible says, "He that being often reproved hardeneth his neck, shall *suddenly* be destroyed, and that without remedy."

"The saddest word of tongue or pen,
  The saddest are these, 'It might have been.'"

Not Next Month But Today

An earnest Christian doctor called to see an elderly patient, suffering from bronchitis. The doctor promised to get some medicine ready, and was about to say goodbye when the wife asked, "When must John take the medicine, sir?"

"Let me see," said the doctor. "You are not very ill. Suppose you start to take it one month from today."

"Oh," said the patient, "I may be dead then."

"That is true," said the doctor, "but you are not very bad yet. Perhaps you had better begin to take it in a week."

"Sir," cried the old man, "I may not live a week."

Then the doctor said, "When would you propose to begin taking the medicine, John?"

"Well, sir, I thought you would tell me to begin today."

Kindly, the Christian doctor said, "Begin *today* by all means. I only wanted to show you how false your own reasoning is when you *put off* taking the *medicine* God has provided for your sin-sick soul. Just think how long you have neglected the remedy. For years, you have turned away from the Lord Jesus, saying, 'Next week, next year, perhaps on my death bed, I will seek the Lord, but I won't do it *now*,' and yet, John, the *present* is the *only* time you are sure of. God's offer is *only* for *today*. 'Now is the accepted time; behold, *now* is the day of salvation.' You may be dead tomorrow!"

Give Him the Best

In the University of Edinburgh, Scotland, there was a young medical student named Macfarlane. He was a fine athlete, and everyone liked him. One day, he was stricken with typhoid, which proved fatal. One of his friends visited him during his sickness. He begged the young student to turn to the Saviour.

During the years of health and strength, Macfarlane had neglected the Lord. Now, he said to his friend, "Wouldn't it be a shabby thing to turn to Christ now when I am sick and about to die?"

"Yes," replied the friend, "it would be a shabby thing, but it would be shabbier *not* to turn to Him at all. He loves you; He wants you to turn to Him."

Poor Macfarlane did turn to the Lord. He was saved before his death. But how sad he was that he had not given his best days in service for the Saviour!

Let us offer the Lord Jesus the *best*, the *finest — our youth*!

> "Give of your *best* to the Master;
>   Give of the strength of your youth;
> Throw your soul's fresh, glowing ardor,
>   Into the battle for truth.
>
> "Jesus has set the example;
>   Dauntless was He, young and brave;
> Give Him your loyal devotion,
>   Give Him the best that you have!"

"Now, or When?"

A boy sat one day beneath the tall Gothic Towers in Yorkshire. A great question was troubling his heart. The question was: "Shall I give my heart to the Saviour?" The tempter whispered, "Put it off a while. There is plenty of time." Then, another Voice said, "Don't put it off. Decide at once for Christ." The conflict went on through the long bright summer afternoon. At last, the boy lifted his eyes, and looked at the sundial, which marked the progress of the day. On the sundial, he read these words, inscribed as a motto: "*Now, or when?*" He thought, "When shall I give my heart to God, '*now, or when?*'" The shadows of evening were coming. Suddenly, the boy exclaimed aloud, "*Now*, I will give my heart to Jesus!" Jumping up from the ground, he ran home. The joybells of Heaven were ringing in his heart!

"Time Enough Yet"

A bright little boy heard the Bible verse, "My son, give Me thine heart." Satan whispered, "Time enough yet." He put it off.

Ten years passed by. The little boy was now a college student. Again, he heard the verse, "My son, give Me thine heart." Again, the tempter whispered, "Time enough yet."

Twenty more years passed by. The little boy was now a great statesman. He heard from the lips of an aged minister the Bible text, "My son, give Me thine heart." Again, the tempter said, "Time enough yet," and he *put it off*!

The statesman went to visit foreign countries. In Paris, he became very sick. As he lay dying, his last words were, "*Too late*!" How sad it was that the little boy did not decide for Jesus.

"Behold, *now* is the accepted time; behold, *now* is the day of salvation!"

Get Ready Now

A fable is told that once upon a time a wild boar of the jungle was sharpening his tusks against the trunk of a tree. A fox, passing by, asked him why he did this, when neither hunter nor hound was near. "True," said the boar, "but when danger arises, I shall have something else to do than to sharpen my weapon." Now is the time for you, boys and girls, to get ready for life. Give the Lord Jesus your heart. Let Him have the control of your life.

He Made a Mistake

A young man in the southwest felt God's call. He knew that he should come to Jesus, the Saviour. The young man said, "Not now. I want to work hard. I want to build a nice home, and get married, and have little children. I want to have a fine business. I have *no time* for God now. After I get rich, then I will come to Jesus."

The young man worked hard. He got his nice home, and his family. But he forgot *all* about God. Then, one day, God sent trouble upon that young man. His business failed. He lost his fine home.

Then the young man said, "I made a mistake. I left God out of my plans. I had no time for Him. Now, I am coming to God. I want Him to save me from my sins. I want to give Him my heart and life. He will come *first*, before my business, before my home, and before my family." How greatly did God bless the young man when the young man remembered Him.

God's Word says to all boys and girls, "Remember *now* thy Creator in the days of thy *Youth*." Boys and girls, if you will remember the Lord now, and put Him *first* always, how greatly will He bless your life!

The Snare of Riches

Two gentlemen were riding past a fine mansion, surrounded by fair and fertile fields. "What is the value of this estate?" asked one. The other replied, "I don't know what it is valued at, but I know what it cost the late possessor: it cost him his *soul*. Early in life, he professed faith in God. He started out in a small way as a clerk in a mercantile business. Then, he rose until he became a partner in the firm. As he rose higher in business, he paid *less* and *less* attention to his soul. The care of this world choked out the Word. He became exceedingly rich in money, but he was so poor and miserly in his soul that no one would have ever suspected he had been interested in God or the church. At length, he purchased this large estate. Then he took sick and died. Just before his death, he said, 'My prosperity has been my ruin.' "

The Forgotten Promise

A young man in Texas promised God that if God would bless him, he would serve Him faithfully. The young man's business prospered. He married and had a lovely wife and a fine little girl. He had a beautiful home. He became so taken up with his business, that he began to neglect his church, and his God. He had no time for Bible study, or prayer. As the years passed by, he wandered farther and farther from his first love for the Lord.

Then, God chastened the young man. His little girl was taken sick suddenly, and went to be with Jesus. The terrible sorrow brought the young man back to God. He had forgotten God, but sorrow made him remember God. With bitter tears, he sought God's forgiveness for His sin. God forgave the young man, and soon, he was busily occupied with the things of the Lord.

Reminders

A boy said one day, "Sometimes I think I am not a Christian. I don't seem to have the same interest that I had when I first joined the church. It is not easy for me to remember God!"

"What about the time when your father was away from home so long? Was it hard for you to remember him?" asked the minister. "Not a bit," said the boy. "We had letters from him which we read; and we kept talking about him, and looking forward to the time when he would come home. There wasn't much chance to forget him!"

"Suppose you had read no letters from him? Suppose you had never talked about him? Suppose you had never thought about him? Would that have made a difference?"

"Oh, yes," said the boy, "I guess it would have made a difference."

"Well, don't you see that it is the same with God? God has given us His Word to read. He has given us His house where the members of His family can meet and talk about Him. If we don't read His Word; if we don't go to His house and talk about Him, then it is easy to forget Him. We allow too many things to crowd Him out of our lives."

"I see," said the boy. "A fellow needs all the reminders of God that he can have in a world like this!"

His Only "Forgotten" Son

An Army chaplain was talking with an unsaved soldier in a dimly lighted railway station. The chaplain opened his New Testament to John 3:16, and asked the soldier to read it. In the dim light, the soldier read with difficulty, "For God so loved the world that He gave His only FORGOTTEN Son." Is Jesus the "forgotten" Son to you?

FAITH

The Meaning of "Believe"

Dr. John Paton was translating the New Testament into the language of some South Sea islanders. He could not find a native word which meant "believe." Everyday he listened carefully to the natives as they talked, but he never heard them use a word which he could use for "believe." One day he was working in his study. One of his native teachers came in, hot and tired from a long walk. The native threw himself on a chair. He put his feet on another chair and used a native word which meant "I am resting my whole weight here." Instantly Dr. Paton had the word he needed for "believe." The natives of that Pacific island now know that to believe in Jesus, or to have faith in Jesus, means that you rest your whole weight of mind and heart on Jesus.

Looking Over Our Troubles

One day John Wesley was walking with a man who was in great trouble. The man even doubted the goodness of God. He said, "I don't know what I shall do with all this worry and trouble." At that moment Wesley saw a cow standing in a pasture and looking over a stone wall. "Do you know why that cow is looking over that wall?" asked Wesley. "No," replied the troubled man. "I will tell you," said Wesley. "The cow is looking over the wall because she cannot see through it. That is what you must do with your wall of trouble. You cannot see through it, so you must look over it and above it."

Faith enables us to look over and above our troubles to God who is our helper.

Quietly Waiting

F. B. Meyer was a minister. He had a dog which he used to feed at his table. His wife objected. The dog seemed to know what had happened. So he stayed out of sight. When the family was at their meal, he crawled under the table, and rested his nose at his master's knee. He had faith that the master would feed him. Quietly he stayed there until Dr.

Meyer would slip some food under the table and put it in his waiting mouth. When we have faith in God and wait for Him, He will never fail us.

"Let My Father Hold the Rope"

One summer, some English botanists went to Switzerland to collect rare flowers. One morning, they left a little village, and went toward a near-by mountain. They climbed for several hours and came to a precipice. Looking down, over the precipice, they saw some beautiful, rare flowers. They looked at the flowers through their field glasses. They wanted some of the flowers.

A little boy came by. He watched the botanists. One of them said, "Boy, let us tie a rope around your waist. Then we will lower you over this precipice. If you will dig up one of those plants for us, and bring it back without harming it, we will pay you well."

The boy ran away. In a short time he returned, bringing with him a man who was bent and gray. The man's hands were rough from hard work. The boy said to the botanists, "Sir, this is my father. If you will let my father hold the rope, I will go over the precipice, and get the plant for you!" The boy had *real* faith in his father.

Take God at His Word

In a sporting goods store in Seattle, Washington, there was a box containing vacation pamphlets. A sign on the box said, "Take one!" So many persons took one, that the pamphlets soon disappeared. Right next to the box was another box exhibiting some prize-winning fish.

Presently, a woman came along. The pamphlet box was empty, but the sign remained reading, "Take One!" She unfolded a newspaper, took the largest fish she saw, wrapped it up and went home with her dinner problem solved. The store owner took down the sign.

God has offered us many blessings. No blessing is greater than this one, "Whosoever will, let him take the Water of Life *freely*"! Will you not take God at His Word? Will you not take the "Water of Life *freely*"? It is yours through faith in Christ.

Already Hers

Two little girls were counting their pennies. One said, "I have five pennies." The other said, "I have ten." "No," said the first little girl; "you have five pennies, the same as I have." " 'But," said the second girl, "my father said that, when he came home tonight, he would give me five pennies, and so I have *ten pennies!*"

The child was counting as *already hers* the five pennies which her father had promised to give her. She had *real* faith in her father's word.

> "It is strange that we trust each other,
>   And only doubt our Lord;
> We take the word of mortals,
>   And yet distrust God's Word;
>
> "But, Oh, what light and glory,
>   Would shine o'er all our days,
> If we would always remember,
>   *God means just what He says!*"

Unclaimed Blessings

A fable is told of a king who prepared a city for some of his poor subjects. Not far away were large storehouses. There everything the subjects needed was stored. All they had to do to get what they needed was to send in their requests and be on the *lookout* for the answer.

There was one desponding, sad subject. He never expected to get what he asked for. He felt that he was too unworthy. Day by day, he sent in requests for what he needed, but he never expected to get the answer and never watched for the packages. One day, this man was taken to the king's storehouse, and there he saw many packages with his name and address on them. Everything he had requested had been sent to him, but his door had been closed. He had not been on the *lookout*, and now they were piled up and marked, "Unclaimed!"

God wants to shower His blessings upon us. He wants to give us many good gifts. How few of us have faith in Him, and are ready to claim and receive His blessings!

No Need for the Cane

Two men were once examining a painting, showing the healing of two blind men of Jericho. Everything was very clear. The painting showed the blind men standing before the Lord Jesus as He healed them. One of the men said, "The most remarkable thing in the painting is the fact that one blind man left his cane behind him. He *knew* that he would need it no more. He rushed to the Lord, as though he could already see!"

Time to Halt

A small boy attended Sunday School for the first time. He was greatly pleased with a picture card which was given him. On the picture card was written the text, "Have faith in God." On his way home, the precious card slipped from his fingers, and fluttered from the open streetcar window. Immediately, a cry of distress arose: "I have lost my faith in God. Stop the car!" The good-natured conductor signaled; the car was stopped; and the card was recovered while the passengers smiled.

How wise it would be if older people would call a *halt* when they find themselves rushing ahead on some road, without faith in God.

Little Faith in a Great God

George Allen, with his wife, visited the famous Mueller Orphan's Home in Bristol, England. Mrs. Allen looked at the large building, and then she turned to Dr. Burton, and said, "It must take a lot of faith to keep all this going." Dr. Burton answered, "Mrs. Allen, little faith in a strong plank will carry me over the stream. Great faith in a rotten plank will land me in it!" How truly did Dr. Burton speak. Little faith in a great God will carry us safely through life.

Faith and Power

A lady went through a corn mill. It was built close by the river. All the wheels were still. The lady asked, "What makes the wheels go round? Where is the power?" Someone showed her a handle and told her to touch it. When she touched it, the big wheels began to move, and the corn was ground. Our faith is like the handle. It starts the power of God moving. When we have faith in God, He does wonderful things for us.

Importance of Faith

Dr. Howard A. Kelly, the great scientist and brilliant surgeon, was seated in his library one day. He was surrounded by many books on medicine and surgery. He was talking to a friend. Said he, "Faith in Christ is the *one* really important thing in life! It is *more* important than my profession, than any scientific research, than *all* the activities of my life!"

Henry J. Heinz, of the "fifty-seven variety" fame, said, "Throughout my life, in which were the usual joys and sorrows, I have been wonderfully sustained by my faith in God through Jesus Christ!"

When Everything Is Dark

A missionary met Madame Chiang Kai-shek during an air raid. She found her a charming woman with great faith in God. The Madame said, "God has eyes. He can see. He knows that our cause is righteous. The darkest hour comes before the dawn. The easy time to trust God is when all goes smoothly. But when everything is dark, then it means *faith*!"

"I Knew He Would Hear Us"

In India, there was a little orphan girl who was to be sold as a slave. She begged a missionary, from a nearby village, to take her home with her. She wanted to live on the mission compound and go to the mission school. The missionary sadly said, "We have no room. We have no money to build more room!" Kara looked very sad. The missionary's heart was touched. She said, "You pray for God to send us money, so we can take you. I will pray, too!"

When the missionary returned to her home in the near-by village, she found a letter from America. The letter contained the money which was needed for

Kara. Early the next morning, the missionary sent a messenger for Kara. It was a long day's journey to Kara's village. But in just a few hours the messenger returned with Kara to the mission compound. Little Kara said, "You prayed to God to send the money, and I prayed to God to send the money. I *knew* He would hear us, so I thought I might as well start!" She had walked half way to the mission compound when the messenger met her.

Christ, the Rock

One stormy night, a vessel was wrecked off the coast of Cornwall, England. Everyone on the vessel perished, but one Irish lad. He was hurled by the waves upon a jagged rock. There, he managed to find a place of refuge. In the morning, searchers on the beach spied him through their glasses. A boat was launched and rowed out to where he clung to the rock. He was almost dead with cold and exposure. Tenderly, he was lifted to the lifeboat and brought to shore. A few hours later, he was warm and fed and feeling bright and able once more. He was asked, "Lad, didn't you tremble out there on that rock in all that storm?" He replied in his Irish way, "Tremble? Sure I trembled, but do you know the rock never trembled once all night long!"

If you have trust in Christ, the Rock, you will find that this Rock is firm and secure, no matter what storms may enter your life!

Absolutely Certain

Some years ago, there was a boys' club made up of newsboys. They were tough fellows, but they were loyal to each other. One ten-year-old boy accepted Christ as his Saviour. He began to witness everywhere for Jesus. He told the boys in the club about Jesus. He told his customers about Jesus. One of his customers said, "Peter, maybe you only think you are saved." "Oh, no, sir," replied Peter; "I don't only think. I'm absolutely certain! Jesus said that he wouldn't cast anybody out who came to Him. I came to Him, and now I am saved for KEEPS! Jesus couldn't make a mistake!"

Trusting Jesus for Everything

An old woman in the Congo was wonderfully saved! The day for her baptism arrived. At the door of the church, she hesitated, and said that she *must* go and get something from her house. When she returned, she walked to the front of the church, and laid a small fetish on the ground. Then, she quietly took her place with the other woman. Serious looks were on every face. They all knew that she had put away her "lightning medicine." The last thing that any of them were willing to give up was their "lightning medicine." Her father had been killed by lightning years before, and since then she had never been without the fetish to protect her from the same fate. She belonged fully to the Lord Jesus now, and she was willing to trust Him for *everything*.

Trusting All the Time

A Christian, who was in great trouble, was telling another Christian about the various efforts he had made to find deliverance. He concluded by saying, "It is all in vain. There is literally nothing for me to do now, but to trust the

Lord!" "Alas!" exclaimed his friend, "has it come to that?" We should trust in the Lord always: in the times of trouble, and in times of joy; in sickness and in health; in want and in plenty. When we have troubles, we should, without delay, take them to the Lord. God is waiting to help His dear children.

"Trusted One Million Times"

Shott's Drugstore in Galveston, Texas, was open day and night for twenty-six years. At the end of this long period, all the prescriptions for medicine, which had been filled, were placed in one of the windows. Above them was placed a sign which read, "Trusted one million times!" People had trusted that drugstore to give them the right medicine one million times. God has been trusted times without count, by millions of His children. He has *never failed* one time! Surely, with all of our hearts, we can trust the Lord. We will cling unto Him, no matter what happens.

The Lord Never Fails

A Christian man, who had been very wealthy, lost all his riches overnight. In speaking of his experience, he said, "I think I am going to enjoy trusting *wholly* in the Lord. I will enjoy resting on Him for my daily needs. I never did it before in my life. I do not even know where the rent for next month is coming from, but I am not worried. I am wondering why I should sleep *better* when I am resting on banks and human beings, and be a bit nervous when I am resting on the Lord. The Lord will *surely* supply *all* my needs. I can safely trust in Him. He will *never fail!*"

"He Will Hold Us Fast"

An old Negro had been serving the Lord for more than fifty years. A friend said, "Well, Uncle, after keeping the faith for so long, you must feel pretty confident of holding out to the end." He replied, "I reckon it's not a question of my holding out; it's only a question of whether the Lord can hold unto me, and I *know* I can trust Him!"

"I Still Trusted God"

Some years ago, a big business man in New York City said, "I went to bed one night worth a million and a half dollars. I felt that I was ready to retire from business, for I was over sixty years of age. I had plenty to care for all my needs, and to give large sums to the Lord's work. I went to bed worth a million and a half dollars. I woke up the next morning worth *nothing*! The financial crash had come. Everything I had was swept away. If I had not known the Lord, I would have gone up to the top floor of my office building, the twenty-sixth floor, and I would have jumped out of the window! Four others did that very thing the day things collapsed. If I had not believed in God, I would have ended my life! But I had trusted in the Lord when I had plenty of money, and now that my money was gone, I *still* trusted Him!"

"Keep up the song of faith,
    And let your heart be strong,
For God delights when you can praise,
    Though dark the night and long!"

Stop Supposing

A poor Negro woman earned her living by hard daily labor. She was always happy and joyous in the Lord. One day, a gloomy Christian said to her, "Ah, Nancy, it is well enough to be happy now, but I should think thoughts of the future would trouble you. Suppose you should have a spell of sickness and not be able to work. Suppose your present employer would move away, and no one else would give you work. Suppose —." "Stop!" cried Nancy. "I never supposes. The Lord is my Shepherd, and I shall not want. It's those supposes that make you so miserable. You had better give them all up and *just trust the Lord*!"

The Pet Parakeet

In our home we have a little bird. He is a parakeet. His name is Rob Roy. We got Rob Roy when he was just a baby bird. We taught him how to talk. He says, "God bless you"; "Good boy"; "Come to me," *etc.* He is not afraid of us. He flies to us and lights on our head, or our shoulder. He eats from our hand. He loves us and trusts us. If a little bird can trust us like that, surely we can trust God, our kind, Heavenly Father.

Charlie's Letter

Charlie was a little boy whose mother was dead. His father was sick. They did not have enough to eat. Charlie went to Sunday School. He had been taught to take his troubles to Jesus. Charlie knew that Jesus would help him in his trouble if he would but ask Him. So, he wrote a letter. The letter said, "Dear Jesus: Papa is sick. We have no money to buy food and medicine. Please send us a little very soon, and when I get big, I will pay it back. Charlie Boyden, 23 Rock Street."

He put the letter in an envelope. On the envelope, he wrote, "Lord Jesus in Heaven!" When he went to the mail box, he found that it was a little too high for him to reach it. He asked the man standing nearby to drop the letter in for him. Then, he went home. He felt *sure* Jesus would help them in their need.

The man, who took the letter, saw the words on the envelope, "Lord Jesus in Heaven." He opened the letter and read it. God put it in his heart to go and see Charlie and his father. He gave them the money they needed to buy food and medicine. He sent the little boy to school. He took care of them until Charlie's papa was well and able to work again.

It is good to trust in the Lord in times of need and trouble. It is good to trust in Him when we need nothing. He loves us. He is always ready and willing to help us. Never doubt Him. One has said, "If we trust, we don't doubt; if we doubt, we don't trust!"

Distrustful

One morning, a Christian lady wanted to feed the birds. It was cold and the ground was covered with snow. She stepped out of doors and flung them handfuls of crumbs, but the birds were afraid. They sat off on the branches, cold and hungry. They did not trust the lady. As she watched and waited, she thought, "How like us are the birds. God loves us. He offers us His bounties. He plans, waits, hopes, and longs for our good. But so often, He has to watch and wait, because we are so distrustful, and so afraid."

" 'Careful and troubled'—so filled with unrest,
Dreading the dawn with its toil and its test,
Trust Him your courage and strength to renew,
He will give grace for each task you must do.

"Nothing is hid from His all-seeing eye,
Never a teardrop, nor even a sigh;
'Careful and troubled' you never need be,
Trust Him completely and doubtings will
flee!"

He Trusted the Wrong Thing

In a city in California, it was announced that the "Human Fly" would climb up the front of a tall building. When the day arrived, a great crowd of people came to watch him. Slowly and carefully the "Human Fly," a young man, started his upward climb. Up and up he went! The crowd was breathless. No one cheered. They watched closely. How could the man climb such a tall building? Would he fall? The man was almost up to the top. Looking up, he saw something he thought he could hold to. Reaching up, he caught hold of it. But it was not strong and secure. It crumbled away in his hands! The man fell to the sidewalk below! He had trusted in the wrong thing.

FAITHFULNESS

Not Success, but Faithfulness

A young missionary in Central America wrote a letter in which he told a little of the trials and hardships of his work. Said he, "The work is hard. I go about on fishing boats through the day. At night, I sleep on piles of hides on the deck. The people do not seem much interested in the Gospel message I bring. Sometimes, I am tempted to be discouraged, because there seems to be little success. But I take courage and press on anew when I remembered that God does not hold me responsible for *success*, but for *faithfulness!*"

God Is Faithful

Some years ago, Dr. Russell Conwell was conducting a prayer meeting. He asked those who had tithed through a number of years to give a simple testimony, telling of God's faithfulness in blessing them. Seven stood. Six gave glowing testimonies of the blessing received through the years. Then, the seventh, a frail, gray-haired woman said reluctantly, "I have skimped and saved and denied myself through many years in order to tithe my income. I wish I could give testimony to the faithfulness of God. But now I am old. I am losing my position. I have no means of support. I do not know what I shall do!" Those who heard her words were depressed.

Next day, Dr. Conwell was the guest of John Wanamaker at lunch. At the dinner table, Mr. Wanamaker said, "Dr. Conwell, you will be interested to know that we are beginning a pension system for our employees. We have thought of it for years, and the plan has finally been worked out. Today, we are to issue our first life pension to a woman who has served our firm for twenty-five years!" Then Mr. Wanamaker mentioned the name of the woman, and it was that of the lady who had given such a sad and hopeless testimony in the prayer meeting the night before. God *was* and *is* faithful to His dear children!

A Heathen Woman's Faithfulness

A missionary in Madras came to a little village where once many of the natives had confessed faith in Christ. A little church had been built for them, but now the converts had fallen away. They had returned to their idols and only one poor woman remained faithful. The missionary said to her, "There is no use to keep the church open any longer. You may as well give the key to me." Noticing the sad look on the woman's face, he added, "There is Christian worship in the village three miles away. You can go to church there." Earnestly the woman pleaded, "Oh, sir, don't take the key away. I at least will still go daily to the church. I will sweep it clean. I will keep the lamp in order, and every day I will pray that God will again visit us in our village." The missionary left the key with the old woman. The time came when he preached in that very church, when it was crowded with repentant sinners. God had answered the faithfulness of that one poor woman.

Faithful Though Unseen

A boy was hired by the owner of a large hardware store. He was sent up to the attic where there was a large box full of nails and screws of all sizes. He was told to put the box in order. The attic was gloomy and dusty. The work seemed useless and was tiresome. Nobody was watching the boy and he was tempted to take a nap. But instead, he kept at the work and tried to do it well. He made compartments in the box and sorted the nails and the screws. He worked at the task for three days. Finally, the work was done. Then he reported to the man who had hired him. The man inspected the boy's work. Then he said, "All right, you have done a good job. That was a test job which I give to see whether a boy

is worthy of a better place. Now you will be given a place at a counter down in the hardware store."

When we are faithful in the unseen places, then God can trust us to work for Him in the larger places.

A Brother's Faithfulness

Two brothers were fighting in the same company of soldiers in France. One was felled by a German bullet and left on the battlefield. The brother who had escaped asked his officer to allow him to go and bring his brother in. "He is probably dead," said the officer. "There is no use for you to risk your life to bring in his body."

After further pleading, the officer finally consented. The young soldier went out on the battlefield, found his wounded brother, and brought him back to the line on his shoulders. Just as he reached the line, the wounded man died. "There, you see," said the officer. "You risked your life for nothing." "No," replied Tom, "I did what my brother expected me to do and I have my reward. When I crept up to him and took him in my arms, he said, 'Tom, I knew you would come. I felt sure you would come.' "

The Lord Jesus expects us to be faithful. Even if no one else expects us to be faithful, the Lord Jesus does. If we satisfy Him, isn't our reward grand and glorious?

"I Will Never Look Back"

When Dr. F. B. Meyer was seventeen years old, he told his mother that he wanted to go into the ministry. She suggested that such a step would involve sacrifice. She hinted that if he regretted the step later, he would be able to leave the ministry. The boy looked straight at his mother and said, *"Never!* That would be putting my hand to the plow and looking back!"

F. B. Meyer never looked back. He did a wonderful work for his Lord and Master in many lands. Perhaps, his success in God's work can be traced back to the day when he said, *"Never. I will *never* look back!"

Ten Years More

A young man was being ordained to the ministry. In the examination, he was asked. If you were to preach ten years, and see *no results*, what would you do?" He answered, "I would preach ten years more!" That answer was of God. God wants His servants to remain faithful always. God's Word says: "Therefore, my beloved brethren, be ye steadfast, unmoveable, *always* abounding in the work of the Lord, forasmuch as ye *know* that your labour is not in vain in the Lord" (*1 Cor. 15:58*).

"He Can Stand Fast"

Henry Ward Beecher one day saw a little boy standing by an old horse that was lank and lean. Mr. Beecher asked the little boy, "Can your horse run fast?" "No," replied the little boy, "but he can *stand fast."* Can *you* stand fast? God help *us* always to stand fast in Him.

Faithful Unto Death

One day, as a train was approaching the city of Montreal, the engineer saw a large dog on the track. The dog was barking furiously. The whistle was blown, but still the dog stayed on the track. Just as the engine came upon him, he crouched down across the track. He was struck by the engine and killed. Suddenly, the engineer noticed on the front of his engine a piece of white cloth fluttering in the wind. He discovered that it was a part of a child's dress. He backed his train to the place where the mangled body of the dog lay. There he found a little child.

The child must have wandered along the track and fallen asleep there. The dog, her faithful companion, seeing the train approach, had tried to stop it. Failing, he had covered her with his own body, and died with her. He had been faithful unto death.

May we be faithful unto death in our service for God. The Bible says, "Be thou faithful unto death, and I will give thee the crown of life" (*Rev.* 2:10b). No matter what others do, or fail to do, *be faithful.* Never give up loving the Lord and faithfully serving Him.

Faithful Richard

One day, a father left his little boy near a certain gateway. He told his boy to stay there until he returned. The father was very busy. He went about the village attending to his business, and forgot the boy.

Night came, and the father returned to his home. The mother asked where the boy was. "Dear me," said the father, "I left Richard this morning standing in a gateway. I told him to stay there until I came for him! He must be there now!" The father hastily went to the place where he had left his boy. There he found Richard, faithfully waiting for him.

May we be as faithful in obeying our Heavenly Father as Richard was in obeying his earthly father.

Practicing Needed

A famous devotional writer was with his family on a steamer about to sail. The wife was busily occupied with a number of things that needed attention. Her husband was finally located in his stateroom. There, he sat writing — finishing a chapter on the importance of faithfulness in the little commonplaces of life. He was *so busy writing about* being faithful in the commonplace things of life that he had left his poor wife to attend to *all* of the necessary things before sailing.

A Faithful Boy

A worker of the American Sunday School Union organized a S u n d a y School one fall. It was in a faraway place. He was not able to visit the Sunday School for several months. Then, one Sunday morning, he made his way through deep snow to the schoolhouse, to see how the work was coming along. Smoke was coming out of the chimney. As he drew near, he heard the bell ringing. But when he entered the schoolhouse, he found *only one* person there, a boy of fourteen. "How has the Sunday School been getting along?" he asked.

"Oh, it got along fine until the bad weather came. Since then, it has not been doing so well!" The man and the boy sat by the warm stove, and talked for awhile. They waited, but no one else came.

"How many were here last Sunday?" the missionary asked.

"Just me!" the boy replied.

"Well, that is not very encouraging."

"No," was the reply, "but I thought that if I would come and build the fire, and ring the bell, somebody else might come."

"How many were here two weeks ago?" asked the missionary.

"Just me," said the boy.

The man asked the boy if he wanted to quit. The boy said, "Oh, no. I want to *go on* serving the Lord. Then maybe, some day, someone else will come!"

Will *you* "*go on*" serving the Lord, no matter what happens? Will you be faithful to Him always?

Laziness

A motorist in the south stopped at an old, dilapidated house to ask for water. A barefooted man was gazing across the field grown up with weeds. "How is your cotton this year?" asked the motorist. "Well sir, I ain't got no cotton. I didn't plant none 'cause I was afraid the boll weavil might be bad." "How is your corn?" "Well, I didn't plant no corn either 'cause we might not get rain." "How are your sweet potatoes?' "Well, stranger, I didn't plant no sweet potatoes 'cause I was afraid the bugs might take them. No sir, I didn't plant nothing. I just played safe."

How much like the steward who hid his talent away in a napkin! How displeasing we are to God when we do nothing. God wants us to be busy in His work. If we will work, He will bless our work.

FATHERS

In Daddy's Shoes

One day there was loud laughter in a home. The father went to see what was causing it. Down the stairs his little boy was coming. He was all dressed up in one of father's suits. He had tied strings on the buttons of the pants and pulled them way up under his arm.

Then he had rolled them way up at the bottom. The vest came down to the boy's knees and the coat touched the floor. The boy's feet were almost lost in a pair of father's big shoes. The little boy shouted gleefully, "Daddy, I'se a-coming in your shoes."

The father turned to the mother and said, "This shows me that my boy wants to be like his daddy. He wants to walk in his daddy's shoes. I will have to be mighty careful how I walk. May God help me to walk the right way."

Thankful for Father

A little girl was kneeling at her Mother's knee to say her evening prayer. As usual she prayed, "God bless Mother and —." The prayer suddenly stopped. With a look of sadness the little girl lifted her face and said, "Mother, I cannot pray for Father any more." Her little lips had always asked a blessing upon Father whenever she prayed, but now Father was dead. He had gone to be with Jesus. Mother urged the little girl to go on with her prayer. The little girl hesitated and then she said, "Oh, Mother, I cannot leave him out. Let me say, 'Thank God that I had a dear Father once.' Then I can still go on and keep Father in my prayers." So the little girl began her prayer again. She prayed, "God bless Mother, and thank God that I had a dear Father once."

A Father Will Do

A young minister in London lost his wife. He had a little girl. For several years he cared for her. One Sunday, the minister came into the church, leading the child. They walked past the crowded pews. Then, the little girl sat in the corner of the front pew. In his sermon, the minister spoke of a mother's love and care. He said, "Think what a child's life is without a mother's love. Who can tend, who can cherish, who can tend like a mother?" His voice halted. Suddenly, a sweet childish voice spoke out clearly, "A father will do every bit as well, Papa, dear!"

How wonderful it is that we have a kind Heavenly Father whose heart is filled with love for us. He will never leave us. He will never fail us in times of distress. How glad we are that we can call Him: "Our Father!"

Love Won

In a home in England there was a boy who was a bad boy. The mother was dead. The father and the brothers and sisters were very sorry about the boy. Often, they coaxed him to change his bad ways. Often, they scolded him and threatened him. But he would not listen. One Christmas day, the boy came home drunk. The brothers and sisters were shocked. They had no patience with him. They went to their father and asked him to drive the boy away from home.

That night, the father talked to his son. He said, "Henry, your brothers and sisters want me to put you out of the house. But, son, I love you. I will never put you out of our home!" The loving words of his father made the son sorry for his sin. He decided that he would come to Jesus, the Saviour; that he would give up his sins and live a different life. Love worked when everything else had failed. That son became a great preacher, Henry Moorehouse!

FELLOWSHIP

"Blest Be The Tie That Binds!"

It was Sunday morning in Kiangsu, China. The morning church service had begun in the little Chinese church. Suddenly, there was excitement. Women uttered suppressed cries of fear. They clutched their children to them. Men half rose from their seats. A Japanese soldier was stalking up the aisle! The Japanese troops had recently taken over Kiangsu. When the soldier reached the front of the church, he put his hand in his pocket. Then he laid an offering on the table. Picking up a hymn book, he turned the pages until he found the number he wanted. He showed the number to the organist. Evidently, he wanted to join with the Chinese congregation in singing. The organist began to play. Then the Japanese soldier and the Chinese Christians all sang together:

"Blest be the tie that binds,
  Our hearts in Christian love!"

Fortunate for the Sailor

After many adventures, an Australian destroyer reached a port in the Solomon Islands. The crew was given shore leave. A young Christian sailor finding himself free for the day, decided to spend the day quietly by himself in Bible study. He saw a trail running into a forest. He followed it until he came to a quiet spot where he sat down and began to read his Bible. Suddenly, he saw standing by his side a huge, almost naked, native carrying a club. Before the sailor could cry out, the native pointed to the open Book and asked, "That Bible?" The sailor replied, "Yes." Then the native remarked, "Me read Bible, too. Me Christian!" Taking the Bible from the sailor, the native read aloud a chapter from the Book of Isaiah. Then, handing back the Bible with a smile, he went on his way!

"We All Walks With Him!"

In a Southern Negro church, Homer Rodeheaver had just finished singing the song, "I walk with the King, Hallelujah!" Down the aisle came a dear Negro "auntie," stepping high. When she was about half way down the aisle, she said, "Hallelujah! I walks with Him, too, Brother!" Instantly, the audience all responded, "We all walks with Him down here!"

Fellowship With Christ

When Count Zinzendorf was a little boy, he used to write notes to the Saviour and throw them out of his window, hoping that Jesus would find them. He always had strong faith that the Lord Jesus was with him, and was his constant Friend and Companion.

Once Count Zinzendorf was travelling. He asked his friend to drop behind so he might converse more freely with the Lord, with whom he spoke audibly.

Cultivate the friendship of the Lord Jesus. Carry every burden to Him. He is an unfailing, sympathetic friend.

"What a friend we have in Jesus,
  All our sins and griefs to bear,
What a privilege to carry,
  EVERYTHING to God in prayer!"

FORGIVENESS

"Won't Somebody Forgive Me?"

A little boy did something wrong. He was taken into a room where his grandfather and grandmother and his uncles and aunts were seated. All of these people looked very stern. They did not look kind and forgiving. The little boy looked from one face to another, and then he burst into tears. He asked, "Oh, won't somebody please forgive me?"

How glad we are that God is ready to forgive us when we ask Him to forgive us. The Bible says, "Who forgiveth *all* thine iniquities" *(Ps. 103:3 f. c.)*; "But there is forgiveness with Thee" *(130:4 f. c.)*; "In whom we have redemption through His Blood, the forgiveness of sins" *(Eph. 1:7 f. c.)*.

God Keeps His Word

Dinny Malone was an old sea captain eighty years old. He sat reading his Bible one day when the minister called. He said, "I am trying to find God." "Well," said the minister, "I guess you will find Him in that Book!" "But I haven't," said Dinny. "For six years, I have been trying to get Him to forgive my sins." The minister asked, "Have you repented?" Dinny replied, "Yes." The minister asked, "Have you trusted in the Lord Jesus to save you?" "Yes," said Dinny, "but I have never felt His forgiveness in my heart. How can I know that God has forgiven my sins?"

The minister took the Bible, turned to a verse and said to Dinny, "Read it." Slowly Dinny read, "If we confess our sins, He is faithful and just to forgive us our sins." "Dinny," asked the minister, "When you give your word, do you keep it?" "Sure I do," roared

Dinny. "A gentleman always keeps his word." Then the minister asked, "Dinny, don't you think God keeps His Word?" A bright light came to Dinny's face. He said, "I see it now! God *does* forgive me. He says He will, and now I *know* He does!"

Won by Forgiveness

A native was dusting the furniture of a missionary in India. He carelessly upset a beautiful vase. It fell to the floor and broke in many pieces. The frightened native ran to the missionary. He fell down at his feet and begged for mercy. The missionary smiled and said, "I forgive you." The native looked up at the quiet face of the missionary. There was no anger in his face. Leaping to his feet, the native cried, "I believe in your Lord Jesus!" He then told the missionary how he had gradually come to know Christ as he lived in the home of the missionary, and now the kindness and forgiveness of the missionary had won him completely to Christ.

Struck On the Cheek

Richard Weaver worked in a deep pit. He was a Christian. One day, a man working near him said, "I have a good mind to smack you on the face," and he struck him. Weaver turned to him the other cheek. The man struck that cheek. This happened five different times. Not once did Weaver strike back. When the man turned away, Weaver cried, "The Lord forgive you for I do! And the Lord save thee!" The next morning, Weaver's enemy came to him and said, "Oh, Richard, do you really forgive me for striking you?" Together, they knelt and prayed. And the enemy of Weaver gave his heart to Jesus. He, too, became a loving and faithful follower of Jesus.

He Got His Wrongs

A little boy attended a meeting in a church. Some of the brothers in the church were angry with one another. One man stood to his feet and, with clenched fists, said, "I will put up with a good deal, but I will not allow you to put anything over on me. I will have my *rights*!"

An old man nearly deaf said, "What did you say, brother? I did not get it!"

The man shouted, "I say I will have my rights!"

The old man said, "But you don't mean that, do you? If you had your rights, you would be in hell, wouldn't you? You have sinned, and so have we all. You are forgetting, aren't you, that Jesus did not get His rights here on earth. He got His wrongs. He even died on the Cross. He did not deserve it, but He died for us!"

The man, who had been so angry, dropped his head, and said, "Brethren, I have been *wrong*. I will forget. I will forgive! Handle the matter as you think best." Then, he sat down, and all the troubles were settled in a minute!

A Beautiful Scene

Some cowboys in Texas were having a camp meeting. One night, they sat in a circle on the hillside. The leader for the evening was a cowboy who had been saved by the Lord Jesus the night before. The leader said, "Before I read the Bible, I want to tell all of you something: Last night, I was saved. I took a public stand for Jesus. That means, I must not hate any one. For a long time, I have been hating a certain cowboy who is here tonight. He did me a lot of wrong, and I did him a lot of wrong. I want to say, 'I am sorry.' I want to ask him if he will forgive me. I stand ready to forgive him!"

Quickly, the other cowboy jumped to his feet. He said, "Bill, I'll forgive you, and I am plenty glad you are forgiving me!" Then the two cowboys put their arms about each other, and wept for joy! What a beautiful scene that was!

His Only Worry

A young explorer in Canada spent his last days alone in a hut. When his body was found long afterward, on the table there lay a letter which said, "The sun is shining, Mother, but I feel so cold. I have not eaten for so long. I haven't seen another human being for forty days now. There are some magazines here, but the stories are so silly. I have some cards, but I don't want to play solitaire. The *only* thing I want, the *only* thing I worry about is God's forgiveness for my sins!"

The Clean Slate

One day a little boy disobeyed his mother. She had told him not to play near the pond. He went close to the pond, and fell into the water. When he reached home, he was told that his mother was sick. The nurse said that he could not go into mother's bedroom. How sad he was. He wrote on a little slate this message: "Dear Mother, I have been bad. I am sorry. If you will forgive me, please rub this out!" The nurse carried the slate to the mother. In a few moments she came back with the slate. The slate was perfectly clean. All the writing had been rubbed out.

How like God who said, "I have blotted out, as a thick cloud, thy transgressions [sins] and, as a cloud, thy sins: return unto Me; for I have redeemed thee" *(Is. 44:22)*.

Forgiveness Is Free

A Christian visited an old man, who seemed anxious for God's forgiveness. The Christian said, "Suppose I go to a shop to buy something for you. I pay for it, and tell you to go and get it. Need you take any money with you?"

"No," said the old man, "it would be paid for."

"Do you need to make any promise to pay for it at some future time?"

"No," said the old man, "I would have it for nothing."

Said the Christian, "So it is with forgiveness of sin! The Lord Jesus has paid the *full* price for it. He had *all* the pain and punishment that sin deserved. He bore it *all*. He paid the *whole*. Now, forgiveness is *yours* simply for the taking!"

"Oh," said the old man with tears in his eyes, "I see it now. It is forgiveness for nothing. Christ has bought it, and He gives it to me!"

No Saviour Like That

Years ago, in northern India, Bishop Warne was preaching to a congregation seated on the ground. He told how the very people whom Jesus came to save, seized Him, mocked Him, spat upon Him. He told how they led Him to Calvary. Vividly, he described the sufferings of Jesus on the Cross. He told how in the midst of it all, Jesus cried out, "Father, forgive them, for they know not what they do."

When the bishop reached this point, an old Hindu priest rushed forward, threw himself at the bishop's feet, and cried out, "You must leave India." The bishop asked why. The Hindu replied, "Because we have no story like this. We have no saviour who lived a sinless life, died for his enemies, and prayed for the forgiveness of those who took his life. If you keep on telling this story to our people, they will forsake our temples and follow your Saviour!" Since that time, thousands in India have forsaken their heathen temples and have followed the Saviour, the *only* Saviour from *sin*!

Forgiveness Accepted

A boy had sinned against his mother. When she lay on her death bed, he was convicted of his sin. He went to her room, knelt by her bed, and sobbed for forgiveness. She drew him near, and whispered in his ear, "My dear boy, I would have forgiven you long ago if you had only accepted it."

The Lord Jesus died for our sins. He would have forgiven us our sins long ago if we had accepted His pardon.

Unexpected Forgiveness

A man saw a boy stealing flowers in his garden. He slipped up behind the boy and laid his hand on his shoulder. The boy was frightened. The man said, "My boy, answer me one question: Which is the best flower in my garden?" The boy looked around and pointed to a beautiful moss rose, and said, "That rose is best." The man, still keeping one hand on the boy's shoulder, reached out and plucked the rose and gave it to the boy. Then he released him, saying, "There, take it my boy!" The boy was amazed. He said, "Ain't you going to punish me, sir?" The man replied, "No, but I am giving to you the best flower in my garden. Now you will never steal my flowers again, will you?" "Never, sir, as long as I live. But, please, sir, ain't there some little errand I can do for you?" Free forgiveness and a token of love had won the boy's heart! From that hour, he was the willing servant of the man.

When God Forgives He Forgets

A little girl had been good for a whole week. She asked some favor from her aunt, reminding her aunt how good she had been all week. The aunt said, "I know you have been good all this week, but you were bad all last week." The little girl exclaimed, "Oh, auntie, you are not one bit like God. When He forgives, He forgets! He doesn't keep throwing up our sins at us afterwards."

Polished Boots

A big sergeant in a Scotch Highland regiment told how he was brought to Christ. He said, "In our company there was a private who was converted when we were in Malta. We gave that fellow an awful time. One wet night, he came in very tired and very wet. Before he went to bed, he knelt down to pray. My boots were heavy with wet mud. I threw one at him and it hit him on the side of his head. Then I threw the other boot and hit him in the other side of his head. He just went on praying. The next morning I found my boots beside my bed. They had been beautifully polished by the

private. That was his reply to me. It just broke my heart. I was saved that day."

Don't Kick Back

One frosty morning a little girl stood looking out of the window into the farmyard. In the farmyard there stood many cows, oxen, and horses, waiting to drink. The cows stood very still until one of them attempted to turn around. She happened to hit the cow nearest her, whereupon that cow kicked and hit another. In five minutes all of the cows were kicking one another in fury!

The mother of the little girl laughed and said, "My dear, do you see what comes from 'kicking' when you are hit? Just so, I have seen one cross word set a whole family saying angry words!"

Later, when the little girl and her brothers were irritable, mother said, "Take care, my children, remember how the fight in the barnyard began. Never give back a kick for a hit, and you will avoid lots of trouble."

Kind Enemies

During World War II, a man was left for dead, by the side of a trail in New Guinea. Later, he became conscious. He lay there badly wounded. He expected every moment that Japanese soldiers would arrive and kill him. Soon four Japanese soldiers did arrive. To his surprise, they did not kill him. They lifted him gently and carried him to a trail in another part of the forest. There, they put him down. One of them said in English, "You will be safe here. Soon, some Americans will arrive and pick you up. We are Christians. We hate war." Then they left.

Little Chin

When the Japanese were at war with the Chinese, a little Chinese boy said to his mother, "Mother, shall I pray for the Chinese soldiers tonight? Shall I pray that they will kill many Japanese soldiers and win the war?"

"No, Chin," said the mother; "you must pray for the little Japanese children whose fathers are fighting and dying tonight." Then little Chin, the Chinese boy, knelt down and prayed for the little Japanese children.

We should always pray for our enemies. Jesus did. As He hung upon His Cross, He prayed, "Father, forgive them; for they know not what they do."

Good for Evil

Hudson Taylor was a missionary in China. One day, he was dressed in Chinese costume. He stood waiting for a boatman to take him across the river. A richly dressed Chinaman came and also stood waiting. The boat drew near. The Chinaman wanted to get in. He did not notice that Mr. Taylor was a foreigner. He struck him on the head and knocked him into the mud!

When the boat arrived, the Chinaman looked at Mr. Taylor and saw that he was a foreigner. He said, "What? You, a foreigner, did not strike me back when I knocked you into the mud?" Mr. Taylor said, "This boat is mine. Come in and I will take you where you want to go!" After they got into the boat, Mr. Taylor told the Chinaman about the Lord Jesus, the Saviour. Tears ran down the Chinaman's face, as he heard the Gospel.

Mr. Taylor suffered for Jesus gladly, because he loved Jesus. He won the Chinaman for Jesus because he was kind and forgiving like Jesus.

Coals of Fire

In the early days of our country, a fine master had a good slave whom he loved very much. One day, the slave went with his master to the slave market. There they saw an old Negro who was to be sold. His hair was gray. His form was bent. He trembled with weakness. The good slave implored the master to purchase the old Negro. The master was surprised, but he did what his good slave wanted him to do. The old man was bought, and carried home.

The good slave carried the old man to his own cabin, and placed him in his own bed. He fed the old man. He gave him water. When the old man was cold, he carried him into the warm sunshine. When the sun was hot, he carried him to the shade.

"What is the meaning of all this?" asked the master of the good slave. "Is this old man your father?"

"No," was the reply.

"Is he your friend, or brother?"

"No," said the good slave. "He is my enemy. Years ago, he stole me from my home in Africa. He sold me to be a slave. I am now doing what the Bible says, 'If thine enemy hunger, feed him; if he thirst, give him drink: for in so doing thou shalt heap coals of fire on his head.'"

A Brave Hero

Years ago there lived a young Englishman whose name was George Atley. He loved Jesus with his *whole* heart. He was willing to suffer "the loss of all things" for Jesus. He went to Africa as a missionary.

One day, a party of very bad men attacked George Atley. He had a rifle with him. It was loaded. He could have easily defended himself. He could have easily taken the lives of those wanting to kill him. But, he thought to himself: "If I kill these men, the mission and the cause of Jesus would suffer much. If I allow them to take my life, Jesus will be glorified, and the mission will suffer no harm." So, like Jesus, he was led "as a lamb to the slaughter." When his body was found later in the stream, his rifle was also found with its ten chambers still loaded!

GIVING

"Nothin' for Nobody"

A little girl told the story of the feeding of the five thousand to the other children in her primary class. She concluded her story by saying, "The boy gave all of his lunch to Jesus and because He blessed it, there was enough for everybody." The teacher asked, "What do you think would have happened if the boy had said, 'I can't share my lunch with anybody; there is just enough for me'?" The little girl thought for a moment and then said, "It would have squinched up and squinched up, and there wouldn't have been nothin' for nobody."

A Doll for Jesus

In a church they asked all the boys and girls to bring some gifts to be sent to a mission hospital in India. They were asked to bring especially toys for the heathen boys and girls who have so few such things. They were told to bring the things to a missionary service on a certain day.

The appointed day arrived. Many boys and girls came to the missionary service, bringing their gifts. One little girl sat in the church, crying as if her heart would break. In her arms she clasped a doll she had brought for some little girl in India. Everyone could see that she was having a struggle to give up her "baby."

At last it came time for the little girl to carry her gift up front. Smiles broke through her tears as she ran down the aisle. As she handed up the doll, she said, "I forgot that I was doing it for Jesus."

William Colgate

Many years ago, a lad, sixteen years old, left home to seek his fortune. The captain of a canal boat, a Christian man, said to him, "Be sure you start right, and you will get along well." The boy told the captain that he wanted to be a maker of soap. That was the only trade he knew anything about. The captain said, "Someone will soon be the leading soap maker in New York. It may be you! Be a good man; give your heart to Christ; give God *all* that belongs to Him. Make an honest soap. Give a *full* pound. God will prosper you, and, one day, you will be a rich man!"

The boy arrived in New York. He remembered the words of the old captain. He became a Christian, and united with a church. He gave God a tenth of the first dollar he earned. After that, ten cents of every dollar he earned went to the Lord's work. He engaged in the soap business. He made an honest soap and gave a full pound. He never forgot to honor the Lord God. How greatly did God honor him! He prospered and grew richer than he ever hoped. Then, he promised to give the Lord two tenths, and then three-tenths, four-tenths, and finally five-tenths! This is the story of *William Colgate*.

"I'll Hide Under the Bench!"

It was time for the offering in the church. A little girl noticed a fine lady who was sitting by her looking over the things in her handbag, searching for a SMALL COIN. Failing to find the coin, the lady closed her purse and folded her hands. She intended to appear in an attitude of worship while the offering plate passed in front of her. The little girl thought it was wrong for any one to be in church without an offering. She had her own offering in an envelope which she had brought from home. She felt very sorry for the lady. Reaching over, she put her envelope in the lady's hand, and whispered, "Here, you put this in the offering, and I'll hide under the bench!"

The Little Lame Girl

A preacher made an appeal for funds for a missionary. He invited the people to bring their gifts and lay them on the altar. The aisles were filled with people who were bringing their offerings. A little, lame girl came slowly toward the front. She took a little ring from her finger and laid it, with the other gifts, on the altar. Then, she adjusted her crutch and started back up the aisle. After the service, the preacher said to the lame girl, "My dear, I saw what you did tonight. It was beautiful! But the people responded well tonight and the offering was large. We don't need to keep your ring. So I want to give it back to you." The little girl looked up

at the minister and said, "I didn't give that ring to YOU. I gave it to Jesus!"

Not too Much for an Indian

An Indian once came to Bishop Whipple, and asked him to exchange a two dollar bill for two one-dollar bills. "Why?" asked the Bishop, thinking that, perhaps, the Indian wanted to give one dollar to God's work. The Indian replied, "I want one dollar for me to give to Jesus, and one dollar for my wife to give to Jesus!" The Bishop asked him if it was all the money he had. "Yes," replied the Indian. The Bishop was about to tell him that it was too much for him to give. Just then, an Indian clergyman who was standing nearby whispered, "It might be too much for a white man to give, but it is not too much for an Indian to give who has this year heard for the first time of the love of Jesus!"

Into the Pierced Hand

A minister was taking an offering for missions. He said, "My friends, as you give this morning, feel that you are placing your money into the pierced hand of Christ." A wealthy lady who was present had thought that she would place a quarter in the offering. But when the minister spoke, she changed her mind. She said to him after the service, "I could not place a quarter into the pierced hand of Christ. So, I am going home and get a ten dollar bill. I will give that for missions!"

All from God

A little girl told a friend that she was going to give her father a pair of slippers for his birthday. The friend asked, "W h e r e will you get your money?" She replied, "Why, Father will give me the money!" Let us know that all we have comes from our Heavenly Father.

Given to Christ

A missionary society was having a difficult time. The members of the society were not doing much to help spread the Gospel around the world. Then, the society thought of a new plan. Each time the offering was taken it was said, "This offering is given to the Lord Jesus Christ!" From that time on, there was a marked increase in the offering.

There will always be an increase in our offerings for God's work if we will but remember that we are giving to the Lord Jesus.

She Wanted to Give All

In a Chinese school for blind children, there was one little girl who seemed too stupid to be taught anything. One day a lady visitor asked how she might help. The nurse said, "Give that poor little girl a piece of money. She has never had a coin of her own!" The lady gave her a five-cent piece.

The little girl was delighted! Each day, she planned to spend the five cents. Some times, she thought she would spend it on herself. Again, she thought she would give it to the kind nurse who cared for her.

A meeting was to be held at Foochow for the Bible society which supplied the school with Chinese Gospels, written for the blind. The little girl was too ill to go to the meeting, but she asked the nurse to take her five cents and put it in the collection. The nurse said, "Part of it would be enough. You give part of it, and keep part." The little blind girl insisted on giving all her five cents. She said, "I have never been able to give God anything before, and I want to give it ALL!"

Robbing God

A Negro church was making a drive for funds. Two sisters called upon Uncle Rastus, and asked him for his donation. Uncle Rastus exclaimed, "I can't give anything. I owe nearly everybody in this town already." "But," said one of the sisters, "don't you think you owe the Lord something, too?" "I do, sister," said the man, "but He ain't pushing me like my other creditors are."

Why Do You Give?

In a dream, one saw the people placing their offerings in a basket at church. In the basket, each gift became what it was in God's sight. A little girl shyly placed a nickel into the basket. She gave to please her Sunday School teacher. The nickel became a daisy. A little boy placed a dime in the basket. He gave it because his father told him to. The dime became a cent. A rich man placed a gold piece in the basket. He gave so others could see how generous he was. The gold piece became brass. A young woman placed a small coin in the basket. She was poor; she worked hard. She gave because she loved God. She gave willingly and cheerfully the little she had. Her gift became a shining gold piece.

Always remember, boys and girls, that God wants us to give willingly and cheerfully, according to what we have. We must always give with a heart filled with love for Christ if we want to please Him.

God Beats Us Giving

Captain Levy of Philadelphia used to give great amounts of money to God's work. Some one asked him, "How are you able to give so much and still have so much left?" "Oh," said he, "as I shovel out, God shovels in, and the Lord has a bigger shovel than I have." Remember, boys and girls, you can't beat God giving.

"May the Giver of gifts give unto you,
That which is good and that which is true;
The will to help, and the courage to do;
A heart that can sing the whole day through,
Whether the skies be gray or blue!
May the Giver of gifts give these to you!"

Sacrificial Giving

A missionary in India told of a mission church which was being built. Many converts brought gifts for the erection of the church. One poor leper came, clad only in a rag. His body was thin from lack of food. He brought an offering of one and one-half cents. It meant privation and hunger to him to give that amount, small as it was. Surely, in the eyes of the Master of the treasury the gift became the "riches of liberality."

The Pumpkin

An old man in India lived thirty-five miles from the mission station. Some times, the missionary came to the village where the old man lived, and preached. The old man became a Christian. He wanted to give something to Jesus. The only thing he had to give was a great, big pumpkin. He had grown the pumpkin with great care. He had protected it a long time from thieves. Now, it was ripe. He did not know when the missionary would come again to his village. So, he picked the pumpkin and placed it upon his head. He walked for thirty-five miles to the mission station.

The pumpkin was heavy. It weighed nearly thirty pounds. The road was hot and dusty. But the man's heart was filled with happiness. He was taking the missionary a gift for Jesus. The pumpkin was worth only four cents in India, but it was the only gift the old man had. How happy he was as he carried it to the missionary. May we always be happy as we bring gifts and offerings to Jesus!

The Best Doll

A missionary suggested to her little daughter that she give one of her many dolls to a little heathen girl. The little girl looked at her dolls. She loved all of them. The doll she loved best was named, "Miss Lou." The little girl thought she would give some other doll to the little heathen girl. Then she thought that the little heathen girl had never known love or kindness. She had never had a doll. The missionary's little daughter prayed. She asked God which doll she should give to the little heathen girl. When she got up from her knees, she said, "God loves that little heathen girl, and I love her, too. I want to give her the *best* doll I have." So she gave "Miss Lou" to the little girl.

The Heart of the Christian Life

A man once came to his minister and said, "I get tired of hearing you say, 'Give, Give, Give.' It seems every time I come to church, you are talking about giving. Is that all there is to the Christian life?" The minister replied, "Brother, I have never thought about that before. But the heart of the Christian life is giving."

A Little Girl's Gift

A missionary lady told about her work in China. When she had finished, a little girl came forward and gave her twelve pennies. "Please," said she, "I have been saving these pennies. Now, I want them to help in the missionary work in China." How happy the missionary was to receive the offering from the earnest, little giver!

Months passed by. One day a letter came to the little girl which read, "With your twelve pennies, I bought twelve penny Gospels of John. I gave one to each in my class of Chinese girls. They read about Jesus in their own little Book! Today, all twelve gave their hearts to Christ!"

Two Bricks

A little girl went with her mother to prayer meeting. The minister and members of the church prayed about a new church building. They needed a new church building badly. On the way home, the little girl asked her mother many questions. She was told that they needed a larger church, and so must build a new one.

The next morning, mother missed the little girl. She followed her little footsteps out of the yard to the minister's house. In the minister's front yard was little Mary. In her toy wheelbarrow, she had two bricks. She had brought the two bricks to the minister to start the new church.

The next Sunday morning, the minister told what little Mary had done. God touched the hearts of the people. Many of them gave money and bricks to build the new church. Before long, a beautiful new church building was ready for use.

All He Had

One time, an offering was being taken to build a new church. A small boy gave *all* that he had in the offering: A top and five marbles. He had no money to give. Afterwards someone started to laugh at the boy's offering. But a Christian man said, "That little boy gave all he had. I will give you one hundred dollars for the top, and I have Christian friends who will give you twenty-five dollars each for the marbles!" The man gave a hundred dollars for the top, and he took the marbles to his friends. His friends gave twenty-five dollars each for the marbles.

God blessed the gift of the little boy. He always blesses our gifts when we give Him the best we have. When the cornerstone was placed for the new church, under it were laid the top and five marbles which the little boy had given.

Fifty-Seven Pennies

On North Broad Street in Philadelphia stands the great Temple Baptist Church. There is an interesting story connected with the building of this church.

Dr. Russell Conwell preached in a small church. It was so small that it could not care for the growing congregation. One Sunday morning, as Dr. Conwell approached the church, he met a little girl who was crying. He asked her why she was crying. She replied that there was no room for her in the Sunday School so she was going home. Dr. Conwell put his arms around the little girl and said, "I will find a place for you."

Some time later, the little girl was taken suddenly ill and died. Under her pillow was found an old pocketbook. In it were fifty-seven pennies, and a scrap of paper on which was written, "To help build the little Temple bigger, so that more children can go there to Sunday School." Little Hattie had worked and saved her pennies to help build a bigger church.

Dr. Conwell told the touching story of little Hattie to his people. T h e i r hearts were touched. They all began to give money for the enlargement of the little church. The papers told the story far and wide, and within five years those fifty seven pennies had grown to be $250,000!

Today, on North Broad Street, you can see the great Temple Baptist Church which seats 3,300 people! All the children who want to attend may go to Sunday School and be comfortable there. Little Hattie was only a *little* girl, but she gave what she could, and God increased her offering. How true is the saying, "When God is in it, little is much!"

A Cheerful Giver

A Negro preacher was taking an offering for God's work. He said, "I want everybody here to give something. I want everybody to give as you are able. I want everybody to give cheerfully. Now, come up to the front and lay your offering on the table." Men and women, boys and girls, filled the aisles. They passed by the table in front and laid their gifts on it.

Presently, a so-called "wealthy" member came by. He placed a dollar bill on the table. The Negro preacher said, "Wait a minute, Brother. You did not give as you are able to give." The brother put the dollar back in his pocket, and then placed a five dollar bill on the table. He had a scowl on his face. The preacher said, "Brother, you have given as you are able, but you did not give it cheerfully. That will not do!" The brother took up the bill. Then, with a smile on face, he placed it back on the table. "That will do, Brother," said the preacher; "you have given what you are able to give, and you have given it cheerfully!"

The Bible says, "Every man according as he purposeth in his heart, so let him give; not grudgingly, or of necessity: for God loveth a cheerful giver" (*II Cor. 9:7*).

GOSPEL

A Sure Cure

Some years ago, in the Southland, a Methodist bishop was wending his way home. A prominent physician, passing in his car, stopped, and offered the bishop a ride. As they rode on together, the physician said to the bishop,

"I am surprised that a man of your intelligence should believe as you do." The physician was an outspoken unbeliever.

There was silence for a few moments, and then the bishop said, "Doctor, suppose that some years ago some one had recommended to you a prescription for tuberculosis. Suppose that you had the dread disease; that you procured the medicine, and took it as directed and were completely cured. And suppose, Doctor, that you had used that prescription in your practice ever since, and had never known it to fail when it was taken according to directions. What would you think of a man who was dying with tuberculosis, and who refused to try your prescription?"

"I would say that that man was an unpardonable fool," replied the doctor.

Then the bishop said, "Doctor, twenty-five years ago, I was a lost sinner, dying in my sin. I tried the Gospel of the grace of God. It made a *new man* of me. Since then, I have preached the Gospel to others. Whenever it has been believed, I have seen men changed. I have never known the Gospel to fail. I have seen it make the proud, humble; the drunkard, sober; the profane man, pure in his speech; and the dishonest man, true! The rich and the poor; the learned and unlearned; the old and the young have all been healed of sin's diseases when they have believed and received the Gospel!"

The doctor said, "Bishop, you have caught me. I have been a fool!" Then and there, the doctor received the Gospel, and became a *new* creature in Christ Jesus!

Saved by the Gospel

A man had been a member of a church in England for some years. One day, he was reading the Book of Acts. He read about the peace and joy of the early Christians. He wondered why he did not have peace and joy. He decided to pray. He prayed for hours, but his life was not changed. He decided to fast. He went without food until his friends feared for his health. One day, in his room, he felt that he could no longer go on with his *empty life*. He cried out, "W h a t must I do to be saved?"

Suddenly, the man knew his answer. He found it in the Book of Acts: "Believe on the Lord Jesus Christ, and thou shalt be saved." Praying had not been enough; fasting had not been enough. But believing on the Lord Jesus Christ was sufficient. His whole life was changed. His heart was filled with peace and joy. The Gospel had saved him. His friends said, "My, but you do look different!" And he was different. He began to preach the Gospel to his friends, and before long, many of them had found the Lord Jesus sufficient.

Must Be Applied

A soap manufacturer, who was not a Christian, was walking with a minister. The soap maker said, "The Gospel you preach has not done much good in the world. I see lots of wickedness, and wicked people!" Just then, they passed by a child who was making mud pies. His face, his hands, and his feet were very *dirty*.

The preacher said, "Soap hasn't done much good in this world. I see lots of dirt, and many dirty people!"

"Oh," said the soap maker, "but you must remember that soap is useful only when it is applied."

"Exactly," replied the minister; "and so it is with the Gospel. It can help you, only if you *apply it:* You must believe in the Lord Jesus, and then you will be saved!"

Giving the Gospel at Home

A great insurance company in New York had a convention for its many agents. They came from all over the country to attend the convention which was held at the main office in New York City. Great was the astonishment when one of the agents from the West insured the barber, the elevator man, and a waiter in the restaurant, all of whom had been employed for years by the insurance company in the great building. No one had ever thought of offering life insurance policies to these men working in the home office building.

Many Christians think of going across the ocean to preach the Gospel to perishing souls, but they never think of giving the Gospel to the lost ones in their *own* town, in their *own* neighborhood, and even in their *own* homes.

The World Needs the Gospel

A noted preacher once said, "I would not cross the street to give India a new religion. I would not cross the street to give China a new religion. I would not cross the street to give Japan a new religion. But I would go around the world again, and yet again, to tell India, China, and Japan and the rest of the world:

"There is a Fountain filled with Blood,
 Drawn from Immanuel's veins,
And sinners plunged beneath that flood,
 Lose *all* their guilty stains!"

The Effect of the Gospel

A traveler in China asked a native if he had ever read the Gospel. "No," was the answer, "but I *have seen it.* There is a man in my village, who was the terror of his neighborhood. He had a violent temper; he was an opium smoker, a criminal, and a dangerous man. But the Gospel has made him gentle and good. He has left off his opium. No, I have never read the Gospel, but I *have seen it, and it is very good!"*

GRACE

Just as Much Grace

During a testimony meeting in a certain church, a man rose and told how Jesus had saved him from a life of law-breaking, liquor, and all manner of evil. Then a little lady got to her feet and said, "Jesus saved me from a life of ease, luxury, and selfishness. It took just as much grace to save me from my easy chair as it did to save our brother from the gutter."

The River Where You Washed

A missionary had roped off his space and had begun to build the little hut in which he would live during his stay in Africa. The little black children gathered around to watch him in open-eyed wonder. They had never seen a man working with white hands before. By and by, one little fellow mustered up courage to crawl under the ropes. He crept across the grass to the place where the white man was working. Then he touched the missionary's trousers with his little fingers. Finally his fingers moved up until they took hold of the wonderful white hand. Then a childish voice asked, "Oh, missionary, won't you please tell me the name of the river where you wash your hands?"

Have you washed your dark and sin-soiled soul in the river of God's grace? If you have, your soul is now as white as snow in God's sight.

The Door of Grace Is Open Wide

One warm summer afternoon, a little bird flew through the open door into a little chapel where a service was being held. The frightened bird flew from the ceiling to the windows seeking a way out into the sunshine. In vain it beat its wings against the windows. A lady, watching it, thought how foolish it was not to fly through the wide open door. The bird, wearied from its effort, landed on a rafter near the ceiling. Suddenly it saw the open door and flew out into the sunshine, where it began a joyous song.

The lady thought, "Am I not as foolish as that bird? I have long been struggling under the burden of my sin, and longing to get free. All the time the door of God's grace has stood wide open." Then and there the lady decided to enter the door.

His Recommendation

One day, a dirty ragged little boy came to Dr. Barnardo and asked for admission to the London Orhpanage. Dr. Barnardo said, "But, my boy, I do not know you. Who are you? What have you to recommend you?" The little boy held up his ragged coat before Dr. Barnardo and said, "If you please, sir, I thought these here rags would be all I needed to recommend me!" Dr. Barnardo caught the little boy up in his arms, and said, "You are right, little fellow! Welcome to our orphanage!"

All we need to recommend us to God's grace are our sinful, needy lives.

A Wonder of God's Grace

One night there wandered into Water Street Mission a strange looking man. He was known as the "old colonel." He was about six feet tall and about sixty years old. His dirty gray beard was a foot long and his dirty gray hair hung over his shoulders, long and ragged. His eyes were bleared. His face looked as if it had never been washed. His old ragged overcoat was fastened with a nail. His trousers were filled with holes. Instead of shoes, he had on his feet rags tied up in strings. Whiskey had brought the old man to this condition. He was a college grad-uate; he had studied law; but the de-mon drink had ruined his life.

Down in Water Street Mission the "old colonel" heard the story of the cross. For six nights he went to the mission services. One night he cried out, "Oh, Lord, if it is not too late, forgive this poor sinner." On the seventh night he arose and said, "I am saved." From that moment the "old colonel" hated whiskey. God's grace worked a wonderful change. His intel-lect became keen again. His youth re-turned. He became a dignified Christian gentleman and was faithful to the Lord to the day of his death.

God's Grace Sustains

A lord in Scotland gave his old ser-vant, Donald, a little farm. The lord said, "Donald, I'm giving this farm to you so you can spend the rest of your days on your own property. You are to work it for yourself." Donald said, "It is no good to give me a farm. I have no money. I can buy no horses and cows." The Scotch lord looked at Donald and said, "I think I can manage to give you what you'll need." "Oh," said Donald, "If it is you and me for it, then we will manage."

Remember, "I can do all things through Christ which strengtheneth me"; "My grace is sufficient for thee."

Grace Day by Day

A little boy was helping his Mother. She a s k e d him to bring her some apples. He put his little arms around many apples and tried to bring them all to her. But every step he took, the apples fell. Sometimes one, sometimes two, sometimes three. Apples began to roll all over the floor. Mother laughed. Then she said, "Daniel, I want to teach you a lesson." She put one apple in Daniel's hand and then she said, "Now, bring me that and then go and get another."

God wants us to bring one day to Him at a time. He will give us grace for that day. We must not try to put our arms around a year. We must not try to put our arms around next week. We must just live for God one day at a time. He will give us the grace we need for today. Then He will give us the grace we need for tomorrow.

GROWTH

A Baby Elephant

A baby in New York was fed on elephant's milk, and it grew one hundred pounds in a few weeks, but it was a baby elephant to begin with. A human baby, fed on elephant's milk, would not have grown the same. One could feed on the best of food for a child of God, and *not* grow like a child of God unless he *is* a child of God to begin with. To grow like a Christian, we must first be a Christian. Boys and girls, if you are not a "born again" Christian, a *real* child of God, will you not *today* put your faith in Jesus Christ, the Saviour? Then you will receive a new nature and become a child of God. Then you, too, can grow as a Christian should grow.

Keep Moving

An old farmer was telling his Christian experience in prayer meeting. He concluded his testimony by saying, "Well, friends, I'm not making much progress, but I am *established* in the faith."

Next day, the farmer was getting out some logs. His wagon sank in the mud, and he could not move it. As he sat on top of the logs, a neighbor came along and greeted him. "Well, Brother Jones, I see you are not making much progress, but you are *established!*"

We ought to be established, "rooted and grounded" in the faith. But God wants us also to be m o v i n g. He wants us to grow in faith and in knowledge and grace. He wants us to become more like Christ day by day.

No Growth

A minister once asked a lady, "How long have you been a Christian?" She replied, "About twenty-five years." Then he asked her, "How much more unworldly are you; how much more devoted to the Lord are you *now*, than when your Christian life first began?"

"Alas," said the lady, "I fear that I am not nearly so much so."

How sad it was that the lady had been a nominal Christian for twenty-five years and had not grown in grace, and in knowledge of the Lord, and in love for Him!

Rocking Horse Christians

Rowland Hill once saw a child riding a rocking horse. After watching the little boy awhile, he remarked, "He reminds me of some Christians. There is plenty of motion, but no progress!" Let us not be "rocking-horse Christians." Let us make progress in the Christian life. Let us grow in the Lord.

Forward!

Marshal Foch was a great French general. Often, he said to his soldiers, "Forward!" When he gave this word of command, his soldiers would go forward, no matter what happened. God says to each one of us, "Forward." Let us go forward with Jesus, no matter what happens.

Building

"We are building every day,
In a good or evil way,
And the structure as it grows,
Will our inmost self disclose.

"Till in every arch and line,
All our faults and failings shine;
It may grow a castle grand,
Or a wreck upon the sand.

"Do you ask what building this,
That can show both pain and bliss,
That can be both dark and fair?
Lo! its name is character.

"Build it well whate'er you do,
Build it straight and strong and true,
Build it clean and high and broad,
Build it for the *eye of God!*"

Still Growing

At Hampton Court Palace in England is a famous grapevine. The vine grows over a high trellis under a glass roof. The vine has been growing for one hundred and sixty years. In a recent year, it bore six hundred fine clusters of delicious grapes. It has had the best of care, and shows no signs of dying.

Would that our lives were like the grapevine in Hampton Court Palace. Would that we would keep on growing and bearing fruit in our lives for Jesus, until we come to the end of life's journey, and pass into His presence!

GUIDANCE

One Step at a Time

One time, a father gave his little boy a letter to mail for him. They were staying at a woodland camp. The letter had to be mailed in the village. The father showed the little boy a trail which led to the village. "But, Father," said the little boy, "I don't see how that path will ever reach the village." The father answered, "Do you see the trail as far as that big tree down there?" "Oh, yes, sir, I see the path that far." "Well, when you get to that tree, you will see a little further on. Just follow the trail until you get in sight of the houses. When you reach the houses, you will find the little post office, and can mail my letter!"

The King Knows

During the war, many little children were evacuated from London. One day, a train, packed with children, was leaving. Many of the children had never been on a train before. Most of them had never been in the country. The parents of a small boy and girl had just said goodby to their precious children. The little girl began to cry. She said that she was afraid because she did not know where she was going. Her little brother brushed his own tears away. Then, he put his arm around her and said, "I do not know where we are going either, but the King knows! So, why should we be afraid?"

We do not need to be afraid. We do not know where we are going, but our King knows. We can safely trust His guidance.

Guided by the Homing Pigeon

A guide in the deserts of Arabia never lost his way. He always carried with him a homing-pigeon with a fine cord attached to one leg. Whenever he was in doubt, as to which way he should take, the guide would throw the pigeon into the air. The pigeon would pull at the cord, trying to fly in the direction of home. Then, its owner would follow. They called that guide, "The Pigeon Man."

The Holy Spirit is the Heavenly Dove, willing and able to lead us if we will allow Him to do so.

A Short Sermon

A guide was taking some tourists through the Mammoth Caves in Kentucky. In the "cathedral," they came to a rock which is called, "The Pulpit." The guide said he would preach a sermon. It was a short sermon. All he said, was, "Keep close to your guide!" The tourists soon found that it was a good sermon. If one does not keep close to his guide in the Mammoth Cave, he is soon lost.

In this world, it is important for us to keep close to our Guide, the Lord Jesus.

The Lost Receipt

Once a poor widow was greatly troubled at receiving a bill. She knew that she had already paid the bill, but she could not find the receipt which would show that she had. She hunted high and low for the receipt, to no avail. She was afraid that she would have to pay the bill again and she had no money to do it. Being a Christian, she took her trouble to God, praying earnestly that He would help her out of the difficulty by showing her where the receipt was.

Several days later the storekeeper who had sent her the bill, called at the widow's home to collect the money. He declared that he would wait no longer for his money. He threatened to have her turned out on the street and her furniture sold to pay his claims.

Just at that moment a butterfly flew in through an open window. The widow's little son began to chase it. The butterfly flew behind a big box of tools which had belonged to the little boy's father. The box was too heavy for the little boy to move so he asked the tradesman to do it.

When the box was moved, a little piece of paper was seen lying on the floor. The widow stooped and picked it up. It was the lost receipt. God had answered the widow's prayer by using a butterfly to guide her to the place where the lost receipt was hidden.

HABIT

Ty Cobb

Grantland Rice, the well-known sports writer, had an interview with Ty Cobb, the great baseball player. Rice asked Ty Cobb why he always held his hands so far apart when he was batting. Cobb answered, "It all started when I was a kid of twelve. I was a stringy youngster, and all the bats were too big and heavy for me. I had to put my hands far apart so I could swing the bat. Once you build up habits as a kid they are hard to change. I have held my hands that way ever since I was a kid!"

It is important to build right habits when you are young.

* * *

"I AM A HABIT"

"It is mighty hard to shake me;
In my brawny arms I take thee;
I can either make or break thee;
I am Habit!

"Through each day I slowly mold thee;
Soon my tightening chains enfold thee;
Then it is with ease I hold thee;
I am Habit!"

— Selected

* * *

Attention

A boy was a practical joker. One day, he saw a man who had spent years of service in the army going home from the store. He was an aged man. The joker suddenly called, "Attention!" The former soldier stopped, and, as he "snapped" to attention, the bundles he was carrying fell to the ground. His military training had been so thorough that it had become second nature to him. When the boy saw what happened, he laughed and went whistling down the street.

Boys and girls are living in the habit-forming ways of life. The habits you are forming now will stay with you as long as you live. Why not form good habits which will help you — habits of clean speech, kind service, regular Bible reading, prayer, and worshipping in God's house? These habits will make your life a joy, and a success.

Christ Can Break the Chain of Habit

In a large steel mill, there was a big muscular Scotchman who was one of the bosses. Nearly all the men from his department were hard drinkers. He was no exception. But a change took place. He became a Christian. When pressed by his fellow workers to take a drink he refused.

"I shall never take a drink any more lads," he quietly said.

They said, "Wait a bit till the hot weather comes, till July. When he gets hot he will give in. He can't help it."

But the hot weather came and the Scotchman went through the hottest month with sweat pouring out in streams, but he never took a drink. At last the time keeper of the mill said to him, "You used to drink a lot. Don't you miss it?"

"Yes," he replied.

"How do you manage to keep away from it?"

"Well, it's this way. Today is the 20th of the month. It is now 10:00 o'clock. From seven till eight I asked the Lord to help me. He did. So I put a dot down on the calendar right near the twenty. From eight till nine

He kept me. So I put another dot down. From nine till ten He kept me and now I put down the third dot, and give Him the glory. Every time I mark these dots I say, 'Oh, Lord, help me. Help me to fight it off for another hour.'"

How glad we are that Christ can help us to break the chain of bad habit.

Habit, A Chain

Ned was watching Grandpa put on his shoes. "Why do you always turn your shoes over and shake them before you put them on, Grandpa?" he asked. "Do I?" asked Grandpa. "Why yes, you shook them just now but I didn't see anything come out. I have to shake my shoes sometimes to get sand out." Grandpa laughed, "I didn't know that I shake my shoes, Ned. I must have gotten into the habit of shaking my shoes every time before I put them on when I was in India." "Why did you do it there?" "Oh, to shake out any scorpions or centipedes or other vermin that might be hiding in them." "But you don't have to do it here. We don't have such things here." "I know," said Grandpa, "but I formed the habit and now I do it without thinking."

"Habit is a queer thing, isn't it?"

asked Ned. "It is a very strong thing," said Grandpa. "A habit is a chain that grows stronger and stronger every day. A bad habit will grow just as strong as a good one. If you want to have good habits when you're old, you'd better form them while you're young."

The Power of Habit

A cow used to graze near the pumping station of the water works in a little Oklahoma town. A tank stood just outside of the building. It was kept full of water. The cow always got her morning drink from this tank. One time there was a storm. After the storm, water covered the valley. It rose until it came within two or three inches of the top of the tank. The cow wanted her morning drink. Instead of drinking of the water all around her, she made her way to the tank. Twice she got stuck in the mud. Once she almost drowned. But she kept going toward the tank. Finally she reached it. She drank long and then she turned and slowly made her way back to the dry land some distance away. She was satisfied that she had done the usual thing. She had gotten her drink of water from the tank.

HEAVEN

Answering the Roll Call

When Dr. R. E. Neighbour was a little boy, he had a d r e a m about Heaven. He dreamed that he was standing outside of Heaven in a great crowd of people. Near him stood his father, mother, two sisters, and a brother. The angels were calling the names written in the Lamb's Book of Life.

Presently, the angel called the name, "William Webster Neighbour." Little Eddie's father answered in a clear voice, "Here am I," and started to go through the gate into Heaven. Little Eddie took his father's hand, and said, "Oh, Father, let me go with you." The father said, "No, Eddie Boy, you must wait and see if your name is in the

Book of Life. You can't go on my name!" After a while the angel called, "Julia Maria Neighbour." Little Eddie's mother answered, "Here am I." As she started toward the gate, little Eddie seized her hand, and said, "Let me go with you, Mother." But mother said, "No, Eddie, you can't go with Mother. You must wait until your name is called." Presently, the name of Eddie's sister, Edith, was called. She answered and went through the gate into Heaven.

Little Eddie felt sad and lonely. Anxiously, he waited for his name to be called. Finally, he heard his own name called: "Robert Edward Neighbour!" With a glad shout, the little boy answered, "Here am I!" He answered the name so loudly, that it awakened him, and awakened his father and mother who were sleeping in a bedroom downstairs.

Little Eddie never forgot that dream. How glad he was that Jesus was His Saviour. How glad he was that his name was written in the Lamb's Book of Life! Little Eddie loved Jesus, and wanted to go to Heaven, and be with Jesus forever and ever.

Why The Journey Wasn't Hard

A small boy sat quietly in a seat of the day coach of a train running between two western cities. It was a hot, dusty day, and very uncomfortable for travelling. The train was passing much desert land, and the view out of the window was not very interesting. The little fellow sat patiently watching the fields and fences hurrying by.

Finally, a motherly old lady leaned forward and asked, "Aren't you tired of the long ride and the dust and the heat?" The little lad looked up brightly, and replied, "Yes, ma'am, a little. But I don't mind it much, because my father is going to meet me when I get to the end of it!"

When life seems wearisome and monotonous, we can look forward to the end of the journey, when God, our Father, will meet us!

From Poor House to a Mansion!

A woman in the poor house was dying. The doctor, leaning over her, heard her whisper, "Praise the Lord!" "Why, auntie," he said, "how can you praise God when you are dying in a poor house?" "Oh, doctor," she replied, "It's wonderful to go from the poor house to a mansion in the skies!"

At Home with Him

A young Christian visited an aged saint of God. He asked, "Shall I read to you the sweetest verse in the Bible?" "Yes," was the reply. The young man read, "In My Father's house are many mansions: if it were not so, I would have told you. I go to prepare a place for you." "No," said the aged saint, "that is not the sweetest verse. *Read on!*"

The young man read on: "And if I go and prepare a place for you, I will come again, and receive you unto Myself; that where I am, *there ye may be also.*" "That," said the aged saint, "is the sweetest verse. It is not the mansion, that I want to see, but *Jesus Himself!*"

A Beautiful Place

A little girl was walking with her father one night. She looked up at the starry sky. Then she said, "Father, if the wrong side of Heaven is so beautiful, what will the right side be?"

In Heaven, many mansions are being prepared for God's children. The Lord Jesus said, "In My Father's house are many mansions: if it were not so, I would have told you. I go to prepare a place for you" (*John 14:2*). A mansion is a beautiful home! How beautiful must be the mansions which the Lord Jesus is preparing for us!

Prepared for Us

A mother received word that her daughter, who had been away for a long time, was coming home. The mother made ready for the daughter's coming. She cleaned her little bedroom. She put new curtains up at the window. She put flowers in a vase on the mantel. She placed a new book on the table near the bed. Everything in the room showed that the mother loved the daughter, and had prepared for her coming. How wonderful it will be when we get to Heaven and see the beautiful things which the Lord has prepared for us.

Close by His Side

Over in Africa, a little boy was taught by his parents to worship idols. A missionary told him about Jesus, and His love. When he heard about the love and death of Jesus, he no longer liked his idols. He no longer worshipped them. He gave his heart to Jesus. One day, he became very ill. The missionary went to see him. "I am very happy," said the boy; "I hope I shall not get well again." "Why?" asked the missionary. The little boy replied, "Because I want to go to Heaven where I can see Jesus. I want to be close at His side always!"

The Way to Heaven

One Sunday morning, a city preacher gave a message in a little country church. After the sermon, someone said to Farmer Peter, "That was a fine sermon, wasn't it?"

"Maybe," returned Farmer Peter.

"Why," said the friend, "that man knows more about the Bible than any minister in the country. He knows a lot about Bible history, and geography."

"Well," said Farmer Peter, "maybe the trouble was with me. But you see, I thought I should hear something about the way to Heaven. I only learned something about the way from Jerusalem to Jericho."

Everyone needs to learn about the *way* to Heaven. Heaven is a beautiful place. It has golden streets where the children play. It has a beautiful river. It has many mansions which God is preparing for His dear children. It will be filled with joy. It will be filled with singing. Do *you* want to go to Heaven? Then, trust in Jesus. He is *the way* to Heaven. Jesus said, "I am the Way, the Truth, and the Life: *no man* cometh unto the Father, but *by Me*" *(John 14:6)*.

A Prepared Place

A weary traveler in the desert longed for a stopping place. A native lad met him, and told him that just ahead there were tents and palm trees, a place where he could stop, and refresh himself. (Desert custom would require him to spend at least three days there.) Then, the lad quickly mounted a horse, saying, "I will go and prepare a place for you." How happy the traveler was as he continued on his tiresome way! A place was being prepared for him, just ahead.

How it cheers our hearts as we journey through life to *know* that the Lord Jesus is preparing a place for us *just ahead*! How we long for the time to come when we will enter the Father's House of many mansions, the place of unending joy and bliss!

"I Shall Meet You There"

One Sunday, a Christian man heard Dr. Charles E. Fuller announce on the radio that he would talk about Heaven the following Sunday. The man immediately wrote Dr. Fuller as follows: "Next Sunday, you are to talk about Heaven. I am interested in that Land because I have held a clear title to a bit of property there for over fifty-five years. I did not buy it. It was given to me, without money and without price.

But the Donor purchased it for me at great sacrifice. For more than a half century, I have been sending material over there, so the great Builder of the universe could use it in building a home for me. That home will never be in need of remodeling or repairs. It will suit me perfectly. It will never grow old. The foundations can never be destroyed, for they rest upon the Rock of Ages. Fires cannot destroy it. Floods cannot wash it away. I hope to hear your sermon, but I have no assurance that I shall be able to do so. When the call comes, I must go immediately. I am *ready*. My ticket for Heaven has no date marked for the journey. It has no return coupon. It has no permit for baggage. I am all *ready* to go, and I may not be here when you talk on Heaven next Sunday. But I shall meet you there some day!"

HELPFULNESS

Where Are Your Good Intentions

Little Dot was drawing a picture with pen and ink on a paper. It turned out to be a cat without a tail. "Where is the cat's tail," asked her Mother. Little Dot looked puzzled for a moment. Then she smiled and said, "Why, it is still in the ink bottle."

Many of our good intentions are like the cat's tail, still in the ink bottle. We need to get our good intentions out and put them to work.

Running Errands for Jesus

A little boy once said, "Mother, I wish that Jesus lived on earth now!"

"Why, my darling?" asked the mother.

"Because, I would like so much to do something for Him."

"What could a little fellow like you do for Him?" asked the mother.

The little boy replied, "I could run errands for Him."

"So you could, my child," said Mother, "and so you shall. Here are a glass of jelly and some oranges that you can take to poor old Margaret. That will be doing an errand for Jesus. When Jesus was on earth, He said, 'Inasmuch as ye have done it unto one of the least of these . . . ye have done it unto Me' *(Matt. 25:40)*. My darling, remember that when you do a kind deed for someone because you love Jesus, it is just the same as doing it for Jesus. You can run errands for Him every day!"

Helping Somebody

Some strangers were going to meet Lord Schaftesbury at a railway station. They asked, "How shall we know him?" The answer was, "When you see a tall man getting off the train and *helping somebody*, that will be Lord Schaftesbury!" The train was met. A tall man alighted from a car. In one hand, he was carrying his own suitcase. In the other hand he was carrying three bundles for a little, old woman walking at his side!

Someone to Share With

A little boy was selling papers on the street. A man stopped to buy a paper from him. While he was searching in his pocket for a coin, the man asked the newsboy where he lived. The little boy said that he lived in a little shack down on the river bank. Then the man asked, "Who lives with you?"

"Jim," said the newsboy. "Jim is crippled, and he can't work, but he's my friend; he's my pal."

The man said, "You would be better off without Jim, wouldn't you?"

"Oh, no, sir, I couldn't spare Jim. I wouldn't have anyone to go home to. And say, mister, I wouldn't want to work and live with nobody to divide with. Would you?"

That little newsboy loved his friend Jim! He was glad to divide with Jim. Good friends are always glad to help one another.

Always Helping Somebody

One day, a man came to a doctor's house. He was looking for the doctor. He asked the doctor's little boy, "Son, where is your father?" The little boy replied, "Oh, he's out helping somebody. He is always out helping somebody!" That is what God wants *you* and *me* to do. He wants us always to be busy helping others. We should follow in the steps of Jesus. He went about "doing good." We, too, must go about doing good.

The Thrush and the Blackbird

One day, a thrush and a blackbird came together to visit the place where food was put for birds. A man noticed that the blackbird picked up the crumbs and put them into the thrush's mouth. He looked closely and saw that a trap, or something, had cut off the thrush's beak close to its head, and it was not able to pick up food. The blackbird had come to the aid of the thrush. It placed the food in the thrush's mouth. What a lesson we may learn from the thrush and blackbird!

"O Lord, Bless Everyone"

"I knelt to pray when day was done,
And prayed, 'O Lord, bless everyone;
Lift from each saddened heart the pain,
And let the sick be well again.'
And then I woke another day
And carelessly went on my way.
The whole day long I did not try
To wipe a tear from any eye;
I did not try to share the load
Of any brother on the road;
I did not even go to see
The sick man next door to me,
Yet once again when day was done,
I prayed, 'O Lord, bless everyone.'
But as I prayed, into my ear
There came a Voice that whispered clear:
'Pause, hypocrite, before you pray;
Whom have you tried to bless today?
God's sweetest blessings always go
By hands that serve Him here below.'
And then I hid my face and cried,
'Forgive me, God, for I have *lied*,
But let me live another day,
And I will live the way I pray.'"

Helping Others

In Chicago, there lives a little Dutch lady, who is known as "The Nurse." She loves the Lord Jesus, and lives for Him day by day. Because she loves Jesus, she spends all of her time trying to help the poor and needy ones. She goes from home to home where there are poor, little crippled children. She nurses many of them back to health. She gives food and clothes to the needy ones. She raises canaries to bring cheer to the shut-ins. She sends "get well" cards to the aged and sick. She tells them all of Jesus.

Even little boys and girls can do *much* to help others. Little Sara Ruth loves to help others. She gives out many tracts, telling about Jesus. She is kind to the little children who are lonely and have few or no friends. She helps her mother in the home. *You*, too, can help others.

Without Delay

The incident is told of a man found dead in a gas-filled room. He had been sad and despondent because he could not get work and had no money to pay his rent. A letter lay just outside his door. The letter contained a gift of money which, if it had arrived *sooner*, might have given him encouragement to fight on. We must remember that we *must* do good *today* as we have opportunity. We must not delay or put off helping others.

"If with pleasure you are viewing,
Any work a man is doing;
If you like him, or you love him,
Tell him *now*!"

The Two Boatmen

One night, an excursion ship, filled with human cargo, was sinking on the River Thames. Two boatmen were mooring their boats for the night. One heard the cries of the people, "Help! Help!" But he was tired and weary. Thinking that the darkness would cover him, he hurried away and went home. The other boatman, hearing the cries, got into his boat and went to the rescue. He filled his boat time and time again, and rowed many away to safety.

Later, when the wreck was being investigated, the two boatmen were questioned. The one who had slipped away without helping anyone was asked, "Did you not hear their cries?"

"Yes," he replied.

"Are you not troubled because you did nothing to help the perishing ones?"

He replied, "I will never cease to hear their cries!"

The one who had rescued so many told the story of his efforts that night, and then he exclaimed, "I only regret that I did not have a larger boat!"

HOLY SPIRIT

No Need to Study Speech

A great professor of speech attended a meeting in Memorial Hall, London. This professor told his pupils how to talk, and how to stand when they talked. As he listened to the preacher, he noticed that the preacher stood very quietly. He did not make many motions with his hands. His language, or talk, was not beautiful. But the preacher spoke with great power. At the end, hundreds of people stood to their feet. They wanted Christ as their Saviour. A friend asked the professor how he liked the preacher's manner. The professor replied, "That man does not need to study speech. *He has the power of the Holy Spirit!*" How truly did the professor speak! When we have the power of the Holy Spirit, then it is easy for us to speak for Jesus!

Lack of Power

A young woman, who worked in a large factory in Philadelphia, said to her pastor, "I'll have to hunt another job. We have a large factory. We have many machines. We have plenty of orders to keep us going all the time. But we do not have enough electrical power to run all the machines at once. My machine has to lie idle part of the week, and I lose much time and pay. I'll have to hunt another job!"

Today, our churches often have plenty of man-made machinery, but not enough power. We have many classes, many committees, many members, but we *lack* the power of the Holy Spirit. God's command to us is this, "And be not drunk with wine, wherein is excess; but be *filled* with the Spirit" *(Eph. 5:18)*.

Give Him Full Place

One time Miss Ruth Paxton visited a college to conduct special meetings. She was entertained in a home where the guest room was over the kitchen, and approached by an outside stairway. An occasion arose which made it desirable for her to enter another section of the house. But she found every other door locked. The only room open to her was the guest room. She felt very lonely.

Returning to her room, Miss Paxton prayed to God. God used this experience to show her how it is with thousands who have the Holy Spirit in their lives, but have never given Him full place. They have forced Him to stay in one little nook, or corner, while He longs to enter into every part of the life and bless it with His fullness.

The Coming of the Spirit

When Nansen went to the Arctic regions to explore, he took with him a carrier pigeon. After two years in the desolation of the Arctic regions, Nansen one day wrote a little message on a piece of paper. He tied it under the pigeon's wing, and let it loose to travel two thousand miles to Norway.

The little bird made three circles overhead, and then, straight as an arrow, it flew south one thousand miles over ice, one thousand miles over the frozen wastes of ocean. At last, the pigeon dropped into the lap of the explorer's wife in Norway. She found Nansen's message under the bird's wing. She knew, by the arrival of the bird, that all was well in the faraway, dark night of the north!

Power

Mary Slessor was a missionary in Africa. Many were amazed when they saw that she, a weak woman, had power to mold savage chiefs to her will. One of the chiefs explained, "You have evidently forgotten to take into account the woman's God." She was filled with the power of God!

An American went with an Englishman to see the whirlpool rapids below Niagara Falls. The American said, "This is the greatest unused power in the world!" "No," said the Englishman, "the greatest unused power in the world is the Holy Spirit of the living God!" Those who have had this power have done mighty things for God and man.

A man met Hudson Taylor for the first time. Hudson Taylor was the founder of the China Inland Mission. He accomplished many great things for God. The man expected to meet a powerful man, with a full, deep voice. Instead, he found that Hudson Taylor was a *little* man, with a quiet and gentle voice. Immediately, he knew that Hudson Taylor's power was not found in himself, but *in God.*

Do *you* have God's power in your life? When you speak, do people *know* that you have been with Jesus?

Hudson Taylor's Power

A minister wrote, "When I first met Mr. Hudson Taylor . . . I expected to see a man with a black beard, and a full, round voice. Instead, I found him to be a little man, with a blond beard, and a quiet, gentle voice. I immediately decided that his power was not in his personality, but rather in God. As the years passed, I found this was true. To the end of his life, Hudson Taylor, the great missionary, won great victories through the power of God. The secret of his power was in his communion with his Father in Heaven!"

He Obeyed the Holy Spirit

A minister, in New Albany, Indiana, was sitting late one night in his study. He was strongly impressed to leave his work and call upon a man who lived a few blocks away. He tried to rid himself of the impression so he could finish the work. But he could not get away from the leading of the Holy Spirit. He went to the home. Twice he knocked at the door and received no answer. The third time he knocked, a light was turned on in the house. The man who lived there opened the door, and invited the minister to enter. The man soon unburdened his heart to the minister. He said that when the minister first knocked he had already turned on the gas in a small bedroom, intending to end his life! This man's life and soul were saved, because the minister *obeyed the voice of the Holy Spirit!*

Helped by Our Guide

On the slope of the Alps mountains lived a little hunchback. He was unable to join the mountain climbers, but each day, he ministered to the climbers who passed by. One day, a famous mountain guide said to him, "How would you like to climb the mountain yourself?" The hunchback beamed, and said, "I would like it very much, but, of course, I can't do it." "Come with me," said the guide. The guide helped the little hunchback go up the mountain. When they reached the summit, the grateful hunchback knelt and thanked the guide. The hunchback had done his best. The guide had done the rest. What wonderful things we can accomplish when we are connected with the power of our Guide, the Holy Spirit.

He Needed Power

Two ladies attended the meetings of D. L. Moody. One night, they said to him, "We have been praying for you. You need power." "What?" thought D. L. Moody, "do I need power? I have a large Sunday School, and a large congregation. Sometimes, people are saved. Do I need power?" Soon after that, the two ladies came to Moody again and said, "We have been praying for you. You need power." Suddenly, Mr. Moody's heart was filled with a longing for the power of the Holy Spirit. He, too, began to pray for power. God answered Moody's prayer. Mr. Moody began to preach with the power of the Holy Spirit. Instead of a few people being converted, hundreds were converted! May God give us the power of the Holy Spirit in our lives.

The Other One Came Too

A Welsh preacher was to preach in a little village church one night. The service began. The people sang many songs. Many prayers were offered. But the preacher did not come.

A lady went to the home nearby to see what delayed the preacher. As she entered the home, she heard the preacher praying. He was saying, "I will not go unless You go with me!"

Quietly, the lady returned to the church. She reported, saying, "The preacher is coming all right, and the other One— the Holy Spirit — is coming too!"

Sure enough, when the preacher came, the other One came too! There was such power in that service that many believed in Jesus and were saved!

Our Holy Guest

A lady was one time visiting in a home. She was told, "Make yourself at home. Be like one of the family." But she found that she was not at home. She was not treated like one of the family. She had to stay in the guest room where she was often lonely. The Holy Spirit is our Guest. He lives in the Christian's heart. We must let Him fill our hearts and lives.

HOME

God Doesn't Live At Our House

Five-year-old Margaret was a frequent visitor in the home of a neighbor. One of the never-ending wonders of the neighbor's home was the prayer time. Little Margaret loved to be there at that time. The daddy in the home read out of a big, black Book. Afterwards, he talked to God as if God were very near and dear to them all. Sometimes, the family would join in singing a song of praise. One morning when little Margaret had been present at the prayer time, the mother in the home asked, "Margaret, don't you pray at your house?" Margaret shook her head sadly and said, "No. You see God doesn't live at our house like He does at yours."

How sad it was that a little girl like Margaret had to go next door if she wanted to meet God, the Heavenly Father. God wasn't included in her family circle.

I Am Different

A girl was always complaining about conditions at home. She was dissatisfied with everything. Her face, her manner, her tone of voice — all showed her discontent. Every trifle irritated her. She would gladly have travelled to the end of the earth to get away from her disagreeable surroundings.

One day a friend, who had not seen her for several months, saw in the girl's smiling face that a change had taken place. "How are things at home?" the friend asked. "Just the same," was the reply, "BUT I AM DIFFERENT!"

Often, IT IS YOU who needs to change and not your home. If you love the Lord, and love others, home will be a different place to YOU.

A Home Without Prayer

Dr. George W. Truett was asked to conduct the funeral of a sixteen-year-old girl. When Dr. Truett called at the home before the funeral he found the mother in deep sorrow. The mother said, "Dr. Truett, she was our only child."

"Yes, but you are not to sorrow as others who have no hope. You are a Christian."

The mother answered, "That is where the trouble is. We have no hope. Our daughter was not a Christian." The mother wept bitterly for a few minutes and then she continued, "It is true that her father and I are both members of the church. We were Christians before our girl was born. It is also true that our darling girl never heard either one of us pray. We never read the Bible to her. We never talked to her about the Saviour. We fear that she is lost because we failed her."

Sacred Memories

How blessed is the home where there is a family altar. When father and mother gather with their children to read God's Word and to pray, that scene is called, "The Family Altar!" Boys and girls who are raised in a home where there is a family altar never get away from that blessed influence.

Two men had lived in a country home in their boyhood. Now, they were rich men. Both lived in the city. Sometimes, they visited the father and mother, living in the old home. Then the father and mother went to Heaven to be with Jesus. The men did not know what to do with the old home. Finally, they decided to tear it down and build a summer home there.

One day, the two brothers went to the old house, and looked around. When they reached the living room, one sat down in a chair. The other walked back and forth in front of the fireplace. Finally one said, "Bob, I've changed my mind. We must not tear down this old house. We must let it stand. It is too filled with sacred memories!"

"That's a strange thing," said the other brother. "I have been thinking about the same thing." Then, he pointed to the chair where his father used to sit. "There is the old chair that Father sat in when he read the Bible in family worship. Here are the chairs where we knelt when Father lifted his heart to God and prayed for us!"

For two hours the brothers stayed in the old home and talked things over. Then they both got down on their knees by the old chair where Father had sat. There, they repented of their sins, and wept their hearts out before God. They went back to the city, saved men, ready to use their money and days for God.

The old house was left standing. Not a single thing was moved out. It was too sacred to tear down, because the family altar had stood there.

"How Do You Behave at Home?"

A Christian girl gave a testimony in a crowded meeting. She told about her love for Christ. A man said out loud, "That's all right for you to say, but how do you behave at home?" Quickly, the girl answered, "There's my mother sitting in front of you. Ask her!" The mother arose and said, "My girl lives at home just like she talks here!" God wants each of us to live beautiful lives for Him.

"Does Christ Live Here?"

A new pastor had come to a village. One day, he called at a certain cottage. When the husband came home from work, the wife said, "The new pastor called today."

"What did he say?" asked the husband.

"He asked, 'Does Christ live here?'; and I didn't know what to answer."

With a flushed face, the husband asked, "Why didn't you tell him that we are respectable people?"

"But that isn't what he asked me," she replied.

"Then why didn't you tell him that we go to church, and say our prayers, and read our Bible?"

The wife replied, "He didn't ask me any of those things, either. He only asked me, 'Does Christ live here?'"

For many days, the husband and wife thought about the question which the pastor had asked. Little by little, there was a change in their lives. Little by little, their home was changed. Then there came a time when they felt that Christ really lived in their home. They felt love and kindness and the radiance of His presence.

Not A Guest

A little girl of five was saying grace at the table. She prayed, "Come, Lord Jesus, be our Guest!" Turning suddenly to her mother, she said, "But mother, I do not want Jesus to be our Guest!" "Why, dear?" asked her horrified mother. The little girl replied, "Well, a guest is one who comes here sometimes. I want Jesus to be here ALL THE TIME!"

No Roof

In Scotland a young man was taken into the home of a well-to-do farmer. He was to be the farmer's helper. After a few weeks, he gave up his new position. A friend asked him why he had left such a good place. "Was the work too hard, or the hours too long?"

"No," was the answer.

"Were the wages too low?"

"No."

"Why then did you leave?"

"I left," said the young man, "because the house had no roof." In Scotland that meant that it was a home without prayer.

How sad it is to live in a home without Christ, without the Bible, without prayer. May God help us to make our homes Christian homes.

What America Needs

The Wall Street Journal once said, "What America needs more than railways, irrigation, bigger wheat crops, . . . is a revival of piety, the kind Father and Mother used to have. Piety that counted it good business to stop to pray daily before breakfast, . . . that quit work a half hour earlier on Wednesday night, so as to get the chores done to get to prayer meeting."

How true it is that America needs Christian homes where Father and Mother and children *all* serve Christ and put Him *first*. Henry M. Grady said that the center of this country is not in the United States Capitol, but in the hovels and cottages and old farm houses, and in every home in this land, where there is a *family altar*. Said he, "The Christian home is the center of American life."

"Thank God for Christian homes that stand
    secure,
Amid life's shifting scenes."

The Value of Family Worship

Someone asked a student in a Bible school, "What does it mean to you to have had a Christian home?" He replied, "It means everything. I am here in Bible school because I had a Christian home. Family worship was a normal part of every day's activity. There was nothing unusual about it. But it made us realize that God was constantly present with us, and it helped me to always put God *first* in my life."

Another student in the Bible school, who was the eldest daughter in a family of four children, was asked the same question: "What does it mean to you to have had a Christian home?" She replied, "In our home, we sang the old hymns at worship time. The singing of those hymns bound us together with strong ties of Christian love. Then Father read the Word, and each of us followed the reading in our own Bibles. Then we had prayer. I was saved when I was nine. The influence of our Christian home molded my life, and that influence will extend to Africa, where I plan to go as a missionary!"

How Does Your Home Look?

Dr. Campbell Morgan once said: "Soon after I was married, my father came into our home. He looked around. We showed him every room. Then he said to me, 'Your home is very nice, but nobody would know, walking through your home, whether you belong to God or the devil.' When Father left, I went and looked through the rooms again and I thought, 'He is quite right.' My wife and I made up our minds that there would be something in *every* room that would tell others that we served Christ, the King. In every room, there must be a Bible, a motto, or a picture to show that we were Christians and had a Christian home!"

Loving Kindness At Home

A young girl from college asked her pastor for the name of someone to whom she could bring Christian cheer during the summer months. He wrote a name upon a piece of paper. He told her not to read the name until she reached her home. On reaching home, the girl looked on the paper, and saw the name of her own father! Her own father needed Christian love and kindness. Will you not be kind and loving to the ones in your home?

Cross At Home

One time there was a revival meeting in a little country church. A young woman went forward and knelt at the altar. She wanted to have her sins forgiven by the Lord. She was weeping as she knelt at the altar. A Christian man knelt by her. He tried to help her.

The young woman said, "I have tried, but the Christian people I work for are not kind to me. The man in the family is very cross with me. It is hard for me to live a Christian life in a place like that."

The man said to her, "You must get another job. For whom do you work?" The young woman raised her bowed head. She looked at the man and said, "For you, sir!"

Instantly, the Christian man was filled with sorrow. He knew that he was cross, and impatient. He knew that he did not live for the Lord Jesus in his home. He burst into tears, and he began to pray and asked God's forgiveness. He asked God to help him live a kind, sweet Christian life in his home.

HONESTY

The Converted Woodchopper

In a certain village, a mean man sold wood to his neighbors. He always cut his logs a few inches shorter than the required four feet. One day, the news was circulated that the woodchopper had been converted. Nobody believed the report, for he was such a mean and dishonest man. While the discussion was under way in the grocery store, a man slipped out quietly. He came running back in great excitement. He shouted, "It's so! He has been converted!" "How do you know?" the crowd asked. "Why, I went over and measured the wood he cut yesterday, and it is ALL a good four feet long!" The crowd was satisfied. They KNEW that the woodchoopper had been converted.

Saying Nothing Can Be Lying

One day all was quiet in the schoolroom, when one of the boys suddenly had a bright idea. There was a whiz and a splash. All the students began to laugh when they saw that a ripe tomato had struck the blackboard. It had made a funny looking spot right in the middle of some examination questions which had been written on the board.

The teacher became very angry, and asked who had thrown the tomato. No one arose. Then the teacher asked everyone in the room to stand. After the teacher had given a severe lecture, he said, "Now all who did NOT throw the tomato sit down." Everyone sat down. The boy who had thrown the tomato did not say a word, but he lied. He lied by his actions. Later he was caught and was suspended from school for several days. We must always be honest in actions as well as in words.

The False Bottom Gone

An old Scotchwoman said to her pastor one day, "Pastor, that was a grand sermon you preached at the Kirk on last Lord's Day."

The pastor asked, "What was the text?"

"Ah, pastor," replied the woman, "I dinna ken the text or the words. But when I came home, I took the false bottom out of my peck measure."

The sermon had done its work. The dishonest woman had become honest.

The Honest Slave Boy

Years ago, at a slave market in a southern state, a smart, active Negro boy was put up for sale. A kind man, who pitied his condition, and who did not want him to have a cruel owner, went up to him and asked, "If I buy you, will you be honest?" The boy replied, "Sir, whether you buy me, or not, I WILL BE HONEST!"

Selling Honor for a Nickel

A young man said, "When I was a small boy, I took a street-car ticket home once, and showed it to my father. I told him the street-car conductor had not taken it, and that I was ahead that much. I planned to use the ticket the next time I rode on the street-car, and thus save a nickel. My father looked at me and asked, 'Son, would you sell your honor for *one nickel?*' When my father asked that, I *knew* that I was *wrong.* I destroyed the ticket, and the next time I rode on the street-car, I paid my fare!"

How important it is for all boys and girls to be honest in small things. Never lie, never steal, never cheat.

Careful to Tell the Truth

A small boy was on the witness stand in an important lawsuit. The lawyer tried to "trip him up" and confuse him. The lawyer asked, "Your father has been telling you how to testify, hasn't he?" "Yes," the boy replied. "Now," said the lawyer, "just tell us how your father told you to testify." "Well," the boy said modestly, "Father told me the lawyers would try to tangle me in my testimony, but if I would just be careful and *tell the truth,* I could repeat the same thing every time!"

The Wrong Change

A young man was employed by a Sunday School board. He went many places preaching. One Sunday, he preached in a church in Nashville, Tenn. He used as his text, "Thou shalt not steal."

The next morning, he got on a bus in Nashville, and handed the driver a dollar bill. The driver gave him back his change. He stood in the rear of the bus and counted the change. There was *one dime* too much. His first thought was, "The bus company will never miss a dime," and then he quickly thought that he could not keep money that did not belong to him. That would be stealing.

The young man made his way to the front of the bus, and said to the driver, "You gave me too much change!" To his surprise, the driver said, "Yes, I gave you a dime too much! I did it on purpose. I heard your sermon yesterday. I watched you in my mirror as you counted your change. If you had kept that dime, I would have known that there is nothing to being a Christian. I would have never had any confidence again in preaching!" How glad the young man was that he had been perfectly honest!

The Honest Italian

A lady answered the door bell one day. There stood a collector of waste paper. The man, an Italian, had taken a lot of paper out of the lady's ash barrel in his weekly collection. Among the waste paper, he happened to find a silver tablespoon. Immediately, he went to the door and returned the spoon to the lady. The lady had missed the spoon for several days. It was made of solid silver and had been in the family for two generations. Naturally, it was highly prized. She warmly thanked the Italian for his honesty, and told him that she would save all of her waste paper for him.

The local newspaper told the incident, and made this comment: "No doubt many will save their waste paper for this *honest* Italian, and he will benefit a great deal more by his honesty than he would have benefited if he had kept the silver spoon."

Honest Abe

When Abraham Lincoln was in the grocery business in his young manhood, he acquired the name of "Honest Abe." This is how it happened: One night, as he was closing the store, he discovered that he had taken six and one-quarter cents too much from a customer. After the store was closed, he walked *three miles* to return the money!

At another time, Abe weighed out a half pound of tea, as he supposed, for a customer. It was the last thing he did before closing the store for the night. When he entered the store in the morning, he found a four-ounce weight in the scales where he had weighed the tea. There should have been an eight-ounce weight in the scales. He saw his mistake. He closed the store, and hurried off to deliver the remainder of the tea to his customer. No wonder that soon he was called *"Honest Abe!"*

Honesty Always Pays

In a Pennsylvania town was a Quaker horse dealer. A farmer wanted to buy a horse. He asked, "How much do you want for him?" The Quaker responded,

"I paid an hundred and fifty dollars for the horse, and I think I am entitled to a profit of fifty dollars. If you want the horse for two hundred dollars, you may have the horse." The deal was closed. The horse was delivered, and proved to be very satisfactory to the new owner.

A few weeks later, the farmer received a check for fifty dollars from the Quaker, and a note which said, "I told you that I paid a hundred and fifty dollars for that horse. On consulting my records, I find I was mistaken. I paid one hundred dollars for the horse. I told you my profit was fifty dollars. So I am sending you my check for fifty dollars to make the deal right!"

The Quaker dealer expected no reward for doing what he *knew* was right. The farmer, however, was so pleased with the Quaker's honesty that he told the incident over and over again. More than five thousand dollars in new business came to the Quaker dealer because of his honesty. Honesty always pays.

God Can Count

A little girl and her brother were carrying a basket of cakes to Grandma. They lifted the cover of the basket and looked at the cakes. They longed to taste them, but Mother had told them not to eat any of Grandma's cakes. They counted the cakes several times. Then, they decided that they would take just *one* of them. Nobody would know about it, and it would taste so good. Just as brother was ready to take a cake, little sister asked, "Can't God count?" That settled the matter. The cover was shut down, and *all* the cakes were carried to Grandma.

An Honest Man

Henry J. Heinz is often called "the man of the 57 varieties." He was the one who placed on the market the famous Heinz canned foods: vegetables, fruits, soups, pickles, *etc.* He was an honest, upright, Christian man.

One day, Mr. Heinz saw a young man working at his factory. The young man was weighing some apples which a farmer had brought to the factory. The young man said, "We are giving you good weight today, Mr. Heinz!" "Fine," said Mr. Heinz. Then the young man said, "You know I have a quick eye and a quick hand, and when I weigh these apples, I can always slip in a few extra pounds for you. The farmer never knows."

A little later, Mr. Heinz called the young man to his office. He said, "Young man, here is your pay. You will leave this place at once." "But, Mr. Heinz," said the young man, "I was saving you money." "You were robbing the farmer who was selling apples to me," said Mr. Heinz, "and you were robbing me of something more precious than money. I am an honest man. I never rob people." Then Mr. Heinz laid his hand on the young man's shoulder and said, "There is only one right way to weigh and do anything else: Always be honest. Be square to the other fellow and to yourself."

HUMILITY

Never Snub People

Sometimes when we wear better clothes and have better homes than other people, we feel that we are better than they are. This is not true.

Thomas A. Edison was a great inventor. When he first went to Boston, he was laughed at, because he wore thin linen pants in the wintertime. He did this because he was poor. Edison brought great blessings to this world, while many who laughed at him were never known.

Abraham Lincoln lived in a log cabin when he was a boy, and wore trousers with patches, but when he became a man, he lived in the White House.

John Bunyan was a very common man, many people thought, because he mended pots and pans. God used John Bunyan to give the world the wonderful story of "Pilgrim's Progress." Those who snubbed John Bunyan never gave the world anything of lasting value.

Never feel that you are better than others. Never snub those who are poorer than you.

Washington's Humility

Many years ago, a rider on horseback came across a squad of soldiers who were trying to move a heavy piece of timber. A corporal stood by, giving loud orders to heave. The piece of timber was a trifle too heavy for the squad to move. "Why don't you help them?" asked the man on the horse, addressing the important corporal. "Me? Why, I'm a corporal, sir." The stranger dismounted, and took his place with the soldiers. He said, "Now all together, boys, heave!" The big timber slid into place. The stranger mounted his horse, and, then turning to the corporal again, he said, "The next time you have a piece of timber too heavy for your men to handle, just send for your commanding general, George Washington." Then George Washington rode away while the corporal stood filled with embarrassment.

Only A Cobbler

One day at a great state dinner, an English officer asked with a snear, "Was not your great Dr. Carey a shoemaker?" Carey, the quiet and humble missionary, overheard the remark. He answered, "No, sir, he was only a cobbler!"

Keep Out of Sight

A little country boy went fishing. He had a switch for a pole. On the switch he tied a string. At the end of the string, he tied a bent pin for a hook. He caught lots of fish. A city man, who had spent much time fishing, passed the little boy. The man from the city had a costly fishing outfit. But he had fished for long hours and had caught nothing. When he came across the country boy, he saw that the boy had caught a long string of fish. The man from the city asked the boy, "How can you catch so many fish?" The boy replied, "The secret is that I always keep myself out of sight!"

When we are humble, when we keep ourselves out of sight, then God can use us. God will give us power and strength when we are small and weak.

Following Christ's Example

Hsu Chu, a lad of eighteen, was from a wealthy Chinese family. He came to the China Inland Hospital, to train as a nurse. He had elegant clothes, and a proud way. A few days after he began to train as a nurse, he refused to clean some shoes given to him. He said he was a gentleman and a scholar and that he would not do the work of a servant.

The superintendent of the Hospital called for Hsu Chu. While he watched, she took the boots and cleaned them! Then she read to him the account of the Lord Jesus washing the disciples' feet. When Hsu Chu heard the story, his face flushed. Then these words were read, "If I then, your Lord and Master, have washed your feet; ye also ought to wash one another's feet" (John 13:14).

The lad's eyes filled with tears, and he said, "May Jesus forgive me for my pride. He did the work of a servant." After that Hsu Chu was not filled with pride. He joyfully scrubbed floors, cleaned shoes, and did other humble tasks.

The Proud Brought Low

A young man once came to his pastor and asked to preach for him in a Sunday morning's service. The pastor said, "Young man, you are just a beginner. Perhaps, it would be better for you to speak Wednesday evening to a smaller group. Later, you may preach in a Sunday morning's service." The young man said, "I am a good preacher. I want to preach in the morning service!" So the pastor arranged for it.

The young man entered the pulpit with his head high. As he stood before the people, he forgot everything he had planned to say. He could not say a word. Hanging his head low, he went down off the platform. The pastor looked at him and said, "Young man, if you had gone up as you came down, you might have come down like you went up!"

Never have a proud and haughty spirit. The Bible says, that if we will humble ourselves, God will exalt us in due season. God helps the humble, and lifts them up. He brings low the proud and haughty ones.

"Remember What Thou Wast"

A nobleman in China carried a chest wherever he went. No one knew what was in the chest. People wondered what was in the chest. Finally, someone asked his highness what was in the chest. The chest was opened. Inside was found the common clothes of a working man. The nobleman said, "I was just a common working man. Our great sovereign stooped and lifted me from the dust. If ever my heart is tempted with pride, I open this chest. I look at these working clothes, and I say to myself, 'Remember what thou wast!' "

As a Servant

A young man wanted to go to China to help Robert Morrison, the great missionary. The mission board said, "You are not fit to be a missionary. But if you want to go as a servant to Dr. Morrison, we will send you." The young man said, "If I am not fit to go as a missionary, I will go as a servant. I will cut wood, or draw water, or do anything to *help*." He went out as a humble servant, but soon, he became a missionary. He was Dr. Milne, one of the *best* missionaries that ever went to China!

Humility Won Them

James Gilmour was a college boy. He went to Mongolia to be a missionary. The people there were hard to teach. They did not want to hear about the Lord Jesus. So James Gilmour humbled himself. He went and lived in tents like the people, amid smoke and dirt and filth. He wore clothes like theirs. He ate food like theirs. Soon, he won some of them to the Lord Jesus.

INFLUENCE

Mother's Influence

A little girl was playing with her dolls one evening. Suddenly, she left her dolls and went to her mother. She asked, "Mother, are you a Christian?" "No, Mary, I am not a Christian." The little girl turned and walked away. She said, "If Mother is not a Christian, I don't want to be one either!"

Mother's heart became sad. She thought, "What kind of a mother am I? I am not a Christian. Now, Mary does not want to be a Christian. What a

bad influence I have. I *must* change my ways. I must become a Christian. I must make room in my heart and life for Jesus! Then, Mary will become a Christian, too!" At prayer meeting the next night. Mother gave her heart to Jesus. Then Mary followed her example. She gave her heart to Jesus, too!

Can't Pack Up Your Influence

A young minister was moving away from a town. An old lady came to tell him goodby. "I see you are very busy packing up your belongings," she said. "Yes," he replied, "but I am almost fin-ished. I have only a few things to put into boxes now." "There's one thing you will not be able to pack up," said the old lady. "You will have to leave it behind." "What is that?" asked the minister. "You cannot pack up your *influence*, sir. You will leave that be-hind. We will always remember your Christian life!"

Influence of a Beautiful Life

A Japanese student had noticed the beautiful life of a fellow student. He said to a minister, "I want a beautiful life like that student. He never thinks of himself. He is always thinking of others. When we pass the food at the table, he will not take anything until all the rest have been helped. I want a beautiful life like his!"

What Would You Say?

A minister was nailing up a trailing vine in his garden. A little boy was watching him with great interest. "Well, my young friend," asked the minister, "are you trying to learn how to gar-den?" "No, sir," said the lad, "I am just waiting to see what you will say when you hammer your thumb!"

All around us there are people who are watching us. They are watching to see how we live. They are listening to hear what we say.

What Is A Christian?

A young man by the name of Wray graduated from Princeton. He volun-teered as a foreign missionary. When he reached his field of labour, he found it difficult to learn the language of the natives. Some of the other mis-sionaries thought that Wray was a fail-ure, because he was unable to learn the language quickly. The natives could not understand his TALK, but they could understand his WALK! One night, in a gathering of the natives, the question was asked, "What is it to be a Christian?" Instantly, the natives re-sponded, "It is to LIVE like Mr. Wray!"

Somebody Is Watching

A man who had been a robber and a kidnapper for twelve years was serving a sentence in prison. There he heard the gospel. There he was converted. Several years later he was discharged from prison. Just before he went out, another prisoner handed him a letter. The letter said, "You know that when I came into this prison I despised preachers, the Bible, and everything. I went to the Bible class and the preach-ing services because there wasn't any-thing else to do on Sunday. You were saved. I said, 'There's another fellow who is taking the gospel road to try to get a parole.' For two and a half years, Roy, I have been watching you. You did not know it, but I watched you when you were in the yard exercising, when you were working in the shop, when you played ball, when you were in the dining hall, when you were on the way to your cell. Now I am a Christian, too, because I watched you. You never slipped. The Saviour who saved you has saved me."

When Roy had finished reading the letter a cold sweat came out on him. He thought, "Suppose I had slipped even once. Then that man would not have been saved."

"I Did Like Mother and it Killed Me!"

A little girl watched everything that happened at her mother's card party. She observed how her mother was dressed; how she dealt the cards; how the women drank cocktails; and how they smoked their cigarettes. The next day, the little girl gathered her playmates together to play party. She dressed in some of her mother's clothes. She slipped into her mother's room and got her mother's package of cigarettes. Returning to her little playmates, she put a cigarette in her mouth. She struck a match. In trying to light the cigarette, she accidentally set fire to the mother's dress which she was wearing. Instantly, she became a "human torch." A few hours later, as she died, the little girl said, "I did like mother, and it killed me!"

How careful mothers should be to watch their influence over their little girls and boys. How careful we ALL should be to watch our influence over others, lest we bring them to destruction!

Evil Companions

When Queen Wilhelmina of Holland was a little girl, she was not allowed ordinarily to eat dinner with the older members of the royal household. Occasionally she was permitted to come in for dessert and sit beside some special friend.

One day the little princess came in for dessert and sat beside a fine, courtly old general. Soon she exclaimed, "I wonder you are not afraid to sit beside me." Everyone in the room heard her remark. A few were embarrassed. The old general said, "I am pleased and honored to sit beside my future queen. Why should I be afraid?"

With a sorrowful expression on her face the little princess replied: "Because all my dolls have the measles."

There is no danger of contagion from dolls, but there is danger of contagion of speech and conduct from evil, bad companions. There is an old saying: "Evil communications corrupt good manners."

A Father's Influence

One time a father wanted to go into a tavern to get some liquor. His little boy was with him. He asked the boy to remain outside for a few minutes. The father did not know it but little Jimmie followed him. He stood right behind his father while he ordered the drink. The bartender served the drink to the father, and then he asked Jimmie, "Young man, what will you have?" Little Jimmie replied, "What is good enough for Dad is good enough for me."

The father heard Jimmie's voice, and whirled around on his stool. He said, "If Jimmie is going to follow me, I will never touch another drop of liquor as long as I live. I don't want my boy to become a drinker." From that day the father was a different kind of man. He wanted to have a good influence, and not a bad influence, over Jimmie.

JESUS CHRIST

Crown Him King of Kings

Soon after Queen Victoria had ascended her throne, she went to hear "The Messiah." She had been instructed by those who knew about queenly conduct that she must not rise when others stood at the singing of the "Hallelujah Chorus." When the beautiful chorus was being sung and the singers were shouting, "Hallelujah! Hallelujah! Hallelujah! for the Lord God omnipotent reigneth," she kept her seat with difficulty. Finally, the singers came to the part where they proclaimed Christ as King of kings and Lord of lords. Suddenly the young queen arose. She stood with her head bowed. She, too, wanted to crown Him as King of kings and Lord of lords.

Let us make Him King of our hearts and lives, and let us every day be loyal to Him.

Why Preach Christ?

Mr. Cunningham was a missionary in South China. One day a native came to him and said, "You have been preaching Jesus for three days. Why don't you preach something else."

"What do you eat for breakfast?" Mr. Cunningham asked. "Rice," was the reply. "For dinner?" "Rice." "For supper?" "Rice." "What did you eat yesterday?" "Rice."

"Why do you eat rice every day?" asked the missionary.

"Because it keeps me alive."

"That is why I preach Jesus. He is our Life. We could not live without Him."

Without Christ Is Hell

A young man received a letter from a former college chum whose life was devoted to money-making. In the letter, the chum wrote, "Bob, poverty is hell." Bob wrote back, "Bill, to be without the love of Christ is hell!" Bob was right. Bob was both happy and rich because he had Christ.

A Superhuman Savior

Daniel Webster was dining with some literary men in Boston. During the dinner, the men began to talk about Christianity. Mr. Webster frankly said he believed that the Lord Jesus Christ is the Son of God, and the Saviour of the world. One asked, "Mr. Webster, can you understand how Christ could be both God and man?" Mr. Webster promptly replied, "I cannot. If I could, He would be no greater than myself. I feel that I need a superhuman Saviour."

All Praise Belongs to Jesus

When Dr. William Carey, the missionary, was very ill, another missionary called to see him. The friend talked about Dr. Carey's great work for God. He spoke of Dr. Carey's sacrifice for God. When the visitor prayed, he prayed about Dr. Carey's great work and wonderful life. As the visitor was leaving the room, Dr. Carey called to him in a feeble voice and said, "Friend, you have been speaking about 'Dr. Carey, Dr. Carey.' When I am gone, speak *nothing* about Dr. Carey. Speak *only* about Dr. Carey's Saviour!"

An Important Question

A chaplain in the World War was ready to preach to a regiment of soldiers, just back from the front trenches. They were tired and weary, and the rain had begun to fall. They were standing in the field, under the open sky, to hear his message. "My text," he began, "is 'What think ye of Christ?'" He paused and then he continued, "My sermon is, 'What think ye of Christ?'" Then he shouted: "*Dismissed!*"

The *most* important question in the world is, "What think *ye* of Christ?" The way you answer this question will determine the way your life will go, and it will decide where you will spend eternity!

Drink Deeply

A little thin boy was brought to a London hospital. The nurse brought him a glass of milk. Before he lifted the glass to his parched lips, he asked, "How deep may I drink?" He came from a very poor home where one glass of milk had to be shared among others. He could hardly believe it when the nurse told him he could drink *all* of it.

When our souls are thirsty, "after righteousness," we may come to the Lord Jesus and drink as deeply as we want. He will satisfy our spiritual thirst. He is the Living Water.

Only Jesus Satisfies

A few years ago, there lived a man who was an atheist. He did not believe in God. He did not love God. This man was sad and wretched. He could not find happiness in anyone or in anything. With *all* of his heart he longed for rest and peace. He tried many things to satisfy the thirst in his heart. But nothing satisfied him. Finally, he turned to Jesus. He found that Jesus satisfied the thirst and hunger of his heart. Then he wrote this beautiful poem:

> "I've tried in vain a thousand ways,
> My fears to quell, my hopes to raise;
> But what I need, the Bible says:
> Is ever *only* Jesus!
>
> "My soul is night, my heart is steel;
> I cannot see, I cannot feel;
> For light, for life, I *must* appeal,
> In simple faith to *Jesus!*"

Crown Him!

A little boy was sitting by the piano while his father played. He asked his father to play the song:

> "Praise Him, praise Him,
> All ye little children!"

The father played the song and sang several verses. He sang, "Praise Him!" Then he sang, "Love Him!" Then he sang, "Serve Him!" When he stopped, the little boy said, "But, Father, you forgot to *crown Him!*" So then the father and the little boy sang together:

> "Crown Him, crown Him!
> All ye little children!"

Have *you* forgotten to crown Him?

No Ordinary Man

Two infidels once sat in a train discussing Christ's wonderful life. One of them said, "I think an interesting book could be written about Him." The other replied, "And you are just the man to write it. Give the correct view of His life and character. Show that He was not Divine. Paint Him as He was: A man among men." The suggestion was acted upon. The book, "Ben Hur," was written. The man who made the suggestion was Colonel Ingersol. The one who wrote the book was General Lew Wallace!

As Lew Wallace was preparing the book, *Ben Hur*, he found himself face to face with an unaccountable Man! The more he studied His life and character, the more convinced he became that this Man was no ordinary man. At length, as he continued to study the life of Christ, he came face to face with the Cross. He was constrained to cry out, "Verily, this was the Son of God!"

All She Needed

An aged Christian had learned many Bible verses by memory. Then her memory began to fail. One precious bit of the Bible stayed with her: "I know whom I have believed, and am persuaded that He is able to keep that which I have committed unto Him against that day" *(II Tim. 1:12)*. Little by little, part of that verse slipped from her memory. Finally, all she could remember was, "That which I have committed unto Him." At last, just before she left this world for Heaven, her loved ones noticed her lips moving. They bent down to hear what she said, and she was saying all she could remember of the verse. She was repeating the precious word, *"Him! Him! Him!"* That one word was all she needed, for in Him, we have *eternal life*.

Christ the Way

A traveler in Switzerland was uncertain of his way. He asked a small lad by the wayside where Kaudersted was. He received this significant answer: "I do not know, sir, where Kaudersted is; but there is the road to it!" There are many things I cannot tell you about the life to come, but I know the Way. The Lord Jesus, the risen Saviour, is the Way!

Rock or Shamrock

A crowd had gathered around a street preacher in London. It was at the time of the Shamrock Races, and many were talking about the event. A rough fellow at the edge of the crowd thought he would have a little fun. So he called out, "Preacher, what do you know about the shamrock?"

The street preacher never paused, but went right on talking about *sin* and the *Saviour*. Again, the would-be disturber called out, "I say, Mr. Preacher, what do you know about the shamrock?"

Still, the preacher paid no attention, but went *right on*, urging his listeners to place their faith in the Lord Jesus. Not to be silenced, the heckler called out the third time, "Mr. Preacher, I'm asking what you know about the shamrock?"

This time, the preacher paused. The crowd became very still! With a clear voice that everyone could hear, the preacher shouted out, "On Christ the Solid *Rock* I stand! All other rocks are sham rocks."

On Our Faces Before Him

Some years ago a group of literary men were gathered in London. One said, "Gentlemen, what would we do if Milton would enter this room?" "Ah," said one, "we would give him a great ovation!" "What would we do if Shakespeare entered?" asked another. "We would arise and crown him master of song," was the answer. "What would we do if Jesus Christ would enter this room?" asked another. An intense silence fell on the group. It was broken by Charles Lamb who said, "I think we would all fall on our faces before Him!"

No Beginning and No End

A six-year-old lad one day asked his mother, "Mother, who made God?" The mother was astonished. She said, "What an awful question to ask! You had better run along and play!"

In the same community, another little boy approached his mother and asked, "Did God make Himself?" His mother, with a silent prayer for guidance, took off her wedding ring. She handed it to her son and asked, "Where does this ring begin, and where does it end?" The boy examined the ring and answered, "There is no starting place and there is no stopping place to a ring." The mother then said, "Just so is God. There is no beginning and no end to God. He always has been, and always will be!"

What Think Ye of Christ?

For centuries, there lay in a shallow brook in North Carolina a big lump of something. People passing that way saw only *an ugly lump* and passed on. One day, a poor man saw *a heavy lump*, and he took it home to hold his door open. One day, a geologist, who stopped at the poor man's door, saw *a lump of gold*, the biggest lump of gold ever found east of the Rockies.

Many people look upon the Lord Jesus. Some see only a Galilean peasant, and turn away. Others see a

Prophet, and stop to listen. Others see in Him, the Son of God, and stop to worship! What do *you* see as you look upon the Lord Jesus? What think *ye* of Christ? Whose Son is He? Your eternal destiny hinges upon your answer to these all-important questions.

The Living Water

There is a strange little plant which grows in South America. It rolls around until it finds a moist place. Then it sends its roots down and becomes green for a little while. When the place becomes dry, the plant draws itself out of the ground, and rolls around again until it comes to another moist place. There, it sends its roots down again and becomes green for a little while. When that place, too, becomes dry, it again draws its roots out, and rolls on to another place. After awhile, the plant becomes nothing but a bundle of dead roots and leaves!

Some people are like that strange little plant. They wander from one thing to another, trying to satisfy the longings of their hearts. But nothing will ever satisfy them fully unless they come to *Jesus, the Living Water.*

The Door to Heaven

For many years, a man thought that one day he would enter Heaven because of his good works. One night, he had a dream. He thought that he was climbing a ladder toward Heaven. Every time he did a good deed, he climbed a little higher. Nearer and nearer he approached Heaven. Finally, as he was about to step off the ladder into Heaven, he heard a voice like thunder, saying, "He that entereth not by the Door into the sheepfold, but climbeth up some *other* way, the same is a thief and a robber." With a great crash, his ladder fell down to earth. The man awoke from his dream. He *knew* that he had been *wrong*. He had been trying to get to Heaven by his own good deeds.

There is *only one way* to get to Heaven, and that is through Jesus. He opened the door to Heaven for us when He gave His precious life on the Cross for our sins. Will you not trust Him *now* as your Saviour? Then you can enter into Heaven through the Door.

> "One door and only one,
> But yet its sides are two,
> Inside and outside,
> On which side are *you*?

> "One door, and only one,
> And yet its sides are two,
> I'm on the inside,
> On which side are *you*?"

"He Must Be God"

When the first missionaries went to Japan, a young Japanese, who wanted to learn English, was given the Gospel of John to translate into his native tongue. In a short time, he became very restless and agitated. At last, he asked, "Who is this Man about whom I have been reading? Who is this Jesus? You call Him a Man, but He *must be God*."

JUDGMENT

Warning

A man who lived on Long Island, one day bought a very fine barometer. A barometer is a small instrument which shows the probable changes in the weather. Sometimes, the barometer says it will rain. Sometimes, it says that it will be clear and sunny. Sometimes, it says that it will be stormy. When the man unpacked the instrument, in his home, he noticed that the needle appeared to be stuck. The needle was pointing to the part that was marked, "Hurricane." A hurricane is a terrible storm which blows down houses and uproots trees. The man thought that the barometer must be wrong. He thought that the needle must be stuck at the word, "Hurricane." He shook the instrument hard, but the needle would not move away from the word, "Hurricane." So the man sat down and wrote a scorching letter to the store where he

had bought the barometer. He told them that the barometer was no good; that the needle was struck.

The next morning, on his way to work, the man mailed the letter. All day long, he worked in his office in New York City. That evening, he returned to Long Island to find that not only was the barometer missing, but also his house! The barometer had been *right*. There *was* a hurricane! His house was gone!

His Reward

When Jonathan Goforth was a lad of fifteen, his father put him in charge of their second farm, about twenty miles distant from the home farm. Jonathan's younger brother, Joseph, was to assist him. When the father handed over the farm to his son, Jonathan, he called his attention to one large field which was choked with weeds. The father said, "Clear that field, and seed it, and at harvest time I'll return and inspect it."

Jonathan put real labor into the preparation of that field. He plowed and replowed it. He left the deadly roots of the weeds lying in the sun until they died, and then he plowed the field again. Finally, he sowed the best seed.

One beautiful morning, just at harvest time, the father arrived. With a thrill of joy, Jonathan took his father to a high place where he could see the whole field of waving grain. The father stood silent for a few moments, as he examined the field for a sign of weeds, but there was none. At last, he turned to his son and smiled. Jonathan Goforth, in later years, said, "That smile from my father was all the reward I wanted for my hard work. I knew my father was pleased!" So will it be if we are faithful in the service of our Heavenly Father."

God's Approval Means Everything

A Christian judge hated wrong doing. In his court, he took a strong stand against all evildoers. Because of this, the evildoers hated the judge and often threatened to take his life. A friend asked him one day, "Don't you think you could shut your eyes a little to some of the wrong doing? If you did that the evildoers would not hate you so much. The world shuts its eyes to much wrongdoing." The Christian judge replied, "My friend, I am living for another world. One day, I shall appear before the Judge of all the earth. I shall be called upon to give an account to Him. God's approval means every-

thing to me. Because of this, I can put up with the disapproval of some wicked men on this earth. I want to please the One higher up."

The Bible says, "So then EVERY ONE of us shall give account of himself to God" (*Rom. 14:12*).

Eternal Loss

Two brothers were brought up in a Christian home. They were sent to the same college to prepare for their lifework. One decided to enter the ministry. The other determined to study law. The one who became a minister of the Gospel did not make a great name for himself, but he was faithful to the Lord, serving for many years a small church in a small town. The one who became a lawyer seemingly prospered in every way. He had a large practice, handled some famous cases, wrote several good legal books, and became a judge at a young age.

The day came when things went wrong with the lawyer. He lost his fortune. His health failed. At length, he went to visit his preacher brother. One day, the preacher heard the lawyer brother weeping as if his heart would break. He went to his brother and asked what was the trouble. The lawyer exclaimed, "Oh, brother, I am so near the end of life and I am not ready to go!"

"You received Christ as your Saviour years ago," the preacher brother replied. "It isn't that," said the lawyer-brother. "I know God has forgiven my sins, but I am not ready to go. I am not ready to stand before Him, and be judged for my life. I can't recall a single soul that I have led to Christ. I can't recall ever having been a good witness for Him! When I stand before Him, I will be like the unfaithful servant to whom the nobleman entrusted one pound. When he appeared before his lord to give an accounting, he had to confess that he had wrapped the pound into a napkin and had not put it to use. I shall stand before my Lord, and tell Him that I have WASTED my talent and my life!"

KINDNESS

Kindness to A Stranger

Years ago, there lived a poor miner who was unable to give food to his little son. The boy had to go out begging. He was a sweet singer. So, he went along the street, begging. One day, a man and his wife, in a house, heard his song. They were deeply stirred by the sweet voice and the sad words of the song:

"Foxes to their holes have gone,
    Every bird into his nest:
But I wander here alone,
    And for me there is no rest!"

The man, whose name was Conrad, went outside to find the singer. The ragged little boy said, "Please, sir, help me for Christ's sake!" The boy was invited into the house. He ate supper there, and spent the night. The Conrads had lost their own little boy a short while before. When they looked at this poor, ragged boy, as he lay there sleeping, they thought that they would like to keep him. The next day, they arranged to have him live with them. The boy went to school. Later, he entered a monastery. There, he read the Bible, and learned that salvation was in Christ ALONE. He became the great MARTIN LUTHER, the founder of Protestantism. Little did the Conrads know, when they gave a home to the ragged, hungry boy, that they were helping a lad, who would become a mighty servant of God'

"Nuisance"

How would you like to be called, "Nuisance"? That was the name of a little Chinese girl who had a hard life. One day, her father was going to take her to market and sell her as a slave. Little "Nuisance" was afraid. In the market, she was bought by a kind missionary, not to be a slave, but to be given a home, and to be taught the Gospel. How she loved the kind missionary! It was not long before she loved the Lord Jesus, too. She became His faithful servant. After some years, she became a faithful missionary to the Chinese people.

Fried Chicken

A new preacher had come to a little country church. On his first Sunday the people drove in from miles around to hear him preach. There was a service in the morning and another one in the afternoon. Between the services the ladies served dinner on the grounds. Long tables were covered with white tablecloths. There were great platters of fried chicken, ham, and other good meat placed on the tables, along with biscuits, corn pone, macaroni, hard-boiled eggs, salads, cakes, pies, and other delicacies. Usually at these dinners the lively boys managed to get in the front line nearest the platters of fried chicken. But this Sunday there was such a large crowd that the boys were asked to wait. Angrily they went off behind a shed and there shot craps trying to get revenge by doing something of which the elders did not approve.

One boy was appointed to keep an eye on the tables and report how things were progressing. Presently he reported that the fried chicken was disappearing rapidly. Then he reported that some of the ladies had brought out more fried chicken. Suddenly he exclaimed, "Say, look at that preacher! He's eaten all he can hold, and now, when no one is looking, he is filling those big pockets in his coat tails with chicken." The boys sneaked around the shed to look. Just then a lady noticed that the preacher's plate was empty, and she exclaimed, "Look at the preacher's plate. You all are neglecting him. Pass the chicken over here." Then the sister heaped up the preacher's plate with choice pieces of chicken. Sure enough, when nobody was looking, the preacher took a couple of clean handkerchiefs out of his pockets, and quickly wrapped the fried chicken up in them, and hid them away in his coat tail pockets.

When those at the first tables had finished eating, the preacher rose with the rest. Carefully he backed away from the others. The boys thought he was going away to hide his "loot." To their surprise he turned quickly and came behind the shed. "Boys," said he, "I saw that the best pieces of chicken were going fast, so I saved a lot of the thighs and drumsticks for you." Then the preacher took four clean handkerchiefs filled with chicken from his pockets and gave them to the boys. How surprised and delighted the boys were. From that day the boys loved the preacher. He had captured their hearts by his kindness. He led all of them to Christ. Several of the boys became foreign missionaries. Three became ministers of the gospel in the homeland.

Kindness Won the Family

A Sunday school worker was hurrying down the streets of Chicago one Sunday on his way to Sunday school. He noticed a little baby who was being held at the window by one of the family. He smiled at the baby, and the baby smiled back. The next Sunday, when he passed the house, the baby was at the window again. Again he smiled and waved his hand and the baby smiled back. The next Sunday, there were several of the family at the window with the baby, and again he smiled and waved. One from the family followed him, and saw him turn to the Sunday school. The next Sunday, some of the children appeared at the Sunday school. Finally, the whole family came, and were won for Christ because of the kindness of the Sunday school worker.

A Glass of Milk

A young medical student was selling books to help pay his way through medical school. One hot summer day, he stopped at a farmhouse, and asked a bright young girl if she cared to buy a book. "No thanks," she replied, "my mother is a widow, and we cannot afford to buy books." Then the student asked for a glass of water. She replied, "We have cold milk in the spring house. Would you care for a glass of milk?" The student thanked her, and drank a glass of cold milk. When he offered to pay for the milk, she refused, saying, "Mother has taught me to be kind to strangers."

Some years passed by. One day, a woman was brought to a hospital. She was too sick to notice anyone. But the *chief surgeon* saw her and recognized her as the girl who had once given him a glass of milk. He took special interest in her case. She was placed in a private room, and had special nurses to wait on her. Weeks passed.

One morning a nurse said, "You are going home tomorrow!" "Oh," said the woman, "I am so glad. But the hospital bill worries me. It must be very large." The nurse said, "I will bring it to you." As the woman looked over the bill, and saw the large amount of it, she began to weep. Then, she looked further, and down at the bottom she read these words: "Paid in full by a glass of milk!" Thus it was that Dr. Howard A. Kelley returned the kindness that a country girl showed to a stranger!

A Kind Chaplain

A chaplain on the battlefield came to a man who was wounded, lying on the ground. He asked the wounded soldier, "Would you like me to read something to you from the Bible?"

The soldier replied, "I would rather have a drink of water. I am so thirsty." The chaplain brought water.

Then the soldier said, "Would you please put something under my head?" The chaplain took off his overcoat, rolled it up, and put it under the soldier's head for a pillow.

"Now," said the soldier, "I need something over me. I am very cold." The chaplain took off his coat and spread it over the soldier.

The wounded soldier looked gratefully into the face of the chaplain and said, "Thank you!" Then he added, "If there is anything in the Bible that makes a man do what you have done for me, you may read it to me."

An Angel's Work

A poor, tired woman got on a train with her children. She sat down with them in a Pullman car. The porter ordered them out. Frightened, they hurried into the next car. It happened to be a coach. They sat down.

A little boy was sitting by his aunt in the coach. He saw the mother, and the children. He noticed that they looked tired and hungry. He said, "Auntie, I want to give them my fruit and my sandwiches. They look very hungry." At first, the aunt said, "No," but the little boy persisted. He said, "Oh, Auntie, they look so very hungry. Please let me give them my lunch." Then the aunt said, "Yes."

The little boy carried his lunch over to the family. "God bless you," said the mother. Then she told him that they had had no breakfast. As the boy started back to his seat, one child asked, "Mother, is that boy an angel?" "Oh, no," said the mother, "but he is acting like an angel. He is doing an angel's work."

Not Mud But a Flower

One day a little girl dressed in white and carrying a bunch of flowers passed a small boy playing in the street. The boy threw a handful of dirt at the little girl. The dirt struck her white dress, and fell on her white shoes.

The little girl stood still. The boy expected her to cry, or say angry words, or throw dirt back at him. But she stood still for a moment, and then she smiled, and threw a flower at the little boy, who was waiting to see what she would do.

He was surprised! He was ashamed! From that day, that little boy was the friend of the little girl. Never again did he throw dirt at her.

A Lawsuit Avoided

A man who had just bought a farm came to his new neighbor and said, "I have just bought the farm next to yours, and I want to tell you that your fence is four feet over on my land, and you are going to have a lawsuit on your hands!" The one thus addressed was a Christian. Quietly, he answered, "Oh, no, we will not have a lawsuit. If my fence is four feet on your land, I will go right now and see that the fence is moved back four feet on to my land!" The kind, soft answer made a friend out of a neighbor who would have been an enemy.

A Friend in Need

An infidel was giving a lecture. He ridiculed all Christians. A man, who was a common laborer, arose and said, "Some months ago I lost my work, for I was ill. To make matters worse, my wife became ill, too. Every one knew of our illness, but *not one* of our *'friends'* came near us. Then, one day, there came to our door a city missionary. I had often made fun of him. Indeed, I had driven him away from my door with threats. He came into our home. He nursed us; he provided for us. If it were not for him, my wife and I would not be alive today. When I was well enough to think, I asked him why he had been so kind to us. He told me that he had done it *for the love of Christ.* I say that a religion which will bring a man to the bedside of one who has hated him and cursed him is a good thing!"

One of His Followers

A little lame boy, in a railway station, was hurrying as fast as he could go on his crutches, toward the passenger gate. He was carrying a basket of fruit and candy. As the passengers rushed through the gate, a man accidentally hit the basket, knocking the oranges and apples in every direction. He stopped long enough to scold the boy for being in his way, and then he hurried on.

A young man passing by saw the lame boy's distress. He stopped and picked up the fruit for the boy. As he placed it in the basket, he put a silver dollar in the boy's hand. With a smile, he said, "Better luck next time."

"Hey, Mister," called the lame boy, "are *you* Jesus?"

"No," answered the young man; "I'm only *one* of His followers!"

Living as We Pray

"I knelt to pray when day was done,
And prayed, 'O God, bless every one,
Lift from sorrowing hearts the pain,
And let the sick be well again.'

"And then I woke another day,
And carelessly went on my way.
The whole day long, I did not try,
To wipe a tear from any eye,

"I did not try to lift the load,
From any brother on the road,
I did not even go to see,
The sick man *just next door to me.*

"And yet again, when day was done,
I prayed, 'O God, bless every one.'
But as I prayed, into my ear,
There came a voice which whispered clear,

" 'Pause hypocrite before you pray,
Whom have you tried to bless today?
Life's sweetest blessings always go,
By hands which serve Him here below.'

"And then I hid my face and cried:
  'Forgive me, God, for I have *lied*,
  But let me live another day,
  And I will live *the way I pray*.'"
                            —Whitney Montgomery

Showing God's Love

Some missionaries were kind to the lepers. They cared for them in their sickness. They told them of the love of Jesus. One day, one of the missionaries asked the lepers, "How do you know that the Lord Jesus loves you?" They replied, "Because of you!" Day by day, the missionaries *showed* God's love and God's kindness to the lepers.

Kindness to an Enemy

Some years ago, in Manchuria, there lived a Chinese farmer named Tung. One day a band of robbers came to his home. They tied Tung up, burned his home, and carried off his belongings. Tung was a Christian. He rebuilt his home and went on with his work.

Two years later, in the city, Tung met and recognized one of the robber band. The robber begged Tung for mercy. He thought Tung would have him arrested and thrown into prison. Tung said, "I do not hate you. Tell me about yourself." The man told Tung about his troubles. He owed money at the Inn. He was hungry. His feet were frost-bitten. Tung gave him some money. and told him to pay his debt and buy some food. Tung said, "I will call for you tomorrow and take you to the hospital."

The robber thought that Tung would surely have him captured and thrown into prison. But next day, Tung came for him and took him to the mission hospital in his own cart. Tung said, "Perhaps, he will learn of Jesus as I did. Then he will come out a different man." The robber did learn of Jesus in the hospital. He was saved and he came out of the hospital a different man!

Kindness Won

John saw some ragged boys and invited them to go to Sunday School. One said he would go, but he had no coat. John gave him his coat to wear, and took him to Sunday School. John went in without a coat. Years afterwards, a teacher of a Bible class told the incident. The teacher said, "I was that little boy that had no coat! John G. Paton, the great missionary, gave me his coat, and took me to Sunday School. His kindness led me to Christ!"

Kindness Shows Love

A little four-year-old African girl was sold as a slave. She did not know what love was. Indeed, her name, "Keodi," meant, "Nobody loves me."

When she was ten years old, Keodi got sick. Her body was covered with ugly sores. Then, her master turned her out. He did not want her longer. The natives would have nothing to do with her. She wandered about homeless, hungry, uncared for.

Some kind missionaries found Keodi. They took her into their home and cleaned her up. They cared for her sores, and put clothes on her. She could not believe that some one loved her. She went about saying, "I am Keodi. Nobody loves me."

The missionaries told Keodi about Jesus. They told her how greatly Jesus loved her, and how He had died on the Cross for her. They told her that they, too, loved her, because His love was in their hearts. Little Keodi looked down at her dress, her clean body, and the bandaged sores, and asked, "Is this love?" The missionaries told her that it was.

We, too, can show the love of God to others by being kind and helpful.

Grandma's Glasses

Two little boys were talking together. The small one asked, "Wouldn't you hate to wear glasses?" "No," answered the other, "not if they were the kind my grandmother wears. They make her see how to mend broken things, and they help her to find lots of nice things to do on rainy days. She sees when folks are tired and sorry, and what will make them feel better. She sees what you meant to do even if you didn't do it quite right. I asked her one day how she could see that way all the time, and she said, that it was the way she has learned to *look at things* since she got older. And so, I knew it was those glasses of hers!"

It was not grandma's glasses, little ones, that made her see how to be kind. It was the love of Jesus in her *heart*.

Her Greatest Happiness

Some one asked a trained nurse if she did not grow weary of her work. She replied, "Yes, I grow weary when I have to care for rich patients who can hire someone else to wait on them. I grow weary and my head aches and my hands became heavy! But let me take a basket of food and medicines and go among the poor who can pay me only with their eyes, and I have the *greatest happiness*. I can hardly wait for my August vacation to come. I am going to spend that among the poor!"

Someone Forgot

On a cold day, a little street urchin sat on a curbstone. His feet were bare. They were cracked open and bleeding from the cold. A man said, "Sonny, I heard that you are a Christian now. Why doesn't God send you some shoes?" The little fellow replied, "I am *sure* that God has told some one to bring me shoes. But they must have forgotten to do it." Let us not forget the poor.

He Had a Friend

A blind man sold papers on the corner of a busy city street. One day the wind was blowing coldly. The hurrying crowds passed by. Suddenly, a sweet voice said at his elbow: "Good morning!" The man turned his sightless eyes toward the speaker. He asked quickly, "Who is it?" A young girl, plainly dressed, said, "It is Marjory Dean. I work nearby. I thought I would stop and say 'Good morning' to you."

The blind man smiled and nodded. He no longer felt the cold wind. He forgot his helplessness. He forgot that he had sold so few papers. Out of the darkness, a sweet voice had spoken to Him. He had a *friend*. Smiling, he said, "Good morning to you. I am so *glad* you stopped to speak to me!"

A Friend to the Poor

A preacher in London called one day to see a street-crossing sweeper in his parish who was ill. He asked if anyone else had visited him. The answer was, "Oh, yes! Mr. William Gladstone came to see me!"

"What?" asked the preacher; "you mean Mr. Gladstone, the Premier of England?"

"O yes," answered the sweeper; "I have known him for a long time. He has always had a kind word for me when he has passed my crossing. When I was not there, he missed me. He asked the man who has taken my place where I lived. Then he called to see me."

"W h a t did he do?" asked the preacher.

"O sir, he read the Bible and prayed with me." What happiness William Gladstone had brought to the poor street-crossing sweeper.

The Best He Could Do

A deacon was requested to come to a prayer meeting in behalf of a poor neighbor who had a large family, and who had broken his leg. The deacon was very busy, gathering his apples. He said, "I can't stop now to pray, but you go down into the cellar, and get some corned beef, salt pork, potatoes, and butter. Take them over to the poor neighbor. *That's the best I can do!*" Surely, that is what God wanted him to do.

When we see a needy brother or sister, neighbor or friend, we are not to withhold our love. We are to show our love in *deed* and in *truth*.

> "Have you had a kindness shown?
>   Pass it on!
> 'Twas not given thee alone,
>   Pass it on!
> Let it travel down the years,
> Let it dry another's tears,
> Till in Heaven the deed appears
>   Pass it on!

> "Be not selfish in thy greed,
>   Pass it on!
> Look upon thy brother's need,
>   Pass it on!
> Live for *self* you live in vain,
> Live for Christ you'll live again,
> Live for Christ, with Christ you'll reign,
>   Pass it on!

The Good Samaritan

One cold wintry night, a mother, with her two boys, sat down to eat their evening meal. Their supper was crusts of bread spread with lard, and some black coffee. The family lived in a little old house on the bank of the Susquehanna River. A blizzard was raging on the outside. The snow lay two feet deep. When the meal was finished, the mother said, "Boys, I don't know what we will do now. We have eaten the *last* bit of food in the house. My money is gone. You have no shoes. I have no warm clothes to go out into the snow!" "Well, Mother," said the older boy, "let's say our prayers. Maybe God will send some one around to help us!" The mother read some verses from the Bible. Then, they all knelt in prayer. The mother asked God to send some *good samaritan* around to help them.

After the prayer was finished, the mother and the boys gathered around the organ. The mother played while the boys sang. Suddenly, there was a knock at the door! All went to the door to see who it was. A man stepped into the room with a basket full of groceries and provisions! There were bread, sugar, rice, potatoes, meat, butter, and other things which were needed. The man left saying that he had another basketful he w a n t e d to bring, and he must get it before the closing of the store. Soon, he returned with another basket laden with good things.

How happy were the mother, and the two boys. "Who ever made you think of us?" asked the mother. "Well, I don't know," answered the man. "I was sitting in our living room, reading, and all of a sudden I thought of you and the boys, and wondered if you were in need of food and coal. I kept thinking of you and so I put on my coat, and went to the store, and got the things. I'm glad that I came! By the way, do you have any coal to keep you warm?"

"No," said the mother; "we have been burning driftwood, and the last of it is in the stove now." The man said, "Don't worry; I will send some coal around in the morning. You just let them put it in, for it's all paid for. If you need anything else, just let me know!"

The family thanked the man, and after he left, they prayed to God *thanking Him* for sending the *good samaritan*. The mother has now gone to be with the Lord in Heaven. The two boys are *fine Christian men*.

A Helpful Girl

An old gentleman said one day, "Once I was young, now I am old. I have never seen a girl unfaithful or unkind to her mother that ever came to be worth a one-eyed button to h r husband. But if one of you boys e er comes across a girl with a face full of roses, who says as you come to the door, 'I can't go for thirty minutes, for the dishes are not washed,' you wait for that girl. Sit down on her doorstep and wait for her, because if you leave, some other fellow will come along and marry her and right there you have lost 'an angel!' Wait for that girl. Stick to her like a burr to a mule's tail!"

Showing Our Love

A group of Christian people met one day to pray for a poor family. They prayed that God would help this poor family. One of the deacons was very busy. He did not attend the prayer meeting, but he sent his boy around to the meeting. The boy came in and said,

"Father was so busy on the farm today that he did not have time to come to the prayer meeting. But he sent his prayers. They are out in the wagon. If some of you will help me, we will take them to the needy family. There are potatoes, flour, a ham, and a lot of other things in the wagon!"

That is the way God wants you and me to help the poor and needy ones. He wants us to love them and pray for them; but he also wants us to *show* our love by sharing what we have with them.

A Medical Missionary

Dr. Richard F. Brown is a Canadian medical missionary to China. When his station was taken by the Japanese, he started traveling through the provinces on foot. He ministered to *all* sorts of people: Chinese, Japanese, Communists! At times, he walked thirty miles a day, working along the road helping the sick from dawn to dusk. In one district, within a radius of three miles, were fourteen hundred sick and wounded without doctors or medical supplies! Dr. Brown helped these needy people. Said he, "It was trying to be wakened every morning by the sick and wounded, pulling at your bedclothes, but you get used to it." How greatly has Dr. Brown shown forth the love of God to the needy people around him!

No Burden

A man from America was walking down the street of a Chinese city. He saw many of the children playing. They carried a burden on their backs. They were carrying on their backs their little brothers and sisters. The man said to one bright little boy, "It is too bad that you have to carry such a heavy burden on your back'" "Oh," said the little boy; "he's not a burden. *He's my brother!*"

When we are helping one another, it is no burden. We love our brothers and sisters in Christ. We like to help them.

Saint Bernard

When Saint Bernard was a young man, he had a beautiful home with everything that money could buy. He wore beautiful clothes; ate delicious food; rode upon a beautiful horse. But he was *not* happy. "How can I be happy," he asked, "when I see so many about me poor, and hungry, and sad?" His father and mother loved their son, but they cared nothing about the poor and unfortunate ones.

One day, Bernard said, "Good-by" to his father and mother. He left his beautiful home, and went to live alone in the mountains, where he could help the poor and needy ones. When they were sick, he nursed them. When they were sad, he tried to cheer them. Always, he talked to them about the Lord Jesus.

Near Saint Bernard's hut, there was a lonely road, where travelers often lost their way in the winter when the snow lay deep. With a big, beautiful dog at his side, and a staff in his hand, Saint Bernard tramped over the mountains, looking for some poor, lost traveler. Tenderly, he would carry the lost traveler to his warm hut, where he would tend him and feed him until he was able to go on his way.

After awhile, some of Bernard's friends came to help him. Together, they built a large house on the top of a mountain. It was called a hospice. Every night, a bright light shone in the window to guide the travelers.

Saint Bernard and his friends had twelve big, faithful dogs to help them in their work. These dogs would go out to find lost travelers. This work of helpfulness went on for some years.

One day, an aged couple came to the door. They seemed poor and tired. Bernard asked them to come in and rest. As they sat by the fire, they told him their story. Years ago, they had an only son. They wanted him to be a great prince, but he went away because he wanted to help the poor and sad. Said the aged couple, "We have traveled far and wide, and searched for him, but we have never found him."

Saint Bernard knew that this couple were his own father and mother. He kissed them and welcomed them to his hospice. He showed them the light that burned all night in the window of the hospice and the great dogs that helped so faithfully. The father and mother were happy, and they asked, "Can't we stay and help you do our blessed Lord's work?" After that, they lived together and went out with the faithful dogs to find lost travelers.

LIGHT

The Guiding Light

A fisherman had a little daughter whom he loved dearly. He used to leave her in his cabin on a cliff while he went out to sea to fish. One time, while he was out fishing, a sudden storm came up. The night was dark, and he could not reach the little harbor before the storm broke. "Oh," said he, "if I only had a little light, perhaps I could make the harbor!" Just then he saw a ray of light, shining out of the darkness. His little girl had made a heap of driftwood, and had set it on fire so her daddy could have a light to guide him. Guided by the light, he soon brought his boat safely to shore.

Are you sending out light from your life to guide boys and girls, who are walking in dangerous ways, to Jesus?

Walking in the Light

A woman in Palestine sat under an olive tree sewing. She was putting beautiful handmade lace on a handkerchief. A tourist paused to inquire the price of the handkerchief. Then the tourist began to chat. She asked, "Do you live here?"

"No, I live over the hill. Let me tell you what happened last night. As I was walking home a panther followed me. Because I carried a lantern and was walking in the circle of light, I was safe."

"Do you mean the panther would not attack you while you were in the light?" asked the tourist.

"That is right, Madam."

What a lesson this is for Christians. We're safe from harm and evil when we are walking in the light of Christ's presence.

Sharing the Light

One day, a man was walking in the City of Glasgow on a narrow street. The houses were high. Little sunshine ever reached the houses on one side of the street. The man noticed a ragged, barefooted boy, who had a small piece of mirror. With his mirror, he was trying to catch the sun's rays, and shine them on a certain window of one of the houses across the street.

The man asked, "What are you trying to do, laddie?"

"Do you see the window up there?" the boy asked.

"Yes," said the man.

"Well," said the boy, "my little brother had an accident two years ago. He can't walk. He is lying on his back in that room, and I am trying to get some sunshine through the window into his room." That little boy wanted to share the sunshine with his little brother.

The Light Must Shine

On the coast of Normandy, a lighthouse keeper lived with his two children in a lighthouse. One day, the lighthouse keeper went to the shore for provisions. While he was gone, a storm arose. He was unable to return to the lighthouse.

The time for lighting the lamp came. Mary said to her little brother, "We must light the lamp, Billy." The two children climbed the long, narrow stairs to the tower where the lamp was kept. Mary pulled up a chair and tried to reach the lamp in the great reflector, but it was too high for her to reach. She went down the stairs and came back with a small lamp in her hand. "I will hold this up," she said, "so the sailors can see a light." Again, she climbed on the chair, but the reflector was too high to catch the light.

"Get down," said Billy, "I know what to do." Mary jumped down, and Billy got on the chair. "Stand on top of me," he said. Mary stood on the little fellow, and then she raised the little lamp high. The reflector caught its light, and the light shone far out across the water. She held the lamp first with one hand, and then with the other to rest her arms. Then she said to her brother, "Does it hurt you, Billy?" "Of course it hurts," he said, "but we must keep the light burning!"

Are we keeping the light of God's love burning, and shining forth in this dark world, even when it hurts?

A Royal Guest

Two young people were walking along a path in the Catskill Mountains. They were talking about a friend who had a radiant, bright personality. One said, "How do you account for it?"

The other pointed across the river to an old castle. "See that wonderful castle?" he asked. "When I was a small boy, my playmates and I loved to sit on the river bank and look across at it. We could tell what was going on there by the number of lights which were burning. If only the family was present, only a few lights would be seen. When guests were entertained, there were many lights, and the palace became truly beautiful! Once, a member of a royal family visited there, and the whole castle was ablaze with lights. I think the reason our friend has a radiant personality is because she has constantly with her a Royal Guest, Jesus!"

How radiant our lives will be when the Lord Jesus is present!

He Kept on Shining

A little Jewish boy was given a Gospel of John by a missionary. He read it and was so pleased with it that he came back to get one of the other Gospels. Before leaving, he gave his heart to the Lord. A little later, he came back to the missionary with twenty-two cards, signed by his friends, asking for twenty-two Gospels.

When the boy went home, his mother asked, "What is it that makes such a bulk in your pocket?" He told her. She took the Gospels and destroyed them all, and gave the boy a severe beating. But the little boy loved the Lord Jesus. He wanted to keep on shining in the darkness. He went and signed up two more children, and returned to the missionary for twenty-four Gospels.

May we be as anxious to shine for Jesus as was the little Jewish boy.

Where It Is Darkest

A little girl was walking along the street in a great city. She was poor, and hungry, and cold. She saw beautiful light coming from a church building. Going closer, she heard beautiful music. She went in, and sat on a seat near the door of the church. She warmed herself as she listened. The preacher used as his text, "I am the Light of the world"!

At the close of the service, the little girl went to the minister and asked, "Did you say you are the light of the world?" The minister replied, "No, dear child, Jesus Christ is the Light of the world. I am one of His lights." The little girl looked at the minister and said, "Well, sir, I wish you would come down in our alley, because it is awful, awful dark down there'"

The Lord Jesus wants His light to shine where it is darkest!

Rudyard Kipling's Lights

Rudyard Kipling purchased a farmhouse on a mountain slope in an unsettled part of Vermont. One day Kipling and his wife went down the mountain back of their house, walked across the valley, and up onto the next mountain. They came to a little house where a woman lived by herself. "Be you the windows across the valley?" she asked. Then she told them how much comfort she had received from the lights shining from the windows across the valley. Suddenly, she looked afraid and asked, "Be you going to stay and keep your lights burning?"

After that day, the Kiplings always kept the lights shining through the windows at the back of their home. They even took down the shades and curtains so more light could shine out.

Boys and girls, today we ask you the question, "Be you going to keep the lights burning?" We are living in a dark world. The world needs Jesus, "the Light of the world!" Will you let Him shine through you so that His light will fill the dark places? Jesus said, "Let your light so shine before men, that they may see your good works, and glorify your Father which is in Heaven" (*Matt. 5:16*).

"His Lamps Are We"

"His lamps are we,
  To shine where He shall say;
And lamps are not for sunny rooms,
  Nor for the light of day;
But for dark places of the earth,
Where shame and wrong and crime have birth;
And for the murky twilight gray,
Where wandering sheep have gone astray."
— Selected

Light Ahead

A man, who had spent his youth in evil ways, was converted. He became a new creature in Jesus Christ. One day, he met an old pal who had known him during his evil life. The pal mocked him for "turning pious."

The man said, "You know what I am — a lamplighter. I turn the lights on in the evening. Late at night, I turn them off. When I go around turning out the lights, I look back, and all the way behind me is darkness. That is like my past life. When I look in front of me, there is a long row of twinkling lights to guide me, and that is like my future since I have found Jesus. My pathway will be filled with light until I come to the end of the road, and then I will not need any light, because that will be *dawn* for me!"

The Light in His Face

When Adoniram Judson, the great missionary, was home on furlough, he passed through Stonington, Conn. A boy there noticed the stranger. He saw in his face a light which he had never seen before. Suddenly, it dawned on him that the stranger was the famous missionary whose picture he had seen. He ran up the street to the home of the Baptist minister, and asked if he really could have seen Judson. The minister hurried back with the boy to see the stranger. The boy was right. The stranger was Adoniram Judson. The minister talked with the missionary and forgot all about the boy.

Years later that boy, Henry Clay Trumbell, became a famous minister, and wrote a book of memories. One chapter in the book was entitled, "What a Boy Saw in the Face of Adoniram Judson." What had the boy seen in the face of Adoniram Judson? It was a light which comes to those who know intimately the Lord Jesus who is "the Light of the world." That light always comes to the faces which are turned toward Him.

Turning on the Light

The Lord Jesus is the Light of the world. When we tell others about Jesus, then we are turning on the Light! A man was sitting in his living room. It was growing dark outside. A lamp lighter passed by. The man could not see the lamp lighter, but as he watched, he saw the lights down the street coming on. The lamp lighter was turning the lights on. When we see people turning from darkness to light, we know that some one has been telling them of Jesus, the Light of the world.

"To Give Light and to Save Life"

On the coast of England stood the famous Eddystone Lighthouse. On this lighthouse were inscribed the words, "To give light and to save life." How beautifully do these words describe the Lord Jesus! He came to give light and to save life. He wants every one of His followers to do the same. The Bible says, "For ye were sometimes darkness, but *now* are ye light in the Lord: walk as children of light" (*Eph. 5:8*).

Light in New Guinea

A soldier in New Guinea was wounded during combat. That night, a dark stormy night, he was carried down the mountainside through the thick jungle by a group of natives. As they walked through the dark night, the natives sang the Christian's hymn:

"Lead, kindly Light, amid the encircling gloom,
 Lead Thou me on;
 The night is dark, and I am far from home;
 Lead Thou me on!"

The young man, who was a Christian, and a graduate of a Southern univer-
sity, decided that if his life were spared, and he got back to the States when the war was over, he would prepare himself for missionary work. He wanted to go and tell other natives in the Pacific Islands about Jesus, the Light of the world!

Giving the Light to Others

A poor blind woman in Paris put twenty-seven franks in a missionary offering. "You cannot afford so much," said a friend.

"Oh, yes, I can," she replied "I am blind, and I asked my fellow-straw-workers, 'How much money do you spend in a year for oil in your lamp?' And they replied, 'Twenty-seven franks.' So I found that I save that much in a year, because I am blind, and do not need a lamp. I want to give it to shed light in the heathen lands. I want to tell the lost ones of Jesus, the Light of the World."

"A hundred thousand souls a day,
 Are passing one by one away;
   In Christless guilt and gloom,
 Without *one ray* of hope or light,
 With future dark as endless night,
   They're passing to their doom!"

When to Shine

A minister asked a young man, who had recently been saved, "Are you shining for the Lord Jesus?" The young man replied, "Not yet. I have been saved only a short time." The minister said, "When you light a candle, when do you expect it to begin to shine?" The young man replied, "Right away!" Then the minister said, "Go thou and do likewise!" The Lord Jesus wants us to begin to shine and give out His light just as soon as we are saved.

"Blowed Out"

A little girl asked her mother, "How can I shine for Jesus?" The mother replied, "You can shine for Jesus by being kind and loving in the home!" The little girl said, "I am going to shine for Jesus every day." Things went well for awhile. The little girl was kind and loving. Then, one afternoon, she became angry. She said unkind things to her little brother. He began to cry. Mother said, "I thought you were going to shine for Jesus." "Oh," said the little girl; "I was shining for Jesus, but I 'blowed' myself out!" She meant that her light had blown out. She was not shining for Jesus now.

LORD'S DAY

Robbing God

A Chinese preacher wanted to show how we rob God when we fail to keep the Lord's Day for His service and work. The Chinaman said, "It came to pass that a man went to market with a string of seven coins. Seeing a beggar who was asking for alms, he gave the poor man six of his coins. He kept one of the coins for himself. The beggar, instead of being thankful, followed the good man and stole the seventh coin. What an abominable wretch! Yes, and would you, to whom God has given six days, steal the seventh day also?"

One Day to Provide Light

An ancient story is told of seven brothers who lived together. Six of the brothers worked. The seventh stayed at home. He cared for the house and kept it clean. He prepared fine meals, and had the meals ready for his six brothers when they came home.

Then the six brothers decided that the seventh must go to work with them. At night, when the seven brothers returned home, the house was dark. No meal was prepared. Then the six brothers saw how foolish they had been! Quickly they changed back to the old way.

God has given us six days in the week to work. He has given us *one day*, Sunday, the Lord's Day, to provide light, and comfort for the other days. If that day is driven out to work, the other days will miss its blessing. How glad we are that God has given us *one day* in seven to be His special day. On that day we will rejoice and be glad!

The Sunday Stone

In a coal mine in England, there is a stone called, "The Sunday Stone." During the week, when the miners are working, the dust flies about. It gets mixed with the water which trickles over the Sunday Stone, and the stone is coal black in color. Then Sunday comes. The mine is quiet. The dust is not stirred up. Clear water falls over the stone, and soon it is washed clean. There it lays, pure white in color.

God has given us Sunday to wash away the dirt and grime of the world. How glad we are that on Sunday we can spend the hours in God's house, worshipping Him, and serving Him! "It is a good thing to give thanks unto the Lord, and to sing praises unto Thy Name, O most High: to shew forth Thy lovingkindness" *(Ps. 92:1, 2).*

LORD'S SUPPER

The Cap Lining

A little waif of the street was admitted to a children's home. He was given a new outfit. He felt real pride in getting a new suit and new boots. But he refused to wear the new cap. He clung to his old ragged cap. The matron insisted that he take the new cap and give her the old cap. Before handing her the old cap, he tore out the lining and stuffed it into his pocket. "Why did you do that?" asked the matron. Tears came into his eyes, as he answered, "The lining of my old cap was part of my mother's dress. It is all I have got left of her." The lining of the torn cap was merely a piece of faded material, but it was a holy symbol to the boy.

The bread and the wine, of which we partake at the Lord's Table, are holy symbols which help us to remember His death upon the Cross.

Where Her Pride Was

There had been much quarreling and bitterness in a certain church. Finally, a split had taken place. One Sunday morning, a member of the church arose from the family breakfast table. She said that she was going to church. "What?" exclaimed the others in the family; "are you going back there after the way our family has been treated? Where's your pride?" Quietly, the one addressed answered, "This is Communion Sunday. I am going to sit at the Lord's table and remember His death for me. As for my pride, I haven't any when I survey His wondrous Cross!"

The Little Red Shoes

A couple lived happily in their married life. Then sorrow came. Their little girl was suddenly taken from them. Their hearts were filled with grief. As time passed, the husband and wife became estranged from each other. In their bitterness, they separated. The wife went home to her people. The husband wrote several letters, trying to get her to return. But she refused to answer the letters. Then, one day, she wrote and asked him to send her all her belongings in a trunk. When the trunk arrived, and was opened, there, in the very top, lay a pair of little red shoes. When the wife saw them, her heart was filled with memories of their former happy home. She remembered how much she and her husband had loved the little girl who had worn the little red shoes. She remembered how much she and her husband had loved each other. Suddenly, she felt that she could not stand the separation from her husband any longer. She wired him, "Am coming home because of the little red shoes!"

Christ has given us something to remember Him by. When we partake of the Lord's Memorial Supper, we remember how much He loves us and how much He suffered for us upon the cross.

In the Concentration Camp

A Lutheran pastor in Russia was sentenced to ten years of hard labor in a concentration camp, because he refused to become a spy. In the concentration camp were other Christians, whose only offense was their Christian faith.

One day, a Finnish believer in the camp received a package from home, containing a little bread and a few apples. Immediately, he thought, "Now it will be possible to celebrate the Lord's Supper!" He went to the Lutheran pastor, and told him of his plans. He had crushed the apples, making juice in a mug. He had a few pieces of bread. He said, "If the Russian guards see us, they will think we are drinking tea." The Christians sat down near a dirty plank.

The pastor quoted the Scripture about the Lord's Supper. Then, they drank the juice and ate the bread.

The altar was the dirty plank. The pastor and his "flock" were dressed in rags. They had only apple juice and a few pieces of bread. But, as they observed the Lord's Supper, they felt the presence of Christ, and their hearts were filled with great happiness!

LOVE FOR OTHERS

Love for the Sinful

A poor woman was being led from the police court. She was dirty. She was crying. A Christian woman saw her. Her heart was filled with the love of Christ. She went up to the poor woman and kissed her. The poor woman had not been shown kindness or love for years. It broke her hard, sinful heart when the good Christian woman showed love for her. It was not long before she came to the Christian woman's Saviour!

Love a Little Harder

A young woman, who had left home because her father was a drunkard, decided to return home. She wanted to win her father to Christ. Someone asked, "What will you do when he finds fault with everything you do?" "Try a little harder," she answered. "What will you do when he is unreasonable and unkind, and you are tempted to lose your temper and answer him angrily?" "Pray a little harder," was the answer. "What will you do if he strikes you like he used to do? Will you leave him again?" "Love him a little harder," came the answer.

No Love in Heathenism

In Japan, there lived a young man who was a carpenter. He was a Buddhist, which means that he worshipped the false god, Buddha, and not the true God. Some one invited him to go to a Christian church. He went. He did not understand the service. He did not know how to find the hymns in the book. His neighbor, a complete stranger, bowed and smiled at him, and then took his book and helped him find the hymns. The young man liked the preaching. He liked the singing. He liked the kindness shown him. He went back to the Christian church again and again. Then he thought that he must return the kindness. So he asked a Christian friend what presents he ought to give to his new friends. He was surprised to hear that no presents were needed; that love and kindness are part of the Christian religion. He said, "How different this is from my religion. There is no love in my religion!" The young carpenter was won to Jesus because the followers of Jesus were loving and kind. Will you not be loving and kind to everyone? You may help win some soul to Jesus in this way.

They Love a Fellow

A little street urchin in Chicago used to go many, many blocks across the frozen streets of the great city to attend Mr. Moody's Sunday School. On his way, he passed many churches and Sunday Schools. Someone asked him, "Why do you go so many blocks every Sunday to attend Sunday School? Why don't you go to a church near-by?" The little boy replied, "I go to Mr. Moody's Sunday School because they *love* a fellow over there." Lost souls all around us are looking for love. They long for love. If we show it to them in our words and in our deeds, we may be able to win them for Christ.

The Cure for Fear

A man, visiting a lighthouse, asked the keeper, "Are you not afraid to live here? This is such a lonely place!" "Oh, no," replied the keeper, "I am not afraid. We never think of *ourselves* here. We only think of keeping our lamps burning brightly, and our reflectors clear, so that those in danger may be *saved!*" How wonderful it is to forget *self*, and to think *only* of *Christ* and *others!* A college boy said, "Christ is *first*; others are second; and I am third."

The Badge of Love

The other day, we saw a little girl wearing a button badge on her dress. This little button badge showed that the little girl was a member of a girls' club. The Lord Jesus wants *all* His followers to wear "the badge of love." When people see how we love others, then they will *know* that we love Jesus and follow His commandment.

Love Won

The father of a certain home was a drunkard. His loved ones criticized him; they scolded him; they pelted him with harsh words, because he drank. There was *one* in the family, however, who never had harsh words for the father. It was his little boy. His little boy *loved him*. He never seemed to notice that he got drunk.

One day, in midwinter, the father received the message that his little boy had been hurt. He hurried home as fast as he could go. He found the little boy suffering greatly. The doctor had said that the little boy could not live. The father bent over his little boy and said, "My little boy is better. He will soon be well!" The little boy whispered, "No, Papa, I will not get well!" The father protested, as he said, "You will get well, and I will be a good man and change my ways'" The little boy whispered feebly again. The father bent low to catch what he said. The little boy's arms went around the father's neck as he said, "When I am gone, Papa, I want you to remember that I *loved you*, even if you did get drunk!"

That sentence broke the father's heart! He went out of the little cottage, sobbing. It was only a few moments before he had yielded himself to the Saviour. *Love* had *won* when scolding and criticism and harsh words had *failed!*

What Is Love?

A young woman visited the office of the editor of a magazine. She had with her a number of poems which she had written. She wanted them published in the magazine. "What are the poems about?" asked the editor. "All about love," she replied. "Well, what is love?" asked the editor. The young woman looked up with a dreamy expression in her eyes, and said, "Love is gazing on a lily pond at night, by the shimmering moonbeams, when the lilies are in full bloom."

"Stop! Stop!" cried the editor; "you are all *wrong*. I will tell you what love is. It is getting up *cheerfully* out of a warm bed on a cold winter morning at 2 A. M., to fill hot water bottles for ailing children. That's *love!*"

Real love for God and for others is *shown* when we put our love in action. It is not enough for us to talk about love. We *must*, boys and girls, *show* our love by our *good deeds!*

LOVE OF GOD

"Deeper Than That"

When Nansen, the explorer, tried to measure the depth of the ocean in the far north, he took a long measuring line. He discovered that his line would not touch bottom, and he wrote in his record, "Deeper than that!" The next day, he tried a longer line, and again he wrote, "Deeper than that!" Finally, he fastened all his lines together and let them down, but his record said, "Deeper than that!" He never found out how deep the ocean was at that point. He only knew that it was deeper than so many thousand feet.

God's love is so broad and so deep that we can never know its greatness. We like these verses from Ephesians: "That Christ may dwell in your hearts by faith; that ye, being rooted and grounded in love, may be able to comprehend with all saints what is the breadth, and length, and depth, and height; and to know the love of Christ, which passeth knowledge" *(Eph. 3:17-19)*.

"He Can't Take His Eyes Off You"

A little boy went one day to see an old lady. She asked him to read a motto on the wall. The motto said, "Thou God seest me." Then she said to him, "When you are older, people may tell you that God is watching you to see what you do wrong. I want you to take the motto home with you. I want you to remember all your life that God loves you so much He cannot take His eyes off you!"

"To write the love of God above
Would drain the ocean dry;
Nor could the scroll contain the whole,
Though stretched from sky to sky!"

Waiting to Bless Us

How glad we are that while we were yet sinners, God loved us. Long before we loved Him, He loved us, and planned to shower His blessings upon us.

A man once gave this remarkable testimony: "I got off at the Pennsylvania Depot one day as a tramp. For a year, I begged on the streets for a living. One day, I touched a man on the shoulder, and said, 'Mister, please give me a dime.' As soon as I saw his face I recognized my old father! 'Father, don't you know me?' I asked. Throwing his arms around me, he cried, 'I have found you! I have found you! All I have is yours.' Men, think of it! I, a tramp, stood there begging my father for ten cents, when, for many years, he had been looking for me, longing to give me *all* he had!" Such is the love of God!

Why God Keeps Us

A minister asked a little four-year-old girl, "Are you worth anything?" "No," she said. Then he asked, "Why does Mother keep you, then?" The little girl said, "Oh, I will tell you why: Mamma loves me!" We do not know why God loves us; but He *does* love us. How thankful we are for His wondrous love! Because He loves us, we love Him. The Bible says, "We love Him, because He first loved us."

God's Loving Kindness

A little boy told what loving-kindness means. He said, "If mother gives me a piece of bread with butter on it when I am hungry, that is kindness. But if she puts jam on top of it, that is *loving-kindness!*"

God shows loving-kindness to us. David said, "It is a good thing to give thanks unto the Lord, and to sing praises unto Thy Name; . . . to show forth Thy lovingkindness in the morning, and Thy faithfulness every night" *(Ps. 92:1,2)*; "Bless the Lord, O my soul; and forget not all His benefits: who forgiveth *all* thine iniquities; who healeth *all* thy disease; . . . who crowneth thee with lovingkindness and tender mercies" *(Ps. 103:1-4)*.

We Can Love Him

One day, there was great excitement in an orphanage. A lady had come to take little Jane home with her. In gentle tones, the lady asked Jane, "Do you want to go with me and be my little girl?"

Timidly Jane replied, "I don't know."

"I am going to give you beautiful clothes, and I have a lot of things for you. You will have a room of your own. In the room is a nice bed, and a little table, and chairs, and a doll in a buggy. Don't you want to go with me?"

Little Jane was silent for a moment, and then she asked, "But what can I do?"

The lady said, "You can love me!"

Quickly, Jane ran forward into the lady's arms. She could love her new mamma!

"I Love Him so Much"

In India, a young American girl was telling the story of Christ to a group of high class Hindu women. Each morning, she told them a chapter in the life of Christ, as the women sat in their apartment working over their embroidery frames. Finally, she came to the story of His death on the Cross. Quietly, she related what happened. Presently, she heard the sound of sobs coming from a young girl nearby. Quickly, she went to her and knelt by her side, asking gently, "What is the trouble? Are you ill? Are you in pain?"

As tears rained down her face, the Hindu girl answered with sobs, "Oh, I cannot bear it! I cannot bear to hear another word! He suffered so much! And you said it was for *me*. I cannot bear it! I love Him so much!"

When the American girl told about it afterwards, she said, "I never knew till that moment how *little* I had loved my Saviour." Have *you* ever thanked the Lord Jesus for dying for *you?*

He First Loved Us

A little girl went to talk to a minister. She was troubled, because she did not love Jesus. She wanted to love Jesus, but somehow she felt that she couldn't. The minister said, "My dear little girl, don't think about your love for Jesus. Think about His love for *you!* Keep saying over and over, 'Jesus loves me.' Say it many, many times. Then, come and see me to-morrow."

The little girl came back to the minister the next day. Her face was shining with happiness. "Oh," said she, "now I love Jesus. How can I help but love Him?"

Surely, when we think upon the love of Christ for us, we will love Him, too. The Bible says, "We love Him, because He first loved us."

God Loves Sinners

When Dr. Ironside was a little boy, he heard a missionary from Africa talk. The missionary said, "Boys, I want to tell you what I preach to the people in Africa. How many of you boys are good boys?" Not one boy raised his hand. "Well," said the missionary, "since you are not good boys, I can give you the same message that I give to the people in Africa: God loves naughty boys; God loves sinners." Little Harry Ironside thought, "That missionary is surely getting mixed up." Little Harry had heard people say, "If you are *good*, God will love you." But the missionary was right! God loves sinners! The Bible says, "God commendeth His love toward us, in that, while we were yet sinners, Christ died for us."

With All Her Heart

A little girl knelt to say her evening prayer. Her mother often suggested things for her to pray about. This evening, the mother asked, "Why don't you ask the Lord Jesus to help you to love Him more?" The little girl replied, "Oh, Mother, I *do* love Him. I love Him with *all* my heart right now!" Do you love Jesus?

The Greatest Is Love

An aged Christian lay dying in Edinburgh. A friend called to say farewell. The dying man said, "I have had three other visitors today. With two of them, I have parted. The third I shall keep with me forever! The first was Faith, and I said, 'Good-by, Faith. I thank God for your company ever since I first trusted Christ, but I am going now where Faith is lost in sight.' The second was Hope. I said, 'Farewell, Hope. You have helped me many times in the hour of battle and distress, but now I shall not need you. I am going where Hope is fulfilled, where Hope passes into fruition.' The last was Love. I said, 'Love, you have been my friend for a long time. You have linked me with God, and with my fellow men. You have comforted me and gladdened me all during my earthly pilgrimage. Now, I cannot leave you behind. You must go with me unto the City of God, for Love is perfected in Heaven.'"

The Bible says, "And now abideth faith, hope, [love], these three; but the greatest of these is [love]" *(I Cor. 13:13)*.

How She Passed the Time

An old lady was alone most of the day. Some one asked, "What do you do during the day?" She said, "I get my hymnbook, and I sing a little hymn of praise to God. Then I get my Bible and read it. God speaks to me when I read His Word. When I am tired of reading, and tired of singing His praises, I just sit still, and *let the Lord love Me!*"

"I Can't Tell That Part"

In Korea, an aged woman was telling a missionary what she knew about Jesus. With shining face, she told about His birth, and about His life. She told how He fed the hungry, healed the sick, raised the dead, blessed the little children. Then, she came to the account of His death upon the Cross. When she started to tell how the nails were driven into His hands and feet, she broke down and began to sob as if her heart would break. Midst her sobs she said, "I can't tell that part. It breaks my heart. Oh, how I love Him!" It was the death of Christ on the Cross which had drawn the aged Korean woman to the Saviour. She loved Jesus, because Jesus gave His life on the Cross for her.

All Alike

A weary teacher fell asleep and had a dream. She dreamed that a message came, saying that the Master was coming to visit her class. She had to get all the little children ready for His visit. She arranged them on benches, putting the little white children first, nearest to where the Master would stand. Behind them, she placed the little yellow, red, and brown children. Far back, she placed the black children. When all were arranged, she looked at them. The arrangement did not seem quite right to her. Why should the black children be so far away? She started to rearrange the children. Just then, the Master appeared! In confusion, she looked up at Him. Then her eyes rested on the children, and she saw that in His presence, *all* shades of color had disappeared! In His presence *all* were *alike!*

How glad we are that *all* are alike before God. We are all sinners in His sight, until we believe in the Lord Jesus. Then we are *all* saints in His sight, saved by His grace alone.

Brothers in Christ

High up in the mountains of Peru, a missionary and a native pastor came upon a group of crude Indian huts. No one was at home. The Indians were away gathering coffee. Looking in one of the huts, the missionary saw a Bible and a hymnbook. He knew immediately that these Indians had heard the Gospel, and that some of them were his brothers and sisters in Christ. Presently, the Indians returned. Their faces showed dismay when they saw the strangers in their little village. The missionary called out to them, "We are your brothers!" Instantly, the Indians began to smile. They hurried into their homes. They got their Bibles and hymnbooks. They gathered around the missionary and the native pastor. They sang Gospel songs together, and prayed, and read God's Word.

The Ground Is Level

At a reception of members in Calvary Baptist Church, Washington, D. C., some years ago, Dr. Greene, the pastor, received into the church on a Sunday morning the Honorable Charles Evans Hughes, a Chinaman, and a washerwoman. As the pastor stood before this unusual group, he said, "My friends, I will have you to notice that at the Cross of Christ, the ground is level!"

The Bible says: "There is neither Jew nor Greek, there is neither bond nor free, there is neither male nor female: for ye are *all one* in Christ Jesus" *(Gal. 3:28)*.

"He Loves Everyone"

In Africa, a missionary told a native boy about Jesus. He told how Jesus was crucified upon the Cross to save us from sin. The little African boy said, "God will save you white people, but not us poor, black Africans." "Yes, He will save you," came the quick reply. "God is no respecter of persons. He loves everyone. The Lord Jesus died for every one!" "Then," said the little black boy, "I'll accept Him as my Saviour!" And the little black boy became an ardent, faithful Christian! Thank God, that the Gospel of the grace of God is a *"whosoever will"* Gospel!

Jesus Loves All the Children

A little Mexican girl attended Bible school in a church in Texas. She heard about the Lord Jesus. She gave her heart to Him. She felt that there was some difference between her and the little white children in the Bible school. Sometimes, the little white children were unkind to her. One day, she went to the superintendent of the school and asked, "Does the Lord Jesus love the little white children more than He loves the Mexican children?" She was assured that it was not true. She was told that the Lord Jesus loves *all* the little children in the world, "black, brown, yellow, red, and white!" She marched out of the church, and soon returned with four other Mexican children, saying, "I wasn't going to bring them to Bible school until I knew that Jesus loves them, too!"

Jesus Loves the Lowly Ones

John E. Clough went to India to preach the Gospel. The high Brahmans were moved. They were willing to hear more about Christ. Then, the low Telugus desired also to hear the Gospel. The high Brahmans did not like this. "You must have nothing to do with those low people," they said to the missionary. "If you help them, you can't teach our children. And we will not listen to your preaching."

What was the missionary to do? Mr. Clough prayed, and read his Bible. He read in the Bible this verse: "But God chose the foolish things of the world, that He might put to shame them that are wise; and God chose the weak things of the world, that He might put to shame the things that are strong" *(I Cor. 1:27, R.V.)*. Missionary Clough had his answer. He must preach the Gospel to the poor and lowly ones. Day after day, he went among the poor, telling them of Jesus Christ, the Saviour. Before a year had passed, ten thousand of the low Telugus confessed faith in Christ as their Saviour!

MISSIONS

Sacrifice

Alexander Duff was a missionary to India for many years. Near the end of his life he went to Edinburgh, Scotland. There he spoke to a great convention. For two and a half hours he held the audience spell-bound while he told about his work on the mission field. He told about the trials and hardships and victories. Suddenly he fainted away and had to be carried off the platform. In a few moments he revived and called out, "Take me back. I must finish my message." His friends protested, saying, "You will die if you go back." He answered, "I will die if I don't go back."

Again Alexander Duff stood before the large audience. He said to them, "Have you no more sons to send to India? When Queen Victoria asks for soldiers, you gladly offer your sons. Christ is asking for missionaries, and you are saying, 'We have no sons to send.' If there are no sons to go, then I will go back. I will let the people in India know that there is one Scotchman who is willing to die to bring the gospel light to those who sit in heathen darkness."

A Dead Church

An artist was asked to paint a picture of a dead church. To the surprise of many he did not paint an old, tottering ruin. Instead he painted a beautiful, modern building. Just within the grand entrance, he placed an offering box bearing the words, "For Missions." Over the slot through which the gifts to missions should have gone, he painted a huge cobweb.

How dead is the church which gives nothing for missions.

No Birthday Party

Every year, a young girl was given five dollars for a birthday party. One year she had been reading about the condition of the people in the far-away lands, who are lost and without hope, because they had never heard the Gospel. Going to her mother, she said, "Mother, I want to do without the birthday party this year. Won't you allow me to give the five dollars to help send a missionary to some of the lost ones far away?"

The mother gladly gave her consent. Her heart was filled with joy because her little girl wanted to help send the Gospel message to others.

God's Second Best

There was once a young girl to whom the Lord was good. She had a fine home, Christian parents, and an opportunity for an education. God had given her special talent, but she did not appreciate the talent, or try to develop it. One day, she felt a clear, definite call to the mission field, but she did not obey it. She married, and had a family.

As the years passed by, heavy cares fell upon the girl's shoulders. Then, one day, there came into her heart a longing to forge ahead for Jesus. She longed to give her life in service on the mission field. But it was *too late*. Home ties and cares held her close. So now, she must be grateful for God's *second best* for her life. She must be happy to do the little things for Him day by day. All the time, however, she is regretful, because she did not enter the door of service, and seize the opportunities when she was young.

Eighty-three Souls a Minute

There was a motto placed over the clock in a certain church. The motto read, "Eighty-three a minute!" It meant that every minute eighty-three souls, who have never heard of Jesus Christ, the Saviour, are passing into eternity. One of the members of the church said, "Can't we take the motto down? It haunts me!"

Surely, none of us can be happy over the fact that so many precious souls go into eternity without hearing about the Saviour. "Neither is there salvation in any other: for there is none other Name under Heaven given among men, whereby we must be saved" *(Acts 4:12).*

Minding Jesus

A Christian man from Korea came to America. He was asked to speak in a meeting on the Christian's duty of sending the Gospel to the heathen. He asked, "Do not the Christians know that Christ has told them to do it?" "Oh, yes," was the answer, "the Christians know that Christ has given them this work to do. But if you will speak to them, they will be more interested." "No, no," said the Korean Christian, "if they do not mind Jesus Christ, they will not mind me."

Neesima

Over in Japan there lived a little boy who was named Neesima. For a long time, Neesima believed what his father told him about the idols. He believed that the idols would take care of him if he gave them offerings and worshipped them. He believed that the idols would punish him if he did not worship them. Then Neesima began to think about the idols. He looked at the idols in his home and saw that they were made by man. He watched them, and saw that they could not eat, talk, see, smell, hear, or do anything. They did not eat the rice or drink the tea that was placed before them.

Neesima began to lose faith in the idols. He bought an idol and buried it in a corner of the garden. Neesima said, "If it comes up out of the dark hole, I will still believe. But if it does not come up, I will never pray to an idol again." The idol did not come up. It stayed in the dark hole. Then, Neesima did not believe in the idol as a god. He did not worship idols anymore. How happy he was when a missionary told him about the true and living God.

Waiting

Over in India, a man came to a missionary. He said, "My village is three miles away. We no longer worship idols. We want the Jesus religion. Come with me. The whole village is waiting for your coming!" Then there came to the missionary a second man and a third man, begging the missionary to come to their villages and tell the people of Jesus. A fourth man stepped forward and said to the missionary, "Sahib, this is the fourth year that I have come to you. Every time you have sent me away sorrowing. The people of my village long for the Gospel. O Sahib, give me a message of hope this time!" With a breaking heart, the missionary said, "Your village is eight miles away. I have no teacher to send to you. Be patient another year. Perhaps, then, I shall have a teacher to send to you. He will tell you of Jesus."

How sad we are that there are not enough missionaries to tell the hungry multitudes about Jesus. All around the world there are millions waiting to hear of Jesus. They are hungry in their hearts. They long for the satisfying Bread of Life, Jesus! Hasten to give Jesus to the hungry ones, before it is too late!

Obeying God's Command

A missionary in India was seated at the dining table in a hotel with a naval officer, an infantry major and his wife, and a sergeant-major and his wife. The naval officer asked, "Why don't you missionaries stay home, and mind your own business?"

The missionary replied, "If you were ordered to take your battleship to Constantinople tomorrow, would you stay here and mind your own business?"

The naval officer's eyes flashed as he said, "If we were ordered to go, we would go, even if every ship were sunk and every sailor were killed in carrying out the orders!"

The missionary said, "You are quite right, my friend. I have orders from the Divine Government to go and preach the Gospel to *every creature*, and I *must* go and obey the command of my Lord, no matter what happens'"

God's Messenger

Dan Crawford was traveling through the tall grass of Africa, accompanied by a native. The native said, "You are angry." Dan Crawford asked, "Why do you say so?" The reply was, "Because you are silent. In our language, we say a man is angry if he is silent. God must be angry with us, too, because He is silent. God is silent."

Dan Crawford was cut to the heart. He knew that God was not silent. God wanted the Gospel to be given to the lost ones in Africa. Dan Crawford went to work translating the New Testament into the language of His African fellow traveler. He built schoolhouses, where the people could be taught to read the Word of God. Then, they knew that God was not silent, for God spoke to them through His Word, and through His messenger, Dan Crawford!

How terrible it is if we, like Jonah, disobey God, and fail to give God's message to the lost ones. How terrible it is if we go about our *own* work, our *own* pleasures, and neglect the lost ones!

The Reversed Version

A young man, before going to the foreign field as a missionary, engaged in colportage work in the homeland. He went to the farmhouses to sell Bibles, and helpful religious books. Often, he gave away the Bibles, and the books if a family was too poor to buy them. At one farm he was met at the door by an old lady. "May I sell you a Bible, madam?" he asked. "Bless you," she replied; "we have more Bibles in this house now than we ever use. We have the Old Testament Bible, the New Testament Bible, the Holy Bible, and the Reversed Version Bible." The old lady should have said, "The Revised Version Bible."

The young missionary thought, "How many Christians must read the 'Reversed Version.' When God's Word says: 'Go ye into all the world', they stay at home. When He says, 'Give' and 'Send' the Gospel to all the world, they think it says, 'Keep the Gospel here. You have enough to do at home. Don't bother to help the lost ones in the regions beyond.'"

Not Miserly with God

A godly Quaker was much moved when he heard a missionary say, "If I were in the homeland again, I would gladly live in one room, make my bed on the floor, and use a box for my chair and another for my table, rather than have the heathen perish for lack of the knowledge of Christ."

The Quaker was so impressed that he lived for years according to what the missionary said. His income was large, but he used just one room, did his own cooking, and wore shabby clothes. Those who knew him called him a miser, but he paid out five thousand dollars to make it possible for two missionaries to go to the Congo, and he paid for the first mission school on the upper Congo River. He sent two missionaries to Assam, and gave largely to other missions as well! All of this was done by *one* man who gladly sacrificed to send the Gospel to the lost multitudes in the gions beyond.' "

A Village Blessed by God

Mrs. Howard Taylor in her biography of Pastor Hsi tells how this earnest Christian taught his fellow villagers that they should worship and serve only the Lord God. The people in the village were suspicious of Hsi when he became a Christian, but soon his careful, upright life won their respect. The time came when they must choose a village elder to be responsible for collecting the taxes, the care of the temple, and other public duties. They asked Hsi to become the elder. He tried to decline, but the office was forced upon him. He accepted the office on two conditions: First, that he would have nothing to do with the temple sacrifices, and would pray only to the true God; secondly, that no one in the village, during his tenure of office, would worship the gods in the temple, or bring gifts to them. Finally, the citizens agreed to his terms. The temple was closed. Hsi then prayed to the *true* God that He would bless the village.

At the end of the year, it was found that the village had never been more prosperous. Hsi was again elected the elder, or head man, of the village. He again accepted the office on the same terms. He prayed that the true God would continue His blessings upon the people and village. Harvests were good. Peace prevailed. Every one had plenty! For three years, Hsi was head man of the village. The temple remained closed. There was no worship of false gods.

At the end of the three years, Hsi refused to be head man again, for he wanted to give his *whole* time to Christian work. When he gave up the office, he said to the people, "By this time, the idols must be starved to death. Spare yourselves any efforts to revive them!" The people gladly heeded his words. They knew that it was the true and living God and not the idols who had blessed their village.

MOTHERS

"Mother, I Love You"

A pleasant-faced Mother got on the street-car one day with her two small sons. The car was crowded because it was the busy noon hour. The smaller boy sat by his mother on one side of the car. The older boy took a seat opposite. He looked out of the window and then he glanced across at his mother. At length he called softly, "Mother." There was no answer. Then he called a bit louder, "Mother." This time Mother looked over at him and smiled. The little boy's eyes shone and he said, "Mother, I love you." The mother smiled radiantly back at him. All over the car, men and women smiled at each other. The street car had become a place of blessing because a little boy had said, "Mother, I love you."

Showing Love for Mother

"I love you, Mother," said little John;
Then, forgetting his work, his cap went on
And he was off to the garden swing
And she had the wood and water to bring.

"I love you, Mother," said rosy Nell;
"I love you more than tongue can tell."
Then she teased and pouted half the day,
Till her mother was glad when she went to play.

"I love you, Mother," said little Nan;
"Today I'll help you all I can;
My doll and playthings I know will keep!"
Then she rocked the baby fast asleep.

Then, stepping softly, she brought the broom,
And swept the floor and tidied the room;
Busy and happy all day was she,
Helpful and good as a child could be.

"I love you, Mother," again they said,
Three little children going to bed.
How do you think the mother guessed
Which of them really loved her best?

—Oliver Plants

No Concern for Mother

A young girl went out to the suburb to spend the day with friends. It was hot and sultry, but she looked sweet and cool and dainty in her thin summer dress. As she sat talking with her friends, she said, "Mamma is not at all well lately. No, thank you; I don't need a fan; I am quite comfortable. I'm quite worried about mother."

"Why didn't you bring her with you? This country air would do her a world of good."

"Oh, she couldn't come today. She's very busy. She has a big ironing to do. She always has big ironings in the summer. And then, as you know, I'm going to the seashore soon and Mamma has a lot of sewing to do for me. She has several dresses to make, beside some other things." Then the girl proceeded to tell her friends about the beautiful dresses Mamma was going to make for her. Her friends were busy with their own thoughts. You can guess what they were.

Not Ashamed of Mother

In the mountains of Georgia there lived a poor widow. She had a few acres of ground on which she raised berries and a few other things. She kept a few chickens and sold some eggs. She took in washings and did any other humble work she could do for a living. God had given her a bright son. He did unusually good work in the district school. One day he told his mother that God wanted him to be a preacher. Then mother decided that he must go to college. The son worked hard and mother helped him. Together they got enough to pay his college expenses. Finally, the time came for him to graduate. He was graduating with honors. Before graduation he went to the mountain home and said, "Mother, you must come and see me graduate." "No," said the Mother. "I have nothing fit to wear and you would be ashamed of your poor old mother before all those grand people." The son's eyes filled with tears as he said, "Ashamed of you? Mother, I will never be ashamed of you. I owe everything I am to you. If you do not come, I will not graduate." Finally the mother yielded. When the graduation day came, she went to the commencement exercises in a plain calico dress. Around her shoulders was a faded shawl. On her head was a simple mountain bonnet. She refused to sit near the front, but found a seat way off under the gallery.

The graduating address was delivered. The son received his diploma along with the other graduates. Then he was called to the platform to receive a gold medal for special excellence in study. No sooner had he received the gold medal than he walked down from the platform and went way back to his mother where she sat under the gallery. He pinned the gold medal on her faded shawl and said, "Mother, this medal belongs to you; you earned it."

In Mother's Heart

A little girl was sitting on her mother's lap. She was very fond of her mother. She called her, her "very own mother," like one who rejoices over a precious treasure. As she sat on mother's lap, she touched the features of her mother's face with her little fingers — her lips, her eyes, her cheeks, and her hair. After awhile she asked, "Mummy, can I see your heart?" The mother replied, "Look in my eyes and see if you can see anything." The little girl climbed up and peered in her mother's eyes and then cried out joyfully, "Oh, Mummy, I can see your heart, and in it there is a wee little girl, and it's me."

She Died For Her Boy T/5/62

A man went west to seek his fortune. He left his wife and son in New England. Soon he succeeded in the west and wrote for his loved ones to come and join him. How happy the wife's heart was. She and the boy went to New York and boarded a Pacific steamer sailing for San Francisco. When they were far out at sea, one day there was a cry of "Fire!" On board the ship there was a Powder Magazine. The captain knew that the moment the fire reached the powder magazine there would be a great explosion and all on board would perish. Life boats were launched. They proved to be too small and too few. Quickly they were overcrowded. As the last life boat was being pushed away, the mother pleaded with the boatman to take her and her boy. He replied, "No, I dare not take another. If I do the boat will sink and all in it will perish." She continued to plead and at last the boatmen consented to take one more. Do you think the mother leaped into the boat leaving her boy to perish with the others on the steamer? No, she seized him, gave him one last hug, and dropped him into the boat. She said to him, "My boy, if you live to see your father, tell him that I died in your place." That boy never spoke slightingly of the mother who went down to a watery grave for him. He always spoke of her with love and tenderness.

"Mother Has Been Praying"

A terrible gale was raging along the coast of England. Many vessels were wrecked. During the height of the storm the *Rising Sun* struck a reef and sank. Only two top masts were left above the dashing and foaming waves. On the shore, life-lines were attached to rockets to be shot out to the men who were clinging to the swaying masts. Before the life-line could be adjusted, one of the masts fell. Just as the rocket bearing the life-line went booming over the water, the other mast fell. The men on shore who had sent out the rocket sadly began to draw in the life-line. Suddenly they felt that something was attached to it. In a few minutes they hauled up on the beach the limp body of a sailor boy. Trained and tender hands worked over him and in a short time he became conscious. Amazed, the boy looked around at the crowd. Then he looked into the weather-beaten face of an old fisherman near him and asked, "Where am I?"

"You are safe, my lad."

"Where's the captain?'

"Drowned, my lad."

"Where's the mate?"

"He's drowned too."

"Where's the crew?"

"They are all lost, my lad. You are the only one saved."

The boy stood to his feet. Raising both hands above his head, he cried out, "My mother has been praying for me." Then he dropped on his knees on the wet sand and put his face in his hands as he sobbed out loud.

How He Loved Mother

A little boy declared that he loved his mother "with all his strength." Someone asked, "What do you mean?" He said, "Well, I will tell you. You see, we live on the fourth floor of an apartment house, and there is no elevator. The coal is kept down in the basement. Mother is busy all the time. She isn't very strong. So I see to it that the coal box is never empty. I carry coal up four flights of stairs all by myself. It takes all my strength to get it up. Now, isn't that loving my mother with *all* my strength?"

A Praying Mother

A preacher was holding some meetings in a country church. He was staying in the home of one of the families. One day, the mother in the home said, "Why are not my boys saved?" The preacher said, "Did you ever take them aside and tell them about Jesus, and pray for their salvation?" The mother said, "No." The preacher said, "You must tell them of Jesus. You must pray for them. You must be burdened for them!'

That night, the mother could not sleep. All night long, she prayed for her boys. She wanted them to be saved. She shed many tears as she prayed. The next morning, the boys said, "Mother, we heard you praying for us last night. We heard you crying and asking God to save us. Mother, we are giving our hearts to Jesus now!"

Mother's Translation

A Bible teacher was telling his class about the different translations of the Bible. The class was greatly interested. One in the class liked the King James version. Another in the class liked the Revised version. Then a young man said, "I prefer my mother's translation of the Bible!" Then he explained what he meant. He said, "My mother has translated the Bible into the language of daily living for me ever since I was old enough to understand it. She has translated it straight, too, and given it *full* meaning each day. Daily, she has lived her life according to the Bible. Whatever printed version of the Bible I may study, it is my mother's translation that has helped clear all my difficulties and doubts!"

A Mother's Influence

Evangelistic singer, F. A. Mills, had a wonderful Christian mother. She raised her children in a Christian home. When she died, Mr. Mills sang at her funeral:

"O, Mother, when I think of thee,
'Tis but a step to Calvary,
Thy gentle hand upon my brow,
Is leading me to Jesus now!"

A Spirit-taught Mother

In the southern part of Argentina, a soldier, in a little town, heard singing. It came from a little mission hall which he entered. There, he heard the Gospel preached. He stayed after the service and spoke to the missionary who asked him if he were a Christian. "Yes, I'm a Christian," he replied. "Where did you hear the Gospel?" the missionary asked. "From my mother. She lives a long way off, but will you come and see her? She has never heard a preacher and she will be so glad to see you!"

The missionary visited the aged Christian woman on the distant farm. No missionary had ever been there before. The aged mother told the missionary that many years before a colporteur had passed that way. He had given her a copy of the Word of God. She had read it. She came to know Jesus Christ as her Saviour. The Spirit of God was her *only* Teacher. She had fourteen children. She began to read the Word of God to them, and to teach them. At the time the missionary visited her, the youngest child was twelve years old. Every one of the children had been won to Christ.

The missionary had the joy of baptizing the *whole family!* That night, he sat with the family in the humble cottage. They read the Word of God together, and then he heard the aged mother open up the treasures of the Word, as she had been taught them by the Holy Spirit!

NATURE

A Lesson from a Watermelon

How beautiful is a piece of watermelon with its green and white rind, its luscious red meat, and black seeds. How tiny are the seeds! It would take about 5,000 of them to weigh a pound. Yet one of them can grow a forty pound melon. When the seed is placed in the ground, it is warmed by the sun and watered by the rain. Soon a miracle happens. A tiny green shoot appears above ground. It begins to gather the material needed to make a watermelon. It covers the outside with a coat of beautiful green. Just inside it puts a layer of white. Within is placed a core of red which is given a wonderful sweet flavor. All through the red core are placed little seeds, each of which is capable of producing more watermelons. I cannot explain everything about a watermelon, but I can enjoy eating it. We know that God's power is behind the watermelon. Only God could produce a watermelon. In the Bible are many miracles which we cannot explain. But we know that God's power is behind the miracles. Only God could produce them.

A Twittering Canary

A man had a sweet singing canary. When spring came he felt sorry for the bird and he hung its cage out on the porch where it could enjoy the sunshine and fresh air. In the trees near the house were many English sparrows. The canary kept listening to the sparrows as they went, "Twitter, twitter." In the fall when the man brought his canary back into the house he found that it had lost its sweet song. The canary had spent the summer in bad company and now all it would sing was, "Twitter, twitter, twitter."

Sometimes Christians who have had a beautiful testimony for Jesus, have lost their testimony because they have kept bad company. It is not good for Christians to stay in the company of sinners.

God's Handiwork

Someone asked a great scientist if he were not lonely when he was away on some mountain side, studying the stars. He replied, "Oh, no, I am never lonely. When I look at the stars, I think of God.

The heavens are God's handiwork. They tell me of His power. They tell me of His nearness!"

Comfort From A Strawberry Plant

A man visited a poor old woman who lived in an attic in the city. He noticed the bare floor and the cracked window. Then he saw on the window sill in a broken teapot a strawberry plant growing. He said, "Your plant is growing nicely. You will soon have strawberries from it."

"Oh, sir," she replied, "I prize it not for the fruit that will come on it, for there won't be much, but for the comfort that it gives me. I am too poor to keep a pet and it is so nice to have a living plant. Day by day it tells me that God is near."

Nature Worshippers

A young boy liked to take hikes in the green fields. Often he hiked on Sunday. His minister told him that he should not forsake God's House on the Lord's Day.

"Can't I worship God in the green fields?" the boy asked.

"Certainly you can," was the answer, "but you don't."

Nature reveals God to us in His power and glory. But nature alone cannot lead us to God.

The Spider

Little Mary was sewing as she sat on the doorstep. She was making a patch for a quilt. Her thread kept knotting, and then her needle broke. Her eyes filled with tears and she cried out, "I can't do it. I can't."

Mother came and told her to look at the spider which was spinning a web on a rose vine nearby. Every time the spider spun a nice thread and tried to fasten it to a branch, the wind blew and tore it away. But the spider kept on trying. Finally it made a thread that did not break and fastened it to the branch. Then it spun other threads to join it.

Mother said to Mary, "What a patient spider that is!"

Mary smiled and took up her work and when the sun went down that day there was a beautiful spider's web in the rose vine and a beautiful patch in Mary's sewing basket.

Changing Clothes

One day a little boy was in the garden with his father. They were watching a little toad. Father took a stick and very gently scratched one side of the toad and then the other. The toad seemed to like it. He rolled from side to side and blinked. The little boy took the stick and did what Father had done. Then he gently ran the stick across the toad's back. What do you think happened? The toad's skin was thin and dirty, and it split right across the back. Underneath there was a bright new coat of green. Then the little toad gently and carefully pulled his outer skin over his head and rolled it up in a ball and swallowed it. How queer is the toad!

Character is not on the outside. We cannot change our character like the toad changes its skin. Character comes from the inside. If we want a good character then we must have a good heart within. Only Jesus can give us that.

Nuts

"I like hickory nuts best," said Ned. "They are very hard to crack, but when they are cracked, they are nicer than any other kind of nuts."

"I think peanuts are better," said Tom. "They are easy to crack and almost always you find two good nuts in one shell."

"I like doughnuts the best," said Jane. "They are the best nuts in the world."

Doughnuts remind us of the optimist and the pessimist. The optimist always sees the good in everything. When he looks at the doughnut he thinks how good it would taste. The pessimist always sees the worst in everything. When he looks at the doughnut, he sees the hole in it. It is better to be an optimist than a pessimist.

Baby Dear

"Where did you come from, baby dear?
Out of the everywhere into here.

"Where did you get those eyes of blue?
Out of the sky as I came through.

"What makes the light in them sparkle and spin?
Some starry sparks left in.

"Where did you get that little tear?
I found it waiting when I got here.

"Whence that three-cornered smile of bliss?
Three angels gave me at once a kiss.

"Where did you get that pearly ear?
God spake, and it came out to hear.

"But why did you come to us, you dear?
God thought about you, and so I am here."
—Selected

The Camel's Stomach

The stomach of a camel is divided into four compartments. The walls of each compartment are lined with large cells which are opened and closed by powerful muscles. When a camel drinks, it drinks a great deal. It drinks for such a long time that you would think it never meant to stop. What the camel is really doing is not only satisfying its thirst, but filling up the cells in its stomach. One by one, each cell is filled with water and tightly closed. After a camel has filled its cells with water, it can go for days without taking a drink. When it becomes thirsty, one of the cells opens and allows the water to flow out. The next time it is thirsty, another cell opens and allows the water to flow out. The camel is useful in desert travel because it can go so long without taking a drink of water.

Christians cannot live like a camel. They must eat and drink often. Christians need daily prayer, daily Bible study, and regular church attendance.

I Saw God Wash The World Last Night

I saw God wash the world last night
  With His sweet showers on high,
And then, when morning came, I saw
  Him hang it out to dry.

He washed each tiny blade of grass
  And every trembling tree;
He flung His showers against the hill,
  And swept the billowing sea.

The white rose is a cleaner white,
  The red rose is more red,
Since God washed every fragrant face
  And put them all to bed.

There's not a bird; there is not a bee
  That wings along the way,
But is a cleaner bird and bee
  Than it was yesterday.

I saw God wash the world last night,
  Ah, would He had washed me
As clean of all my dust and dirt,
  As that old white birch tree.

—William L. Stidger

The Donkey Boy

Once there was a little boy who never wanted to do anything that others wished him to do. When the sun rose in the morning and said, "Little Boy, wake up," he said "No, I don't want to wake up." When his mother came to dress him, he said, "No, I don't want to dress." When he was offered cereal for breakfast he said, "No, no." When he was offered a glass of milk, he said, "No." When it was time to go to kindergarten, he said, "No, no, I don't want to go." When his teacher told him to bring his chair and join the circle he said, "No, no."

One day Little Boy's teacher looked at him and said, "I believe you are going to be a donkey boy. Go look in the mirror and see what you look like."

"No, no," said Little Boy. But teacher took him by the arm and led him over in front of the mirror. What do you suppose? Little Boy's face was getting long. His face didn't have any smiles. It was beginning to look like a donkey. Little Boy cried, "No, no, I don't want to be like a donkey."

"If you don't want to be like a donkey, Little Boy, you will have to learn to obey. Little donkeys always balk. They always say, 'No, no.' You must learn to say 'Yes.'"

Little Boy began that very minute to say "yes," and he did not grow up to be like a donkey at all.

Fishing

One day a man caught a little fish. The little fish cried, "Let me go. I am too small to be worth much. Wait until I am larger."

"No," said the man as he put his fish in the basket. "If I wait until you are larger, you might not bite the hook."

We should win the boys and girls for Jesus while they are little. It is much easier to catch them when they are young. Let us bring all the little ones that we can catch to Sunday School and church where they can hear about Jesus, the Savior.

The Seasons

I love the Springtime with its leaves
And grass of dainty green,
And flowers bursting all around
Of every shade and sheen.

I love the Summer with its weight
Of ripened fruit and grain,
Its sighing winds and singing birds
And silvery falling rain.

I love the Autumn with its wreath
Of rainbow tinted hills,
And Jack Frost hiding in the grass
And by the flowing rills.

And when King Winter comes along
And wraps the earth with snow —
The other seasons I forget
Because I love it so.
— Alice Montgomery Barr

Nature Reveals God

A man asked an old colored man why he believed in God. "Sir," said he, "I have been here sixty years. Every day since I have been in this world, the sun has risen in the East and set in the West. Every night I see the North star in the sky. The Great Dipper and the Scorpion keep on in the same path in the sky. God's works can be depended on. They never change. They never fail. But man's works cannot be depended on. A man makes clocks and watches. They run for awhile, but then they get out of fix and stop."

"It Isn't Raining Rain to Me"

"It isn't raining to me
It's raining daffodils!
In ev'ry dimpling drop I see
Wild flowers on the hills!

A cloud of gray engulfs the day
And overwhelms the town; —
It isn't raining rain to me, —
It's raining roses down!

It isn't raining rain to me,
But fields of clover bloom,
Where any buccaneering bee
May find a bed and room.

A health, then, to the happy,
A fig to him who frets!
It isn't raining rain to me, —
It's raining violets!"
— Robert Loveman

A Queer Animal

The rock cony is a most interesting animal. He "makes hay while the sun shines," just like any good farmer. In fact he works hard all summer long, gathering green grass and storing it in his home under the rocks for winter's use. Then when cold weather comes he is well provided for. Underneath the rocks his nest is warm and clean, and the heaviest snows cannot reach him.

The rock cony, besides being such a good worker, is a very wise little creature. The Bible tells us something about them. Prov. 30:26 says, "The conies are but a feeble folk, yet make they their houses in the rocks." They are wise enough to know they are no match for their enemies, so they do not even try to fight them. They would only lose out if they did, for they are such puny little creatures. But when danger comes they run to the rock for protection, and hidden beneath the rock, no enemy can get at them.

Some boys and girls are not as wise as the conies. Instead of running to the

Rock, the Lord Jesus Christ, they try to fight their battles all alone. But wise boys and girls run to Jesus when they are about to lose their temper, or tempted to cheat, or lie, or do anything that is wrong. Those who run to Jesus and let Him fight their battles are protected from their enemies.

OBEDIENCE

The Faithful Dog

A Negro turpentine worker, with tears in his eyes, told the story of his faithful dog. He had left the dog beside his dinner pail, telling him to watch it. A great fire swept through the forest. The dog did *not desert* his post. He stayed by the dinner pail, and was burned to death. As the Negro finished his story, he said, "I always had to be careful what I told that dog to do, 'cause I knew he would do it."

"Pleased to Obey"

A little boy had a dog whom he loved. One day he said, "I wish I could mind God like my little dog minds me. My dog always looks so pleased to mind me. Sometimes I don't." Surely God's children should be pleased to obey Him.

Prompt Obedience

General Robert E. Lee once sent word to General Stonewall Jackson that he wanted to talk with him at his convenience on some matters not very urgent. Immediately, Jackson rode to headquarters to see General Lee, although the weather was stormy and bad. General Lee expressed surprise at seeing Jackson so soon. General Jackson said, "General Lee's slightest wish is a supreme command for me, and I always take pleasure in *prompt obedience!*" We should gladly and promptly obey God's slightest wish for our lives.

The Drawbridge Keeper

The keeper of a drawbridge received orders to have the bridge closed for a fast express train which was soon to pass over the bridge. A tug boat came up the river, and whistled for the bridge to be opened. The keeper thought he had plenty of time to let it pass before the express train came. So, he disobeyed orders and opened the bridge. Suddenly, he heard the whistle of the oncoming train! He quickly tried to close the bridge, but before he could do so, the express train came down the track, and plunged into the river!

Hundreds of lives were lost because of the keeper's disobedience. The keeper of the bridge went insane. He was placed in a padded cell. There he muttered day and night, "If I only had! If I only had" If he only had obeyed orders, hundreds of lives would have been saved, and his own life kept from ruin.

Without His Hat

Some one said to a Christian man, to whom God had given riches and honor, "Suppose God would direct you to drop everything in your life. Suppose He would direct you to leave your home, your friends, and your business, and go to the heart of Africa for the rest of your days. Could *you* go without complaint, without demur?" The Christian's eyes flashed, as he instantly replied, "I could go without my hat!"

The Best Girl

A group of schoolgirls were asked: "Who is the best girl in your school?" "Lucy Jones," was the quick reply. "Why is she the best?" One girl said, "She recites the best!" Another girl said, "She is always ready. She never keeps the class waiting." A third girl said, "She is never late." A fourth girl said, "She keeps all the rules." Then, a fifth girl said, "I know why she is the best girl in the room: She loves and obeys God, and she loves and obeys her parents."

How wonderful it is when boys and girls love and obey God. How wonderful it is when they love and obey their parents in the Lord.

"Trust and obey,
For there's no other way
To be happy in Jesus,
But to trust and obey."

Obeying Mother

A man needed a boy to help him in his shop. He ran an ad in the morning paper. Soon, his office was filled with all kinds of boys. He did not know which one to choose. So he sent them all away. He ran another ad in the paper. It said, "Wanted: To assist in my shop a boy who *obeys* his mother." Only *two boys* answered the ad. The man knew that he could trust a boy who obeyed his mother. How few such boys there were.

The Wrong Job

A boy on a farm was told by his father to do a certain thing one day. Then the father went to town. The boy noticed that the barn door needed paint. Instead of doing the work which his father had assigned him, the boy got a can of red paint and a brush, and went to work, painting the barn door. He did a good job, but when the father came home, the father was displeased. Instead of being rewarded for his service, the boy was punished.

So it is with Christians. We will be rewarded, not for doing what we want to do; but for doing the work which Christ has given us to do. God wants our obedience, our whole-hearted, cheerful obedience.

All Ear

A missionary wanted to teach the native Christians what obedience to God means. He could not find the right word in the native language, for obedience was not known by the natives. One day, the missionary started home from the village. His dog lingered behind. The missionary whistled, and the dog came running at top speed. An old native man, with great admiration for the dog, said, "Your dog is all ear!" Immediately, the missionary knew that he had the expression for obedience. From that time, he told the natives that we must be *all ear* to our Lord!

Saved by Obedience

One day, near a country station, a switchman was preparing to turn a switch on a track. He wanted to switch the train which was approaching on to a different track to prevent its collision with a train that was coming from the opposite direction. Just as he started to throw the switch, he saw his little son playing on the track where he was going to switch the approaching train! What could he do? If he did not turn the switch instantly, the lives of hundreds of people might be lost! Instantly, he cried to his son, "Lie down!" The son, who was accustomed to obey his father promptly without question, did as his father commanded. The father threw the switch, and the heavy train thundered *over* the boy. As soon as the train had passed, the father rushed forward to where his son lay, fearful lest he would find a mangled corpse. To his joy he found his boy alive and unharmed. His *prompt obedience* had saved him!

Cheerful Obedience

One day, Jack was playing baseball in the lot next to his home. His father came to the front door and called. Jack threw down the bat, and ran over to see what his father wanted. The father asked Jack to go to the drug store and get him some medicine. Jack did not grumble. He cheerfully said, "Yes, sir, I will be glad to get it!" He started down the walk. Father called him back and said, "Son, I want to thank you for being a good boy. I know you were playing ball, and it is hard to leave a game. But you came instantly, and you have not complained. Thank you, Son!"

With a smile, Jack went off to the drug store. When he returned, he found a group of people gathered on his front porch. They were whispering. Some were crying. One of the neighbors said kindly to him, "Jack, your father just dropped dead!" Jack replied, "Oh, I am so glad that I came quickly and cheerfully when he called me from the game. I am so glad I didn't complain!"

Obedience First

A little girl went down to the seashore and gathered shells. Her father had told her not to go down by the shore. He knew that she might be swept into the sea by the outgoing tide. But the little girl disobeyed. She gathered the shells by the shore. Then she remembered how much her father liked pretty shells. She carried the shells to him. She said, "See, Father, I have brought you some beautiful sea shells!" The father took the shells, and threw them away. He said, "My little girl, I cannot receive any gift from you when you have disobeyed me. You know that I told you not to go down to the seashore."

So it is when we disobey God, and go into the ways of sin. When we do this, our worship, our offerings, our service, our sacrifices are *not* pleasing or acceptable to Him.

George Washington

At a banquet, the mother of George Washington was sitting beside a distinguished French officer. Turning to Washington's mother, the officer asked, "How have you managed to rear such a splendid son?" She replied, "I taught him to obey."

Where He Leads

A native in the Congo prayed, "Dear Lord Jesus, You be the needle and I will be the thread. You go first, and I will follow wherever You lead!"

PERSECUTION

A Persecutor Converted

Some years ago, Richard Baxter was riding to a village some distance from his home to preach. Night came on. In the darkness Baxter missed his way. Finally, he saw a lighted house near the roadside. He went to the door and asked to stay overnight. The master of the house consented. During the evening meal, the gentleman asked his guest what his business was. Mr. Baxter quietly replied, "I'm a man catcher, sir." "Oh," said the man; "you are the very one I want. I am the justice of the peace, and I want to catch Dick Baxter who will preach tomorrow morning in a house near by."

Mr. Baxter did not reveal his identity. He agreed to go with his host to the meeting. Early the next day, they went to the house where the people had gathered to hear Dick Baxter preach. The justice of peace found that Dick Baxter had not yet appeared. He said, "I suppose Baxter has heard of my plans to arrest him, and is not going to fulfill his engagement."

After they had waited for awhile, the justice of the peace suggested that his guest offer a prayer and talk to the people. Then Mr. Baxter began the meeting! He prayed a powerful prayer. He delivered a heart-searching sermon. The justice was melted to tears. At the close of his message, Mr. Baxter turned to the Justice and said, "I am the Dick Baxter you are looking for! Take me!"

But the Justice did not arrest Dick Baxter. God's Word had broken his hard heart. Instead of presecuting Dick Baxter, the Justice became a Christian. If we will always let God have His way in our lives, glory and honor will come to His Name in the midst of suffering and persecution.

Jesus Suffered More

An ungodly father beat his boy to keep him from going to church or Sunday School. One day, the boy came to his Sunday School class with black and blue marks on him. The teacher, seeing the marks of violence, said, "I wonder that you do not run away from home." With a surprised look on his face the boy said, "Well, I haven't stood near as much as the Lord Jesus did, and if I stay home, maybe Pa will believe in Jesus sometime."

Persecution on the Mission Field

On the mission fields, many of our missionaries are suffering persecution for Jesus' sake. A missionary in Manila wrote a letter, telling about some revival services which were held in a tent in a town near Iloilo. She told how some of the natives, aroused by a priest, threw stones in the tent. This happened for several nights, and then, one night, when the tent was crowded with people listening to the Gospel, a shower of stones began to fall. Many stones fell near the missionary. The tent was badly torn by the stones. Hymn books and papers were lost. But the people were not harmed by the stones, and many in this meeting gave their lives to the Lord Jesus.

Faithful Unto Death

At the beginning of this century, there was a Boxer uprising in China. The Boxers put many of the Chinese Christians to death. One day, they captured a mission school. They blocked all the gates but one. Then they sent word into the school that anyone who trampled on the Cross would go free. Those who would not trample on the Cross would be immediately killed. The first seven students, who came out of the school trampled upon the Cross, and went free. The eighth, a girl, knelt before the Cross. Then she rose and went on to be shot! All the rest in the line of one hundred students followed the example of this brave girl. They were faithful to Christ unto death.

It is said that more than thirty thousand Chinese converts chose death in 1900 rather than deny their Lord and Saviour. Today, the Chinese Christians are bravely and faithfully standing for Christ. Many are willing to seal their faith with their life's blood.

Christians all around the world have faithfully stood for Christ in times of persecution. A thousand black converts in Uganda, Africa, went to their death by fire.

How can any Christian forsake the Lord Jesus? He is our Lord and Saviour. He is dearer to us than life. "Be thou faithful unto death, and I will give thee a crown of life" (*Rev. 2:10*).

What He Expected

A soldier in the East Indies was the terror of his regiment. He was a strong man, a former prize fighter, and he was always eager for a good fight. One day, he was converted. When the Lord Jesus came into his life, his life was completely changed. The lion became a lamb! Two months later, in the mess hall, some of those who had formerly been afraid of him began to ridicule him. Then one of the soldiers threw a bowl of hot soup over him. There was a breathless silence! They all expected him to almost murder the offender. He opened his coat and wiped the hot soup from his scalded breast. Then, he turned around and said, "This is what I expected to endure when I became a Christian!"

Delivered from the Lions

A little girl in Africa attended Bible school. She heard the story of Jesus. She gave her heart to Him. Her mother was a heathen. She was very angry, because her little girl went to Bible school. She beat her. She put her in the hands of a witch doctor, thinking that he would put fear in the little girl's heart. But the little girl continued to love Jesus, and memorize Bible verses, and sing the sweet Christian songs she had learned. At last, the mother drove her into the forest, and bound her to a tree, thinking that the lions would come and frighten the Jesus belief out of the little girl. She left her saying, "A worthless child art thou to me — but food for lions!" The dreadful black night came.

At dawn, a Christian lad found the little girl tied to the tree. She was unharmed, but he saw lions' track encircling the spot. Not one of the lions had come nearer than five yards. The little girl had seen their glaring eyes, but she had remembered how God delivered Daniel from the lions, and she prayed that God would deliver her, too. All fear had left her. She *knew* that God would not let the lions harm her.

Blessed

One day, Mrs. R. J. Richardson, a missionary, was traveling in China with her two little children. She was stopped and examined by a Japanese soldier, whose rude handling of her person caused her to protest. The answer was a harsh slap on her face. Finally, she was released. She got into her ricksha and rode off.

When she reached a little lane, where nobody was in sight, the missionary gave way to her feelings and began to sob. When the ricksha coolie heard her crying, he turned around and said, "Don't cry, lady. 'Blessed are they which are persecuted for righteousness' sake.'" These words from a humble servant of the Lord brought comfort to the heart of the missionary.

The Child Apostle

The late Bishop of Madras was visiting a mission station in Africa. There he was introduced to a little slave girl who was called, "The Child Apostle." She had won this title because of her zeal for the Lord Jesus. She was constantly telling others of the Saviour. Nothing could stop her witnessing for Jesus. She had suffered brutal persecu-tion. The bishop noticed that her face, neck, and arms were disfigured, scarred by stripes and blows. His eyes filled with tears as he asked, "My child, how can you bear this?" She looked up at him in surprise and said, "Don't you like to suffer for Christ, sir?"

Praying for Enemies

Some years ago, in a village in northern Syria, there lived a man named Abu Dugoom. Abu became a Christian. Then he was severely persecuted. His bride was taken away from him by his father-in-law. The villagers tore down his new house. Finally, when he refused to give up his belief in the wonderful Book, he was led out of the village to be burned to death. He was tied to a pile of wood. Then, he was given a chance to say his last words. He neither cursed nor wept. He knelt down, and prayed for his enemies and persecutors. A miracle happened! One by one, the angry mob stole quietly back to the village. Abu was left alone, but not alone, for God was with him.

PRAISE

Praise Changes Things

A large department store in Chicago hired a young German girl as a saleslady. Her face was large and full. Her hair was coarse and straight. She never had a smile. She always looked glum and stolid. She made no friends and was almost a complete failure as a saleslady. The department manager thought he would have to discharge her. Then he thought of the store's sympathetic matron. He sent the girl up to see her. The girl burst into the ma-tron's office, crying out, "I hate myself. I hate my ugly face and my stiff greasy hair. I don't see why I'm not pretty like the other girls." Then she began to sob as if her heart would break.

In honest surprise the matron said, "I don't think you're ugly. You have a nice complexion and pretty teeth. Here, look at yourself and see if I'm not right." The matron drew the girl over to a mirror that hung on the closet door. The girl looked at herself earnestly for a moment. Then she asked, "Do you really think I am not ugly?"

"No, you're not ugly," replied the matron, "and if I had beautiful teeth like yours, I would smile and show them. Why don't you try it?" Suddenly the girl smiled and said, "I will."

It took the girl some time to cultivate a pleasant look but she kept trying and gradually her face changed. It was no longer sullen. It became bright and happy looking. Even her hair seemed to respond to the change in the girl. Her fellow-workers began to notice the difference in the girl. Then her sales became larger. Before many months the girl was one of the best liked and most capable clerks in the store. The words of deserved praise had brought a wonderful change in the girl who was almost a failure.

"Let It Be Praise"

A young man was summoned to the bedside of his aged mother. She was more than eighty years old, and had been stricken with what was feared would prove her fatal illness. Her children had all gathered in her room, when in walked the pastor. He turned to the aged saint and asked her, "What shall I read from the Bible?" She replied, "Make your own selection, but let it be of praise!" She was weak and old and sick, but there was no gloom or sadness in her heart. In her heart was praise.

Praise 'Midst Suffering

A captain lay on the battlefield seriously wounded. He was suffering greatly. The stars were shining clearly and beautifully above the dark field. He began to think of God who had given His Son to die on the Cross; and that He was up there in Heaven above the scene of suffering. The captain knew that he was soon going home to Heaven to meet and praise God there, and he felt that he ought to praise God even while he lay wounded on the field of battle. With a clear voice, he began to sing:

> "When I can read my title clear,
>   To mansions in the skies!"

Near him, in the brush, lay a Christian brother. He took up the song. Beyond him, there lay another Christian and another. All over that battlefield Christian brothers joined in singing praises to the Lord! The night resounded with hymns of praise!

Songs of Praise

In the Alps, the great tall mountains of Europe, the shepherds have a beautiful custom. At the end of the day, they gather their flocks to go home. When they begin to lead the flocks down the mountain pass, they sing. What do they sing? They sing songs of praise to God. One of their favorite songs says, "Hitherto hath the Lord helped us. Let us praise His Name!" Then, as the shepherds leave one another, they sing a friendly farewell: "Good night, Good night!" It is wonderful to hear the mountains echo the praises which the shepherds sing unto the Lord.

Each evening, each morning, and all during the day, we should sing praises to the Lord.

"Blankets or No Blankets"

An old lady loved the Lord. She had the habit of saying, "Praise the Lord!" Often, when the minister was preaching, she would say, "Praise the Lord!" The minister was some times disturbed when Betty said, "Praise the Lord!" He would forget what he was saying. He offered Betty a pair of wool blankets if she would keep still. Betty was poor and needed the blankets. So she did her best to earn them. Sunday after Sunday, she kept quiet. Then, one day, a visiting minister came to preach. He preached on forgiveness of sin, and all the blessings that come with it. As he preached, Betty thought less and less of the blankets. She thought more and more of the joys of salvation. Finally, she could stand it no longer. She cried out, "Blankets or no blankets, *praise the Lord!*"

Praise Changes Things

A missionary in China was living a *defeated* life. He was always sad and discouraged. He prayed long for victory over sadness and discouragement. Finally, he decided to leave his work and pray until victory came. He went to the home of a fellow missionary to try to find rest and refreshment. On the wall of the guest room was a motto with these words: "Try Thanksgiving!" The missionary saw the motto. He began to think: "Have I been praying and weeping all this time and not praising, not thanking God?" He immediately began praising the Lord, and his soul was flooded with light and sunshine. He found that: "Praise changes things! Praise changes *you!*"

His Last Words

A young man lay on an operating table in the hospital. The surgeon was soon to remove the young man's tongue. The young man had cancer of the tongue. The surgeon asked him to say the last words he wished to say. With a clear voice, the young man said, "Thank God for Jesus Christ!"

The Reason For Haydn's Joy

Haydn was a great composer of music. One of his friends asked him why his church music was always so cheerful and lively. Haydn replied, "I cannot make my music otherwise. I write according to the way I feel. When I think upon God, my heart is so full of joy that the notes dance and leap, as it were, from my pen. God has given me a cheerful heart and I cannot help but serve Him with a cheerful spirit."

Joy in Service

A beautiful young woman one night noticed a poor blind fiddler playing for money on the street. His music was not good. Nobody seemed to notice him. The girl took the violin and stood beside him and began to play. She played beautiful melodies that touched the hearts of the passers-by. They began to drop their gifts in the blind man's tin cup. The girl's face became radiant with joy. There is always joy in service. There is always pleasure in helping the needy. Did not Jesus say, "There is more joy in giving than in receiving"?

Room to Smile

The primary class met in a little room. One Sunday there were so many children in the class that they had to sit very close together. One little girl was afraid that her dress would get mussed up. She began to scold about how crowded the room was. The little girl next to her was having a happy time. She was glad to see so many children there. She did not mind the crowding. Very sweetly she said, "We have room to smile anyway."

There is always room for us to smile. So, let us always be happy and wear a smile on our face.

Joy in the Heart

A poor Chinese coolie was wonderfully saved. With a happy face, he gave this testimony: "I am nothing but a poor coolie. I have no money, and no learning. But in my heart, I have an unable-to-speak-it-out *joy!*"

A wealthy Chinaman came to a missionary and said, "I want to hear about your religion. I never have heard the words of it, but I have heard the laughter in your house, and in the houses of my countrymen who have your religion. If ye have anything which makes people so joyous, I want it!"

How we thank God for the *deep* and *lasting* joy which He gives to His children!

I Am Happier Now

An old man, who had been converted from heathenism, gave this testimony, "I am happier now when I am not happy, than I used to be when I was happy!" That was his way of telling of the joy Jesus had brought into his life. Have you not found that the Saviour has brought joy to you?

> "Joy, joy, joy,
> With joy my heart is ringing,
> Joy, joy, joy,
> His love to me is *known.*
> My sins are *all* forgiven,
> I'm on my way to Heaven,
> My heart is bubbling over,
> With His joy, joy, joy!"

Smiles

An old man once stopped a lady and said, "Excuse me, but I want to thank you for something."

"For what?" asked the lady.

Said the old man, "I used to be a ticket collector. Whenever you went by me, you gave me a cheerful smile, and a 'good morning,' Wet or fine, you always smiled, and said 'good morning.' I used to think, 'Wonder where she gets her smile. Wonder what makes her so happy all the time.' I decided that the smile must come from *inside.* Then one morning, when you came by, you had a little Bible in your hand. I said to myself, 'That's where her smile comes from.' I went and bought a Bible. I read it, and found Jesus as my Saviour. Now I can smile, too, and I want to thank you!"

From Darkness to Light

A girl in a mission school in India sang all day long as she went about her tasks. When she was asked why she was so happy, she said, "I have been redeemed from sin and idolatry. I am set at liberty. It is like slipping suddenly from midnight darkness into the brightest noontime! I cannot but be happy!"

Singing in the Rain

A dear old Christian lady had been a shut-in for many months. One day her pastor called to see her. She said to him, "I have a lovely robin that sings outside my window every day. In the early morning, he serenades me. What I like most about him is that he sings in the rain!"

The most beautiful thing about a robin is that he sings in the rain. The storm will silence almost every other song bird; but the robin sings in the rain. That is what Christians who walk with Christ should do. They should sing not only in the sunshine, but also in the rain.

Comfort in a Cloud

A blacksmith, in a town in Pennsylvania, was always cheerful and happy. One day, he told the reason for his joy. Said he, "A dear old lady taught me always to look for the silver lining to every cloud. She was a very poor woman and had many troubles. Still, she was always cheerful. One day, I said to her, 'Mary, you must have some dark days. You must have some clouds.' 'Yes,' she replied, 'but I have found that there is comfort in a cloud. When I feel very low in my spirit, I go to the window, and if I see a heavy cloud, I think about the cloud that received the Lord Jesus out of sight. And then I think that maybe the cloud in my life is just hiding Him, that He is behind the cloud. So you see, there is always comfort in a cloud.' "

Not Tired Yet

A young man, just out of college, preached in a country church one day. After church, he went home to dinner with one of the members. The man invited him to visit an old blind woman who lived in a little cottage in his cotton field. After dinner, the young man walked through the field. When he neared the cottage, he heard a voice singing,

"O happy day that fixed my choice,
On Thee, my Saviour and my God!"

The young man took his hat from his head and felt like removing his shoes from his feet. He felt like he was coming to holy ground. When the song was finished, he walked up to the door and knocked. "Who is it?" the blind woman called. He told her that she had a visitor, a young man who had preached that day in the country church. She invited him in. Then she reached out in her blindness and pulled a chair close to hers and invited him to sit down. He asked her how long she had been a Christian, and she replied, "Nigh on to sixty years, and I ain't tired yet!"

Sweet As Molasses

A little colored boy down in Mississippi was converted to God. He was so happy he did not know what to do with himself. He laughed, and then he cried. Finally, he said, "Oh, it is sweet! It is as sweet as molasses!"

Long ago, David said, "The judgments of the Lord are true and righteous . . . More to be desired are they than gold, yea, than much fine gold: sweeter also than honey and the honeycomb" (*Ps. 19:9-10*).

Better Higher Up

An old bed-ridden saint lived on the fifth floor of a tenement. A Christian lady who often visited her found her always cheerful. This lady had a friend who always looked on the dark side of things and was constantly complaining. She thought it would do this friend good to see the bed-ridden saint. So, one day, she took her with her for a visit. When the Christian lady and her friend entered the building, the friend said, "How dark and filthy it is here."

"It's better higher up," said the Christian lady. They got to the next story and it was no better. The friend complained again, only to be assured that it was better higher up. At the third floor, it seemed worse, and the friend kept complaining. Again, she was assured, "It's better higher up!" Finally, they reached the fifth floor. When they entered the sick room, there was a nice carpet on the floor. Some plants were blooming in the window, and some little birds were singing. There, they found the bed-ridden saint, beaming with joy. The friend said to her, "It must be very hard for you to lie here." She smiled and answered, "I am not complaining. It's BETTER higher up!"

When we remember that, "It's better higher up," our hearts are filled with joy!

PRAYER

Prayer and Work Belong Together

One time when D. L. Moody was crossing the Atlantic Ocean, a fire broke out on the ship. The crew and some volunteers from among the passengers stood in line to pass buckets of water.

A friend said to Mr. Moody, "Let us go to the other end of the ship and pray."

Mr. Moody replied, "No, sir. We will stand right here and pass buckets, and pray hard all the time we are doing it."

Mr. Moody believed that prayer and work should always go hand in hand.

The Best Medicine

Dr. Hyslop, one of Britain's great physicians, said to the British Medical Association: "The best medicine which my practice has discovered is prayer. It relieves disturbed sleep, depression of spirits, and all the miseries of a distressed mind."

The Strange Birds

In Japan, there lived an earnest Christian man. He had an orchard of one thousand trees. He depended upon the orchard for a livelihood for himself and his family. One morning, he discovered that some peculiar worms had arrived in his orchard. They were destroying his half-grown apples. As he walked through the orchard, he observed that the worms were on every tree.

The man called his family together in the orchard. They called upon God for help. Then, they began to work, picking off the worms and destroying them. They worked all day and on, into the evening. But the pests were multiplying by the thousands, and their efforts were in vain. In desperation, the family again cried unto God for help. Then, weary with their work, they lay down on their straw mats for a little sleep.

The next morning, the family returned to the orchard to begin another busy day. They were surprised to see hundreds of strange birds alighting on the trees! All day long, the birds stayed in the orchard, eating up the worms, but not injuring the trees or the fruit! For three days, the birds came, and kept up their work. On the evening of the third day, the family walked through the orchard and found that it was entirely free of the worms.

A Loaf of Bread

A little, old Christian lady rented half of a double house. The owner of the house lived on the other side. He was an atheist. He often laughed at the old lady, because she trusted in God. One day, the little, old lady began to pray to her Heavenly Father about her needs. She did not have a meal in her house. She prayed loudly and the man next door heard her. Then, he said, "I will play a trick on that old lady."

The man went to the grocery store and bought a loaf of bread. Reaching his house, he climbed to the roof. Near the chimney, he stopped and listened. The little, old lady was still praying. Laughing, he leaned over and let the loaf of bread fall down the chimney. It landed near the feet of the old lady. He heard her give a little cry, and say, "Thank You, Lord. I knew You wouldn't fail me. You have never failed me!"

With a sneer on his face, the man climbed to the ground, went around to the door, and knocked. The little, old lady said, "Come in." Then the man said, "You poor, foolish woman. You really believe that God hears and answers prayer. I am the one who brought that loaf of bread. I dropped it down into the fireplace."

"Well, praise the Lord," cried the little, old lady. "God always helps me when I tell Him about my needs. He helps me, even if he has to use the *devil* to answer my prayers!"

Jesus Heard

Little Marie was five years old. She had a dear, kind father who loved her very much. He played with Marie. He read stories to her. He told her about Jesus. One day, Marie became very sick. As the days went by, Marie became worse. One day, the Christian doctor said to her father, "Marie is very sick. She will die unless *Jesus* heals her and makes her well!" Then he said, "Let us pray together and ask Jesus to make Marie well!" The father and the Christian doctor prayed. They asked Jesus to please make little Marie well. God heard the prayer. He healed Marie and made her well.

Without Food

A young minister and his wife were sent to take charge of a circuit of churches in Vermont. On the circuit were only a few members, and most of them were poor. One day, the young couple found themselves short of provisions. They cooked their last food for breakfast. When the meal was finished, they prayed together and asked God to send them the food they so badly needed! Then, the minister went out to the old barn, and there continued to pray. He told his Heavenly Father how he had laid his *all* on the altar. He told God how his wife had given herself to His service; and that now they were without food. The minister's wife went into her bedroom and there she "poured out her heart" to God.

A few miles away, there lived a young farmer. He was on his way with a number of hands to his mowing field. Suddenly, he stopped. He told his hired help to go on to the field while he went back to the farmhouse. He returned to the house and told his wife that he felt that he *must* stop everything, and go to the minister's house with some good things to eat. He asked her to help him put the things he must carry into the wagon. Into the wagon went a bushel of potatoes, some meat, flour, sugar, butter, vegetables. Soon, there was a wagon load of good things! The farmer drove over to the minister's house. There his gifts were received most thankfully! Had not the minister and his wife told Jesus about their needs? Had not He answered their prayers?

Praying for One Far Away

In England, two little boys had a kind governess whom they loved. One day, the governess left them to go to far-away India as a missionary. Each night, the little boys prayed that God would bless her, and protect her from all harm and danger.

One night, the little boys were burdened for their friend in India. They cried as they prayed. They begged God to keep her from harm.

At that very time, their dear friend in India was on her way home. She had been speaking about Jesus. She was tired and weary. As she walked along the dusty road, she lifted her foot, and started to put it down on a huge snake! God kept her from putting her foot down. She saw the snake, and drew back. With a prayer of thanksgiving in her heart, she went on her way home. God had answered the prayer of the two little boys in England who had prayed for their dear friend.

"I Must Pray First"

Mary, who was nine years old, was taken sick. She grew rapidly worse. Her father and the family doctor took her to the hospital. There, the surgeon examined her and said that an operation was necessary to save her life. Mary's mother was sick at home. Her father was not a Christian. The surgeon said to the little girl, "My dear, an operation is necessary. Before I perform that, I must put you to sleep." The nurse removed Mary's clothing and put on a white gown. Mary said, "I am ready to go to sleep. But *first, I must* say my prayers!"

"Do just as you please, my dear," said the surgeon. Mary knelt down, folded her hands, and prayed: "O Jesus, you know where I am, and that Mamma is sick at home. Please bless dear Papa, my Sunday School teacher, this surgeon, and all for Jesus' sake! Amen!"

Mary's father was overcome. He begged to be excused, and went home and got on his knees. He surrendered to God, and became an earnest Christian. The great surgeon was also moved. He said, "I had not prayed for *thirty years*. That night, after I heard Mary pray, I fell on my knees and begged for God's mercy!"

Mary's prayers were answered. The Lord Jesus was with her, and she rapidly recovered.

"Save Our House!"

In the home of a Methodist preacher, there was a dear little girl, four years old. She loved the Lord Jesus, and each day lived for Him. One night, the fire bell rang. The whole end of town where the little girl lived was in flames. A terrible wind was blowing. The fire was fast m o v i n g toward the church, and the home of the Methodist minister. The air was full of flying cinders. Across the street from the church and the home, was a vacant lot. Furniture from the home was carried to the middle of the lot. Then the little girl was placed near the furniture, and told to remain there until her mother came for her.

Instantly, the little girl dropped upon her knees. She clasped her hands and began to pray. She cried out, "O God, save our house! O God, save our house!" She told Jesus about her trouble. Did He hear her prayer? He certainly did! Quickly, the wind changed. It began to blow the flames back, over the houses which had already been burned. Soon, the fire went out! God saved the home of the little girl. Not only that was saved, but all the homes around the little church were saved.

The Orphans' Prayer

Some years ago, down in Hephzibah Orphanage in Macon, Georgia, the little children awakened one morning to find no breakfast. The pantry was empty! The kind matron at the orphanage called the little children into the parlor. She said, "Children, we have no food for breakfast. God is our kind Heavenly Father. Let us pray, and ask Him to send us some food. He will answer our prayers!"

The little children knelt down and began to pray. They said, "Lord, send us some 'dits (grits), send us some bread, send us some milk!" Earnestly, they cried to God for food.

Suddenly, a knock was heard at the door. The kind matron went to the door and opened it. There stood a man who said, "I have some of the Lord's money. I asked some one where I could best use it for the Lord, and I was told about this orphanage! Will you please accept this money as from God, and buy the things the little children need?" How happy the matron and little children were! God had answered their prayers.

A Little Cripple

A little cripple was distressed because she could not go out and work for Jesus among the lost ones. A minister visited her. He told her that she could pray earnestly for the salvation of others, even while she lay on her sick bed. Soon, a revival came to the village.

Every night, the churches were crowded, and many were saved. The little cripple anxiously asked about the progress of the revival. She asked daily for the names of those who were saved. A few weeks later, she died. Under her pillow was found a paper containing the names of fifty-six persons for whom she had been praying. She had placed a check mark by the names of those who were saved, and there was a check by each one of the fifty-six names! Just think, boys and girls, fifty-six persons had been saved because of the prayers of a little crippled girl!

Intercessory Prayer

A young man, sixteen years old, was wonderfully saved. Each morning and night, he prayed for strength to live a Christian life. He entered college. One afternoon, his roommate had a fall in the gymnasium. He was carried to their room, more dead than alive. A doctor was called. With terror in his eyes, the roommate whispered, "Wilson, I wish you would pray for me!"

The Christian young man knelt down and prayed for his roommate. God answered the prayer. A change came, and the roommate was *immediately* better. Said the young man, "That faltering prayer for my roommate opened to me the wide door of intercessory prayer, *prayer for others.* My Christian faith was weak because I had never prayed for others." Every Christian should be an intercessor.

"Stop Praying"

Hudson Taylor was a famous missionary. He went to China years ago in a sailing vessel. When he was crossing the ocean, the vessel stopped moving because the wind had ceased to blow.

The captain of the vessel asked Mr. Taylor to pray for help from God. Mr. Taylor said, "I will pray if you will set your sails to catch the wind!"

The captain did not want every one to laugh at him. He did not want to set the sails when there was no wind. But Mr. Taylor said, "I will not pray unless you set the sails, ready to catch the wind!" So, the captain set the sails.

Mr. Taylor went into his stateroom, and began to pray. He prayed earnestly for God to send wind. Suddenly, there was knocking at his door. Mr. Taylor answered the knock. The captain stood there. He asked, "Are you still praying for wind?" "Yes," said Mr. Taylor. "Well," said the captain, "stop praying. We have *more* wind now than we need!"

Sure enough, there was plenty of wind, and the vessel was moving along on its way to China! The captain *knew* that God can hear and answer prayer.

A Delayed Answer

George Mueller was the founder of a great orphanage. In this orphanage were hundreds of boys and girls. Mr. Mueller was like a father to them. The needs of the orphanage were supplied by the Lord through Christian friends who sent in money.

A Scotch father sent money to the orphanage for many years. He had a son who was not a Christian. He longed for this son to be saved. For many years, he and Mr. Mueller prayed for this son. The aged Scotchman died. The son was still not saved. One day, the son, now a grown man, came to Mr. Mueller and said, "I was looking over my father's papers, and I saw that he gave many large sums of money to your orphanage. I said to myself, 'My father would like

for me to help that work! I will visit the orphanage and take some money for the work.' "

While the son was at the orphanage, he attended a service for the boys and girls. He listened to the message from God's Word. Then and there, he received Christ as his Saviour. Friends at the orphanage said to him, "We are not surprised that you have been saved. For *thirty-eight years,* Mr. Mueller has never ceased to pray for you at this Home!"

If you pray, and the answer does not come immediately, have faith in God. *Know* that He hears and will answer your prayers in His time and in His way. We have His promise, "He shall call upon Me, and I will answer him" *(Ps. 91:15 f.c.).*

Prayer for Rain

Joao Mbaxi, a native convert, was placed in charge of Gospel work among a cannibal tribe in Africa. It was in the dry season when he took charge. Then the rainy season came; but month after month went by without rain. Then the dry season came again. Every one was suffering from hunger. Starvation was near.

The native chief told Joao that in *all* the years that they had worshipped their father's gods, rain had never failed to visit them. He said that Joao must leave and must take the white man's God away with him.

Joao refused to go. Then the chief said, "You say that your God rules the sky, and the earth. Why doesn't He send rain? If it does not rain by sunrise to-morrow, we will drink your blood and eat your flesh!"

Joao thought of Elijah. He went to

his hut, and prayed that God would send rain, while the heathen were waiting for the sunrise, and getting ready for their cannibal feast. Just before daybreak, thunder and lightning came! A torrential rain began to fall. God had answered the prayer of Joao just like He answered the prayer of Elijah.

PRESENCE OF GOD

There Is a God Here

A little Armenian girl was thrown to the dogs by some Turks, because she would *not* renounce her faith in Jesus. The dogs were fierce and savage, and the Turks thought that they would devour the little girl. The next morning, they saw the little girl on her knees praying. Beside her, the largest and most savage of all the dogs in the kennel stood. He snapped at every dog that came near the child. Terrified, the Turks ran away crying, "There is a God here! There is a God here!" Thank God, there *is* a God who is always with His children!

All the Way

A little boy had to go to a village. When he was ready to start, he said, "Mother, it's so far to the village. I'm not exactly afraid, but would you come a little way with me?" The mother took her son's little hand in her's and said, "My son, Mother will go *all* the way with you! So, with his hand in mother's, the little boy walked fearlessly along the road. He was not afraid now. Mother was with him! We need have no fear, for God is always with us. He will never leave us nor forsake us.

What Sustained Livingstone

David Livingstone, the missionary to Africa, returned to Scotland, after spending sixteen years in Africa. He was thin, and very weary. He had had many attacks of African fever. His arm hung helpless by his side, because a lion had attacked him. The university of Glasgow wanted to honor David Livingstone. The university was going to give him a high degree, Doctor of Laws. As Livingstone stood before the young college students, they looked upon him with wonderment. He told them that he was going back to Africa. Then he said, "Shall I tell you what helped me through all the years I have spent in Africa? I have been among savage people whom I could often not understand. Sometimes they were unfriendly. Sometimes they have wanted to kill me. What has helped me most is God's promise: 'Lo, I am with you alway, even unto the end of the world.' "

God Sees

In Georgia, a father went with his little boy to a watermelon patch. The father told the little boy to sit on the fence and watch. He was going to steal a watermelon. The father looked the melons over in the bright moonlight. He found a nice, big melon. He took a knife from his pocket. Just before he stooped to cut the melon from the vine, he looked around. He wanted to be *sure* no one was watching him. Then, he began to cut the melon.

Suddenly, his little boy cried out, "Pa, you forgot to look one way!" The father was frightened and he asked, "Which way did I forget to look?" The little boy said, "You forgot to look *up!*"

The little boy was *right*. Father had not looked up. Father had forgotten that God's eyes were upon him. Father said to the little boy, "Come on, Son. I guess we won't steal that melon. God sees us!"

Delivered from Lions

An African boy was sent on a lonely journey through a country full of lions. He was frightened. He kept saying, "Heavenly Father is with me. He will look after me." Suddenly the boy turned a corner in the pathway, and there he saw two huge lions, crouching on an ant hill, waiting for him. Trembling, he knelt in the path right in front of the lions and prayed. He asked God, his Heavenly Father, to protect him. Then he said to himself, "I must forget my fears. I must deliver this letter for the missionary." He got up, and walked on past the lions. God was with him. He delivered his trustful child from the lions.

"I Am with Thee'

When John McNeill, the Scotch preacher, was a little boy, he went to town one day. He was late starting for home. He had to walk six or seven miles through a lonely glen. Night came, and the darkness drew deep! His boyish heart was filled with fear. Suddenly, through the darkness, there rang out a strong, cheery voice, "Is that you, Johnnie?" It was the voice of his father.

When telling the story, John McNeill said, "That was the voice of my father — the bravest, strongest man I ever knew. Many a time since then, when things began to get black and gloomy

around me, I have heard a Voice greater than the voice of any earthly father cry out through the darkness, 'Fear not: for I am with thee'!"

What Helped Him

An old lady said to a little boy, "Sonny, remember God loves you. The Bible says, 'Thou God seest me.' Remember God loves you so much, He can't take His eyes off you. Each day, He watches over you."

Safe When He Is Near

A little boy was afraid to go home one stormy night. He had been visiting friends, and when the storm and thunder came, he was afraid to go home. Tears covered his face. Then he went to the window and looked out toward his home. Suddenly, he turned with a smile and said, "I am not afraid to go home now. It is dark out and raining, but I see my big brother coming after me. He has a lantern. And I am not afraid of a storm when my big brothers holds my hand and carries the light. He knows the way home, and nothing can hurt me when my big brother walks with me!"

How glad we are that, day by day, the Lord Jesus walks with us. He knows about every danger, every sorrow, every trouble. We are safe when He is near!

Not Alone

Some years ago, a Bishop was sent for to see a dying man. The night was dark and the way lonely. When he reached the house, there was no one in. He returned home.

Years later, a man in prison told the Bishop that he had sent him a false message that night. He wanted to rob him. The Bishop asked, "Why didn't you rob me, then?" The answer was: "I lay in hiding, and when you passed by, I saw you were *not alone.* A mysterious Stranger walked close behind you. I could do nothing to harm you!"

The Lord Was There

Some years ago, rioters in western China drove out many missionaries from their district. The young treasurer of a mission helped to get the other missionaries out. When he saw that they were cared for, he himself started down the river in a boat. Rioters overtook him, and came on to his boat. He jumped overboard. They began to throw spears at him in the water. He would dart under the boat and come up on the other side, only to find another spear shot at him. Down he would go again and up again. His plight seemed hopeless! Finally, he struck out for the shore. On the bank he was surrounded by a mob of rioters. He thought the end had come. But the chief said, "Let him go!" And the rioters melted away!

Some time later, this young treasurer stood on the platform at Northfield Bible Conference on Missionary Day. He said, "Some of my friends have been curious to know what text of Scripture came to me when I was down under the boat. Friends, no Scripture text came there. *The Lord Himself was there!*"

How it strengthens us to know that the Lord Himself is with us, during times of persecution.

Father Is On Deck

One night a great storm arose at sea. The waves came sweeping against the side of a ship, sailing from England to New York. Everything on the ship that was movable went crashing from side to side. The noise and movement awakened the passengers. Many were filled with fear.

The little eight-year-old daughter of the captain of the ship was sleeping soundly. Some one went and awakened her. She asked, "What's the matter?" She was told that a great storm had come upon the sea, and that the ship and its passengers were in great danger. The little child asked, "Is Papa on deck?" She was told that he was. "Then, I'm going back to sleep," said the little girl. She dropped her head on her pillow without a fear, and in a few moments she was asleep!

With sweet trust in God's love and care, the Psalmist said, "I will both lay me down in peace, and sleep: for Thou, Lord, *only* makest me dwell in safety" *(Ps. 4:8).*

God Present Everywhere

One Sunday morning a man was sharing a seat with a small boy on a shuttle train in Philadelphia. The boy was holding a Sunday School paper. "Do you go to Sunday School, my boy?" asked the man. "Yes, sir," replied the boy. The man thought he would have a little fun so he said, "My boy, tell me where God is and I'll give you an apple." The boy looked up sharply at the man and replied, "I will give you a whole barrel of apples if you will tell me where God is not."

The Nearness of His Father

A little boy was entering school. On the first day, his busy mother packed his lunch and gave it to him, saying, "Go straight up the road, across the bridge, to the schoolhouse." The little boy started out. When he reached the bridge, he saw a little fish in the stream. He laid down his lunch, and started down to the stream to catch the fish. Then he saw a beautiful butterfly. He ran after the butterfly, and tried to catch it. All the time, he got farther and farther from the road. Finally, he gave up the chase. Then, he could not find the bridge. He decided to pray. He knew two prayers. The first one was: "Now I lay me down to sleep!" That did not fit his case. So he decided to pray the other one — The Lord's Prayer. Kneeling down, he prayed aloud, "Our Father!" Instantly, he heard behind him a voice. It was the voice of his own earthly father. Father had followed him, because he knew it was his first day in school, and knew that he might need help. The boy grew to manhood. He said that one of the greatest lessons he ever learned was the lesson that his father was near, not only his earthly father, but his Heavenly Father also.

A Little Boy's Question

A little boy lay on his bed, having just retired for the night. Before going to sleep, he turned in the direction of the big bed on which his father lay and asked, "Father, are you there?" The answer came back, "Yes, my son!" The little boy turned over and went to sleep without any thought of harm. The little boy is now an old man of seventy. Every night, before going to sleep, he looks up to his Heavenly Father and asks, "Father are you there?" And the answer seems to come back, clear and strong, "Yes, my child, I am here!" Then, the old man turns over and goes to sleep without any thought of harm.

Protected from the Bandits

It was a terrible night in a Chinese city. The bandits had come. Hundreds of women and children went to the mission compound for shelter and protection. The missionary, Miss Monsen, was sick with malaria. Satan seemed to say to her, "What will you do when the bandits come here? What will you do when they begin firing on this compound?" Miss Monsen began to pray, "Lord, I have been teaching these people all these years that your promises are true. If your promises fail now, my mouth shall be closed forever." Then she began to encourage the frightened refugees. She encouraged them to pray and trust God to deliver them. Awful things happened all around that mission compound that night, but the compound was untouched.

In the morning, people from three different houses nearby asked, "Who were those four people, three sitting and one standing, who quietly watched from the top of your house all night long?" They were told that no one was on the housetop, but they refused to believe it, saying, "We saw them with our own eyes." Then Miss Monsen told them that God has Guardian Angels to protect his children in the hour of need and great danger.

PROMISES OF GOD

Translated Promises

An aged grandmother had great faith in God, and in His Word. A young grandson, who was attending a theological school, came to visit her. He wanted to have some fun with her and said,

"Grandmother, you know the Bible that you say that you believe in was written in Hebrew and in Greek. Great scholars have translated it into our English language. How do you know that those scholars got it right when they translated it?" "Ah, Jamie lad," she answered, "never mind about the great men. I have translated a few of them promises myself. They are ALL correct! They are ALL true! They are ALL faithful!"

Still True

A minister was going to church one Lord's Day morning. It was very cold and stormy. A neighbor called out to him, "It's very cold, sir!" "Yes," replied the minister, "God is good. His Word is *still true!*" The neighbor asked what he meant. The minister said, "Three thousand years ago, God promised that 'while the earth remaineth, seedtime and harvest, and cold and heat . . . shall not cease.' God is keeping His promise!"

He Never Disappoints

A printer in a large city sends out many packages. On every package he places his trademark. It is just a circle. Within the circle is his name and the words, "I never disappoint!" Every promise of God could bear this trademark: "God never disappoints!" God always keeps His Word!

"Proved"

An old man was visited by his minister. When the minister called, the old man was sitting in his chair holding his Bible. The minister took the Bible and looked through it. He noticed that in many places, in the margin of the Bible,

was written the word, "Proved!" He came to this verse: "God is our refuge and strength, a very present help in trouble." By this verse was written the word, "Proved!" And so it went on through the Bible. The dear old man had written, "Proved!" by each promise of God that he had tried, and found *true* in his own life.

He Will Remember

An aged Christian said to his young pastor, "Pastor, I am dying. For years, I have been resting on the promises of God. But this morning I can't remember one of them. What shall I do?" The pastor said, "Do you think God will forget any of His promises?" The aged Christian said, "Praise God! He will not forget any of His promises. I will just fall asleep, trusting Him to remember His precious promises to me!"

Unclaimed Promises

A poor old lady applied for relief. A man went to her home to investigate her circumstances. As he sat talking to the old lady, he saw something on the wall that attracted his attention. He asked, "What is that on the wall?" She replied, "I don't know exactly what it is, but it is a paper my uncle sent me. I don't like to throw it away, so I just keep it there in remembrance of him." He asked, "Don't you know what it is? It is a bank check. Look! There is the name of the bank on which the check is drawn, and it says, 'Pay to Jennie Johnson the sum of five thousand dollars,' and at the bottom is your uncle's name." "What," cried the poor old lady, "have I been living in poverty all these years when my uncle intended for me to have all of that money?"

In God's Word are many precious promises. God wants us to have faith and "cash in" these promises, but many of us are living in spiritual poverty and are not possessing the blessings He has planned for us.

Examine His Promises

A Christian who had been ill felt that his faith was failing him. A friend said to him, "Are you not making the mistake of examining your faith rather than *the promises of God* upon which your faith should rest? If you were traveling a new highway, and approached a bridge, whose strength you did not know, would you stop to examine your faith in that bridge, or would you get out of the car and examine the bridge, and when satisfied with the bridge cross over it with confidence? So I beg you, dear friend, look not at your faith, but look away to the promises of God. Remember, His promises will *never* fail!"

QUIET HOUR

"It's a Good Deal Cleaner"

A Scotch laddie worked for a farmer. Often when the farmer told him to do something, he would ask, "Why?" This annoyed the farmer. One day the farmer handed the boy a market basket and said, "Go down by the creek and fill this basket with water." The laddie asked, "Why?" The old man said, "None of your 'whys.' I am paying for your time, and you do as you are told to do." The boy went to the creek, waded in, and dipped the basket into the water. When he lifted the basket up, the water ran out. Disgusted, he said, "The basket won't hold water." "Dip it again," the farmer said. The lad obeyed and again the water ran through the basket. "Fill it again," said the farmer. The lad replied, "I'll fill it one more time, and if it does not hold the water this time, you will no more make a fool of me." For the third time the boy filled the basket with water. When the water ran out, he angrily took the basket and flung it over into the grass. The old farmer picked it up good naturedly. Then he held it up between him and the sun and examined it carefully. "It's a good deal cleaner than it was, and that is what it needed," he said.

God wants His children to be clean. We are made clean through the washing of the Word. What we need is daily, thoughtful, careful, prayerful reading of the Word.

A student in college found himself overtaxed with study. It was just before examinations. There was little, or no time for prayer and Bible reading. The student felt that he must have a quiet time with God every day. He had been neglecting the quiet hour and had been missing it greatly. He knew that his spiritual life was suffering because of it. So he began to get up early e v e r y morning and spent an hour alone with God, reading His Word and praying. To his surprise, he DID MORE in his studies in a single week than he had accomplished in a month before. God blessed him because of the quiet hour.

Stopping to Listening

A man, working in an ice plant, lost his watch in the sawdust. It was a valuable watch. So he and his fellow workmen searched for it for more than two hours. But they were unable to find it. They left the plant for lunch. When they returned, they found a little boy with the watch in his hand. "How did you ever find it?" they asked. He replied, "I just lay down in the sawdust and LISTENED and I heard it ticking!"

We cannot find God by intensive, bustling search. We find Him when we are STILL and LISTENING.

"Silence! God Is Speaking

Some years ago, an earthquake rocked the city of Charleston, S.C. An aged Negro preacher was just beginning his sermon when the first tremor of the earthquake came. All was silence for a moment. Then, a great upheaval was felt. Lifting his eyes from his sermon notes, the aged minister said, "God is now speaking. It is time for us to be silent!"

'Midst the upheavals of earth, let us be silent and listen to God's voice.

Food for the Soul

A little boy in Japan went to school one day without eating his breakfast. His teacher asked, "Why didn't you eat your breakfast?" Didn't you have any food in the house?" The little boy said, "Oh, yes, we had plenty of food; but this morning I got up late. I did not have time to eat breakfast. I had only time to take food for my *soul*. So I read my Bible, and I came to school without any breakfast!"

God's Word Makes Us Clean

A man who was dissatisfied with his sinful life, came to Dr. R. A. Torrey and explained his trouble. Dr. Torrey suggested that he read some Book in the Bible twelve times a day for a month. He suggested that the man try the Book of Second Peter.

The man and his wife followed the suggestion. They read the Book of Second Peter, three or four times in the morning, two or three times at noon, and several times in the evening. Soon, the man was talking Second Peter to every one he met. Soon the song of Heaven was singing in his soul. He read Second Peter on his knees, marking the verses which touched his heart. Teardrops mingled with the crayon markings. The man said to his wife, "See how I have ruined this part of my Bible!"

"Yes," she said, "but as the pages have been getting black, your *life* has been getting *white* and beautiful!"

Much Time in His Presence

A dear saint of God said, "It is my ambition to be like Christ every day. I want His meekness, His gentleness, His patience, His holy obedience to the will of God. I talk about the joy of being with Christ when He comes again. That would be mere empty talk, unless I am seeking to be like Him now. How could I talk of the joy of being with Him if I did not give Him five minutes of my company throughout the day. If I want to be like Him day by day I *must* spend much time in His presence."

God's Sunshine

An old violinist was poor, but he owned a violin which never failed to charm others with its beautiful tone.

The old violin always awakened responsive chords in the hearts of the listeners. Some one asked the violinist about his instrument. He held it tenderly in his hand and said, "A great deal of sunshine must have gone into this wood, and what has gone in, comes out."

How much of God's sunshine has entered into your life? How much time do you spend in the radiance of His presence, reading His Word and meditating upon it? If you get His sunshine into your soul, remember that the sunshine will surely come out and your life will bring blessings to others.

REPENTANCE

Penance or Repentance

A minister asked if anyone knew the difference between penance and repentance. A little girl said, "I think it is like this: Judas did penance and he went out and hanged himself; but Peter repented and wept bitterly."

That was a good answer. Judas was filled with remorse for betraying Jesus. He gave back the silver pieces to the priests, and went and hanged himself. Peter was truly sorrowful for denying Jesus. He wept bitterly. He came back to his Lord, and served Him faithfully for many years. True repentance means that we are sorry for our sins, that we forsake our sins, and turn to the Lord.

The Bookseller Needed Repentance

A Christian man tried to lead a young bookseller to the Lord. He read many Bible verses to the young man, explaining the way of salvation. As it was getting late, the Christian asked the young man to go to his room and read the verses from the Bible over again, seek light from them, and return the next evening. When the young man came back there was joy in his face. He said, "Everything is all right now. I surrendered unto Christ at two o'clock this morning."

"What was your trouble?" asked the Christian man. "What was holding you back?"

"Well, you see, I am a bookseller. I sell all kinds of books. Some are good; some are bad; some are indifferent. I sell stuff to the young people that is terrible. If they read it, it will drag them down into hell. I have my living to make. Last night I had a battle to fight in my soul. But I read the verses in my Bible, and at two A.M., God changed my mind. I saw the horror of what I have been doing. God gave me real repentance. Then Christ came into my heart. Now the peace of God floods my soul."

Most Unusual

A gentleman attended church one Sunday morning. On his way home after the service, he was fussing and fuming. Said he, "Here is gratitude for you. My family and I have been most kind to this young preacher. And this is the return we get. He gets up in the pulpit and tells us that we are great sinners unless we repent. He says that our good works go for nothing with God; that we are sinners and need to repent. That sermon would be all right in a penitentiary, but not in a genteel, respectable church. It is most unusual to tell people like us that we are sinners and need to repent."

His Trouble Was Not Doubts

An army officer had two days' leave before sailing for the Pacific battle front. He called upon a minister and said, "I don't want to go into battle in my present state of mind. I have lost my faith. I am beset by doubts. I cannot pray."

The minister said, "Do not tell me about your doubts. Tell me about your sins."

There was a moment or two of silence. Then the minister asked the officer if he had any pictures of his family in his wallet. The offcer did. He took the pictures out and placed them on the desk where they both could see them.

Suddenly the officer burst into tears. Then his story was told — the story of a life filled with sin. What that officer needed was repentance.

Deathbed Repentance

A preacher asked a Christian woman if she thought a deathbed repentance could do away with a lifetime of sin. She answered, "No, it can't, but Calvary can." If we are truly sorry for our sins and turn from them to Christ the Saviour, He will forgive our sins and blot them out forever.

The Meaning of Repentance

A man once asked a Sunday School class what was meant by the word, "Repentance." Then a little girl said, "I think repentance is being sorry enough to *quit!*" God wants us to be so sorry

for our sins that we will turn from them and come to Him.

"Except Ye Repent"

A student from Moody Bible Institute was talking with a man at the Pacific Garden Mission about his soul. The man said, "I do not believe the Bible." The student repeated one verse: "Except ye repent, ye shall all likewise perish."

The man laughed and said, "I told you I don't believe the Bible."

Again, the student quoted, "Except ye repent, ye shall all likewise perish."

The man became angry. He said, "You disgusting fellow. What is the use of telling me that?"

Again the student said, "Except ye repent, ye shall all likewise perish." The man struck the student between the eyes with his fist, sending him one way and his Bible the other way.

Quietly, the student got up and said, "My friend, God loves you. Remember this: 'Except ye repent, ye shall all likewise perish.'"

The next night, the man was in the mission before the meeting began. He said, "I could not sleep last night. All over the wall of my room, I read the words, 'Except ye repent, ye shall all likewise perish.' I saw them on my pillow. When I got up this morning, I saw them at the breakfast table. All day long, I have seen them. I cannot get away from them. I know that except I repent, I shall perish. I have come back here to get right with God!"

Like a Dead Tree

A man was one day felling trees in the woods. He saw a dead tree lifting its dry, leafless branches into the air. Said he, "That tree is fit only to be burned. It is dead and dry; so I will cut it down." Instantly, the thought came, "In God's sight, am I not a dead tree, fit only to be burned?" He struck a few blows with his ax at the dead tree. Then, the thought came, "Will God say of me, 'Cut it down'?" Suddenly, he shouldered his ax, and started home. When he reached home, he fell upon his knees before God, truly repentant. He knew that he was a lost sinner, and he sought God's forgiveness in Christ.

"Please Forgive Me"

Some years ago, a little girl wrote a letter to President Cleveland. Her letter has been saved, and put into a collection of letters which are at the White House. Her letter says, "Dear President, I am in a dreadful state of mind. I thought I would write and tell you all. About two years ago, I used two postage stamps that had been used before on letters. Perhaps, I used more than two stamps but I can only remember doing it twice. I did not know I had done wrong, until lately. My mind is worried. I think about what I have done night and day. Now, dear President, will you please forgive me? I promise you I will never do it again. Enclosed find cost of *three* stamps. Please forgive me. I was but thirteen years old, and I am heartily sorry for what I have done. From one of your subjects!"

RESURRECTION

The Empty Tomb

A missionary was preaching in a bazaar in one of the villages of northern India. As he closed, a Mohammedan came up and said, "We have one thing you have not and it is better than anything you have." The missionary said, "Please tell me what it is." The Mohammedan replied, "When we go to Mecca, our sacred city, we find at least a coffin. When you Christians go to Jerusalem, your sacred city, you find nothing but an empty grave." The missionary smiled and said, "That is the difference between our religions. Mohammed is dead. Mohammed is in his coffin. The founders of all false systems of religion are in their coffins. But Jesus Christ is not here. He is risen. All power in Heaven and on earth belongs to Him."

The Way Home

A little girl was walking in a light-hearted, care-free manner through a graveyard. Night was approaching. Someone asked her if she was not afraid. "Oh, no," replied the girl. "I only cross the graveyard to get home."

Death is the way home, to Heaven.

He Talked with Jesus

Two young men were discussing the resurrection. They said that it was impossible for them to believe that Jesus rose from the dead. Just then, a deacon of a nearby church walked by. One of the young men, in a joking way, called to him, "Say, deacon, tell us why you believe that Jesus rose from the dead." The deacon stopped. He said, "One reason is because I was talking with Him for a half hour this morning!"

We do not need any proof of the resurrection of Christ when we have His living presence in our lives.

He Lives and Loves Forever

A father told his little four-year-old boy how the Lord Jesus died upon the Cross. When he had finished the story, the little fellow had a sad expression on his face. He asked, "Father, did Jesus really die?" "Yes," said the father; "He died on the cross!" "Oh," said the little boy, "then Jesus cannot love me now, because He is dead." Instantly, the father replied, "But son, He can love you now. He did die on the Cross, but He rose from the dead on the third day. Now He lives and He loves for ever."

Which Christ?

A very learned man once said to a little girl who believed in Jesus, "My poor little girl, you don't know whom you believe in. There have been many christs. In which one of them do you believe?" The little girl replied, "I know which one I believe in. I believe in the Christ who rose from the dead!"

The Mighty Deliverer

A little Jewish girl in Russia learned large portions of the New Testament from a boy who had memorized much of the New Testament. It was not long until she gave her heart and life to the Lord Jesus. Then, she could not keep silent about her Saviour. Her father was absent from home. When he returned some days later, she ran to meet him, saying, "Father, I love Jesus. He loved the little children. He is my Sav-iour! He is my Saviour!" The father was very angry. He told her to never speak of Jesus again.

Soon, the child was stricken with scarlet fever. The doctor gave no hope for her recovery. As the girl lay on her deathbed, the father prayed the prayer of the Jews. Suddenly, the girl opened her eyes. She repeated accurately the account of the raising of Jairus' daughter. When she had finished, her head fell back, and she was gone!

The father fell to his knees. He began to pray, saying, "O Jesus, Thou who didst raise up the daughter of Jairus, raise up my little Deborah, and I will believe in Thee, and serve Thee as Israel's Messiah!" The Lord Jesus heard the anguished cry. He raised up the little girl. She rose from her bed, alive and well! That Jewish family became Christians. They believed in the Lord Jesus as their Saviour and Messiah.

They Really Believed

A father and mother lost three little children in one week by diptheria. Only the little three-year-old girl escaped. On Easter morning, the father, mother, and child were in Sunday School. The father was superintendent. He led his school in worship and read the Easter message from the Bible without a break in his voice. Many in the school were weeping. But the faces of the father and mother remained serene and calm. "How can they do it?" men and women asked each other as they left the church.

A fifteen-year-old boy, walking home with his father, said, "Father, I guess the superintendent and his wife *really believe it*, don't they?"

"Believe what?" asked the father.

"The whole, big thing, all of it! *Easter!* You know!"

"Of course," answered the father. "All Christians believe it!"

"Not the way they do," said the boy, and he began to whistle.

Let us believe the "whole, big thing, all of it, *Easter.*"

Getting Our Loved Ones Back

A faithful missionary in distant Korea sat by the bedside of his dying wife. For fifteen years, they had toiled together, preaching the glorious Gospel of Jesus Christ. Now, her summons had come, and the sad husband sat waiting for the end. The wife said to him, "Do not grieve for me, my dear. You will get me back, you will get me back!"

A month later, the missionary sat watching his only little boy who was dying. He was going to be with the same Lord to whom his mother had gone. The little fellow had the same message for the sorrowing father as his mother. Said he, "Don't cry, Papa! I see a great shining light, I want to go. Don't cry, Papa. You will get me back, you will get me back!"

A few days later, the father was riding in the funeral train behind the body of his little boy. He was riding in a chair, covered with curtains, borne by the natives. He heard the voice of a woman weeping outside. Presently, the voice of another Korean woman spoke up and said, "Why are you weeping?"

"I am weeping for the foreigner who has lost his little boy."

Then the answer came, "Don't weep for the foreigner. Weep for yourself. You have lost a little girl, and you will never get her back. I have lost a little boy, and I will never get him back. But these foreigners have a strange way of getting back their dead!"

The Dead Shall Live

The great chemist, Lord Faraday, had a helper. One day, the helper accidentally knocked a little silver cup into a jar of acid. It disappeared, being dissolved by the acid. Faraday, put some chemical into the jar, and in a moment, every particle of silver descended to the bottom of the jar. Then the great chemist lifted it out, a shapeless mass of silver. He sent it to a silversmith, and the silversmith made another cup of it.

If a chemist like Faraday can recover a silver cup, which has been dissolved by acid, and has completely disappeared, surely God can restore the scattered dust of His saints. What a wonderful day it will be when He calls forth His saints from the dead! Jesus said, "Verily, verily, I say unto you, The hour is coming, and now is, when the dead shall hear the voice of the Son of God: and they that hear shall live" (*John 5:25*).

Two Little Slave Boys

An Arab master had two Negro boys who were slaves. He taught them to believe in Mohammed. He told them that the body of Mohammed was preserved in a coffin in the city of Medina in Arabia.

One day, the boys went to market. There they heard a missonairy tell about the death, burial, and resurrection of Jesus. That night, in the darkness of their little hut, they talked the matter over. One of them said, "Our master tells us that Mohammed is dead, and that his body is in a coffin. The white missionary tells us that Jesus, the Son of God, who came to die for us, rose again and is *alive*. What you you think about it?" The other replied, "I think

I would rather believe in the *living One!*" So the little boys placed their faith in Jesus, the Son of God.

Do *you* have *real* faith in Jesus, "the living One?"

Joyful News

When the news of Wellington's victory over Napoleon reached London many years ago, it was not sent by telegraph or radio. The news was brought to the Southern coast of England by a sailing vessel. Then, it was wigwagged overland toward London by semiphore, or signaling flags. Atop Winchester Cathedral, the long-awaited message was spelled out. "Wellington Defeated —." Then a dense fog settled over the land, and the signals could no longer be seen. All of London was in despair: Wellington defeated! Presently, the fog lifted. The signaling on top of the Cathedral became visible again! Now, the complete message was spelled out. "Wellington Defeated the Enemy!" The joyful news spread, and the land was filled with rejoicing!

When the Lord Jesus was laid in the grave, sadness filled the hearts of His followers. It seemed that the enemy, *death,* had defeated the Lord Jesus. Then, the clouds of gloom and darkness were lifted. The glad news that Christ had risen from the grave, thrilled the hearts of the followers of Jesus. The Lord had defeated death!

A Living God is Better

A missionary in India was talking to a group of women. He told them how God loves them, and how the Lord Jesus laid down His life for them. Then he told them how the Lord Jesus arose from the dead, and is *now* a *living* God. Said the women, "The foreigner's God is better than ours. Ours has no life."

The Keeper of the Key

A sweet Christian girl had died and had been laid away in a vault in the cemetery. The sad father turned and gave one last, lingering look behind, as he handed the key of the vault to the keeper of the cemetery. A Christian friend noticed the father's despair, and said, "You think the key to your little girl's last resting place on earth is in the hand of the keeper of the cemetery. That is not true. The key to your darling girl's grave hangs at the girdle of the Son of God. Some glad day, He will come and use it! And your little girl will be delivered from death."

RICHES

A Night's Lodging

A minister spoke to an audience in a mission on the subject, "Such as I have I give thee." These poor people had nothing to give, so they thought. When the meeting was over, all went home but one man. He went to the minister and asked what he could give. He had nothing, except a card for a night's lodging. As he went out, he saw near the door, an old man who was even poorer than himself, and who was shivering in the cold night air. He led this old man to his lodging house where he could have a nice warm bed for the night. Then he himself went out into the snow. He had given what he had.

His Treasure Was Left Behind

Two friends were talking. One told the other about a "good" man who had died and left thirty thousand dollars. The other one said, "What a pity that the man left the money behind when he might have sent it on ahead! He is not likely now to ever hear from his money again!"

The Lord Jesus said, "Lay not up for yourselves treasures upon earth . . . But lay up for yourselves treasures in heaven."

Useless Money

A little girl tightly clasped in her hand a penny. She entered a candy store to make a purchase. Laying her penny on the counter, she looked in the showcase to see what she would like. Finally, she pointed a chubby finger at some candy, and said, "I'll take that." "That costs two cents," answered the clerk. The little girl made another selection. "That costs five cents," said the clerk. Again and again, the little girl made a choice, but the candy all cost too much. Finally, she turned away and started to leave. "Wait, little girl," called the clerk; "you have forgotten your penny!" "I don't want it," was her reply; "it won't buy anything!"

God can use all of our pennies in His work.

Whose Money Was Lost?

A little boy started to Sunday school with two nickels. One was for the Lord, and one was for himself. On the way to church, the little boy lost one nickel. "There goes the Lord's nickel," he said.

How sad it was that the little boy said the lost nickel was the Lord's and not his!

The Difference

A rich but godless farmer heard about the death of an aged Christian, whom he had known years before. The Christian's death had been an happy, triumphant death. When the rich farmer heard about it, he said, "You may wonder why I cannot be quiet and happy when I think about death. But there is a difference: That man went to his treasure, and I will leave ALL of my treasure behind!"

Don't Forget Heaven

Dr. George W. Truett was entertained one time in the home of a wealthy oil man in Texas. After dinner, the man took him up to the roof of his house, and showed him large fields of oil derricks. He said, "Dr. Truett, I came to this country twenty-five years ago without a penny. Now I own everything as far as you can see!" He motioned southward toward the oil derricks. Turning, he motioned eastward toward waving fields of grain. Turning again, he motioned northward toward huge herds of cattle. Then, turning once more, he motioned westward toward a great virgin forest. Said the man, *All this is mine!* Twenty-five years ago, I was penniless, but I worked hard and saved, and to-day, I own everything you can see in any direction from this roof!"

The man paused, expecting to hear Dr. Truett's praise. But to his astonishment, the praise did not come. Dr. Truett laid a loving hand on his shoulder, pointed toward the sky, and asked, *"My friend, how much do you own in that direction?"* The man dropped his head in shame, and said, "I never thought about that!"

How sad it is when one lays up treasures on earth, and forgets about

Heaven. How important it is for all Christians to lay up their treasures, day by day, in Heaven. We must live for God and not for self. We must live for Heaven and not for the perishing things of this world.

Gowns or Crowns

Some years ago, there appeared one day, in the same daily paper, the stories of two American women. One had just spent $70,000 for dresses from Paris. The other, a real Christian, being questioned in a legal matter, had modestly admitted that she had given many millions of her estate to various righteous causes. Someone on reading the two stories said, "It is all a matter of taste. One wants Paris gowns; the other wants Heavenly crowns!"

For Eternity

Roger W. Babson, the financial expert, said, "One dollar spent for lunch lasts five hours. One dollar spent for a necktie lasts five weeks. One dollar spent for a cap lasts five months. One dollar spent for an automobile lasts five years. One dollar spent for water power, or a railroad, lasts five generations. One dollar spent for *God* lasts for *eternity*!"

Considerable Property Above

A minister was driving home with a friend after a funeral. "Poor R—" said the friend, "he did not leave much property. It is too bad. He worked hard and made plenty of money, but he was too tender-hearted. He was always giving his money to help something or someone!" The minister listened politely. Then he said, "I suppose you are right about his being poor, and having no property here on earth, but from what I have known of his life, I believe he must have considerable property to go on to. He must have considerable property *above!*"

Not Taxable

A tax collector called at the home of a poor minister, to find out the value of his property and to determine the amount of his taxes.

"I am a rich man," said the minister.

Quickly, the official sharpened his pencil. Then he asked, "Well, what do you own?"

"I am the possessor of *everlasting life*, which my Saviour purchased for me on the Cross. I have a place in the eternal city, which my Saviour is now preparing for me. I have a brave, pious wife, and Solomon said, 'Who can find a virtuous woman? for her price is far *above* rubies.' I have healthy and obedient children. I have a merry heart, which doeth me good like medicine, and which enables me to pass through life joyfully."

"What else do you have?" asked the tax collector.

"That is all," replied the minister.

The official closed his book, and took his hat, and said, "You are indeed a rich man, sir, but your riches are not subject to taxation!"

How true it is that, "The blessing of the Lord, it maketh *rich,* and He addeth no sorrow with it" *(Prov. 10:22).*

Cheap Imitations

During the war, a lot of cheap, imitation jewelry was sent to the Armed Forces in the Pacific. It was used as barter with the natives. High army and navy officials revealed that the natives of the Pacific Islands would perform most dangerous and hard tasks in exchange for the cheap jewelry. They liked the glitter of the trinkets and baubles!

We smile when we think of the natives doing hard work for mere trinkets. But we must be sure that we are not doing the same thing. Everything that Satan has to offer are mere trinkets or trifles: money, pleasure, fame. The native does not know the difference between precious stones and imitation jewelry. But we should know the difference between the passing, transient things of this earth and the eternal riches of Heaven.

Esau sold his birthright for a mess of pottage. Judas betrayed the Saviour for thirty pieces of silver. What trifle, or bauble, is Satan dangling before *your* eyes to cause *you* to do his work? We must not let Satan fool us. We must never live for the passing trifles of this world. We must live for God and for the eternal riches of Heaven.

He "Died Rich"

Many years ago, a man went west to hunt for gold. At last he found what he thought was gold in the midst of the shifting dunes of Death Valley, California. Soon, because he had not given thought and care, he found himself without water and without food in Death Valley. There was no escape from death. So, he scribbled on a piece of paper the words, *"died rich!"* Then hugging a small boulder of mica, which resembled gold, he passed out into eternity! Only recently, a party of tourists discovered the skeleton in the cabin. An old miner's pick lay near it. A rusty watch, not running, was found also. That man gave his life seeking earthly riches. He thought that he had them within his grasp, but he was mistaken.

The Child of a King

Once there lived in Kansas a little boy named Robert Edward Neighbour. One day, little Eddie went into the Y. M. C. A. building. He heard music. It came from behind closed doors. Peeking through the doors, he saw the son of a wealthy man seated at the piano. The young man was playing a beautiful song. Little Eddy thought, "I wish I were rich and could play the piano like that!"

Just then, the young man began to sing:

"My Father is rich in houses and lands,
  He holdeth the wealth of the world in His hands!"

Little Eddie thought: "My, I didn't know his father was that rich! He shouldn't sing about how rich his father is, but I guess I'll stay and listen."

Little Eddie's eyes grew large as the young man continued singing:

"I'm the child of a King, the child of a King!"
"Of rubies and diamonds, of silver and gold,
His coffers are full, — He has riches untold."

Then the young man came to the chorus of the song and began to sing:

Little Eddie said to himself, "I know better. Your father may be rich, but he is not a king!"

Then, little Eddie heard the words:

"With Jesus, my Saviour,
  I'm the child of a King!"

Suddenly, little Eddie's eyes filled with tears of thankfulness. He said to himself: "Why, I have the *same Father myself*! That is my kind, Heavenly Father the young man is singing about! I, too, am a child of a King!"

Lay Not Treasures upon Earth

The secretary of a missionary society called on a merchant, and asked him to help in the work. The merchant made a check for two hundred and fifty dollars and handed it to the secretary. Just at that moment, a cablegram was brought in. The merchant read it and looked troubled. Said he, "This cablegram tells me that one of my ships has been wrecked and the cargo lost. It makes a great difference in my affairs. I shall have to write you another check!" The secretary understood perfectly and handed back the check.

The merchant wrote another check and handed it over to the secretary. The secretary looked at it with amazement. It was for one thousand dollars! "Haven't you made a mistake?", he asked. "No, I haven't made a mistake," said the merchant. "That cablegram was a message from my Father in Heaven. It said to my heart, 'Lay not up for yourselves treasures upon earth.' "

Who Was Rich?

There once lived a good farmer. He worked hard, but he had no money laid away in the bank. During the years, he used all his money to help others. He never turned a poor man, hungry, away from his door. He gave his four children the best education he could. One became a minister. Two became teachers. One became a civil engineer. He always shared his home with others. He gave a home to some children who were left as orphans when a friend died. He gave a home to his wife's crippled niece. He gave a home to a little boy that he rescued from the slums of the city. God was good to the farmer. God blessed the farm and the crops. Instead of hoarding his dollars, the farmer spent them on *others*. When he died, many were the kind words said about the farmer.

Near-by there lived another farmer. He was mean and selfish. Said this farmer, "So my neighbor, poor old Gould, is dead. He died without a penny in the bank, but look at me! I started with nothing, and now I own all the broad fields, clear down to the creek! When wife and I started to keep house, I got this iron savings bank. Every penny we could save went into its jaws. It's surprising how many *pennies* you can save when you want to. Other people ate meat; we ate molasses. Other wives wore silk; my wife wore calico. Other men sent their boys and girls away to school; I taught mine to work early and late. I have wasted no money on churches, or poor people, and now I own all that land down to the creek! I am worth $100,000!"

This farmer had lived for *self*. He had saved all his riches for *self*. He had given to no one. He had not helped God's work. In God's sight, he was a *pauper*. So are all who lay up treasures for themselves, and are not rich toward God. How greatly does God bless the liberal soul. God says, "The liberal soul shall be made fat" *(Prov. 11:25)!*

SALVATION

Christ Did His Part

A colored man, who had recently been saved from sin and its power, gave his testimony in a meeting. He told how Christ had won his heart and had forgiven his sins and delivered him from the power of satan. He spoke only of Christ and His work; he said nothing of any efforts on his part. The leader of the meeting knew little about salvation by grace, apart from works. As the negro's testimony ended, he said, "Our brother has told us only of the Lord's part in his salvation. It would be interesting to know something of his part. Brother, what did you do before the Lord saved you? What was your part?

The negro stood to his feet quickly and said, "Yes, sah, I clear forgot to tell about it. I did my part for thirty years, running away from God as fast as my sins could carry me. That was my part. Then God took after me until He run me down. That was His part."

How thankful we are for God's part in our salvation. "The Son of man is come to seek and to save that which was lost" (*Lu. 19:10*).

A Saved Sinner

A Scotchman, who was a prize fighter and gambler, was wonderfully saved by the Lord Jesus. He became a mighty preacher and soul winner. One night, just before he arose to speak in a certain city, some one sent an envelope up to the platform. When he opened it, he found on a piece of paper a long list of the sins and crimes he had committed in that very city. At first, he felt that he must run away. Then, he changed his mind. He stood boldly and said, "Friends, I am accused of crimes and sins committed in this very city. I will read them to you." One after another he read the charges. After each one he said, "I am guilty!" When he had finished the whole list, he paused for a moment, and then he said, "You perhaps wonder how I dare to come and speak to you about righteousness and truth with a list of crimes like that against my name. I will tell you: 'This is a faithful saying, and worthy of all acceptation, that Christ Jesus came into the world to save sinners; *of whom I am chief.*' "

Simply Trusting

A doctor had been under conviction of sin. One day, he visited a patient who was a Christian and happy in the Lord. He said to the sick man, "I want you to tell me just what it is — this faith in Jesus that brings peace." The patient replied, "Doctor, I am sick. I know I can do nothing for myself. So I have put my case in your hands. I am trusting you. That is exactly what every sinner must do to be saved. He must trust in the Lord Jesus. He must put his 'case' in the hands of the Lord Jesus, and *know* that all will be well!"

"Is that all?" exclaimed the doctor. "Is it simply trusting in the Lord Jesus?"

The patient replied, "Yes, doctor, He has done the work. He died on the Cross for us. When He died, He said, 'It is finished' (*John 19:30*). 'Whosoever believeth in Him [shall] not perish, but have everlasting life' (*John 3:16*)."

"I get it," said the doctor; "He does the work. I simply trust Him." From that sick room, the doctor went away rejoicing in Christ his Saviour!

The Right Train

An elderly woman was starting a journey on a railway train. Many trains moved from the station in different directions, during the day. She was afraid that she was on the *wrong* train. She asked several of the passengers, "Is this the right train to Bay City, Michigan?" They assured her that it was the right train, but she was not quite satisfied. Presently, the conductor came into the coach. She motioned to him. When he reached her side, she asked, "Is this the right train to Bay City, Michigan?" He said, 'Yes, madam, this is the right train." Completely satisfied, she settled back on her seat, and was fast asleep before the train pulled away from the station!

We want to go to Heaven. We want life eternal. We can safely trust in the Word of God, which says, "Believe on the Lord Jesus Christ, and *thou shalt be saved*"; "He that hath the Son hath life; and he that hath not the Son of God hath not life."

Two Soldiers Saved

Major Whittle related this incident: "When I left home, my mother sent me away with prayer. I was not a Christian. I was wounded in battle one day. When I was taken to the hospital, I started reading the Bible my mother had given me. I began to read the Book of Matthew. The more I read, the more I wanted to read. Soon, I saw that the hope of my salvation lay in the Lord Jesus. He alone could save me from sin. But I delayed to accept God's salvation.

"One day, the nurse came to my bed and said, 'There is a lad of nineteen here who is dying. He wants some one to pray with him. You are the only one I know that can do it.' I told the nurse that I could not help the lad, for I was not a Christian. The nurse asked me to come and do what I could. When I reached the bedside of that dying lad, I knelt down and began to pray. I confessed my *own* sin, and asked the Lord to save me! Then, I began to pray for that boy. Both of us found salvation in Christ."

Not Religion but Salvation

A young man came to the Dr. C. I. Scofield, and, with smiles wreathing his face, said, "Dr. Scofield, I got religion this summer!"

"That's good," replied Dr. Scofield, "and while you were getting religion, did you get *saved?*"

"Why, isn't getting religion getting saved?" questioned the surprised young man.

"No," replied Dr. Scofield, "Jesus didn't come that we might get religion, He came that we might have *life* and have it more abundantly!"

The young man saw "the point," and received by faith, eternal life, God's gift.

Salvation Is Free

A minister was talking with an old man who seemed anxious about his salvation. He had great trouble in making the old man understand that God is ready to pardon our sins; that He is ready to give us the gift of salvation through the precious Blood of Jesus.

Finally, the minister said, "Suppose I were to go to a shop and buy something for you, and pay for it, and tell you to go and get it. Need you take any money with you?"

"No," said the old man, "it would be paid for."

"Need you make any promise to pay at some future time?"

"No," said the old man, "I should have it for nothing."

Then the minister said, "The Lord Jesus has paid the *full* price for the forgiveness of your sin. He had the wrath, the pain, the punishment. He bore it all; He paid the *whole!* Now, you may have pardon for sin, and salvation in Him for *nothing!*"

"Oh," said the old man, as his eyes filled with tears, "I see it now. Pardon for nothing! Pardon for nothing! Christ has bought it, and He will give it to me!"

Not too Late!

One night, Dr. Hall was preaching to a large audience. He suddenly glanced toward the door, where he saw many standing. He said, "Perhaps, among those pressing in at the door, there may be one who is so miserable as to think of throwing himself over yonder bridge. His sins are heavy on his heart. He knows no way to escape. Perhaps, that one says, 'Dr. Hall, it is *too* late to talk to me.' But I say to such a one, 'Stop! Stop! There is hope for you. Christ died for you. He will forgive you. He will save *even* you from the bondage of sin.'"

A few weeks later, Dr. Hall was told that in the audience that night, near the door, there had stood a woman who had made up her mind to throw herself over the bridge that night. She had come into the church to wait until darkness came, so the police could not see her and stop her. As she stood there, she had heard the message of Dr. Hall. Instead of going to the bridge and ending her life, she had come to Christ! She had gone back to her home to pray and to become a *true* and *happy* Christian!

Double Security

A Christian man urged a friend to become a Christian. The friend said, "I will decide for Christ when I go to bed tonight."

The Christian asked, "Why are you putting it off for a few hours?"

The man replied, "I am not sure I can hold out."

The Christian said, "Listen to these words of Jesus: 'Neither shall any man pluck them out of My hand . . . and no man is able to pluck them out of My Father's hand.' You have double security: you will be kept by Jesus, and by God, the Father. Won't you trust Him *now?*"

The friend said, "I will trust Him *now.*"

"He Took Me In"

One afternoon, little Helen came home from a children's meeting. She rushed into her father's study, threw her arms around his neck, and said, "Daddy, I'm a Christian!"

"Well, Helen," said her father, "I am so glad to hear that! When did you become a Christian?"

"This afternoon," she said. He asked her to tell him what had happened.

"Oh," said she, "the teacher said that Jesus Christ was there in the room, and that if we would receive Him, He would come into our hearts, and make us His own. I received Him as my Saviour, and He took me in."

"Well, Helen," said the father, "that is fine, but how do you *know* that when you received Jesus as your Saviour, He took you in?"

The little girl looked into her father's face and said, "Why, Daddy, I *know* it, because Jesus said He would!"

Not Cheap

A miner said to a minister, "I would give anything to believe that God would forgive my sins, but I can't believe that He will forgive them if I just turn to Him in faith. It is too cheap!"

The minister, who was going down into the coal mine in an elevator, said to the miner, "Are you sure that all I have to do to get down into the mine is to get in this elevator? That's too easy! *That's too cheap!*"

Seriously, the miner replied, "It may be cheap for you, but it wasn't cheap for the company. The company spent a lot of money sinking that elevator shaft, and one man lost his life during the work."

The minister said, "My friend, so it is with your salvation. It may be cheap for you, for *all* you have to do is to *believe* in Christ, the Saviour. But your salvation cost God a *lot*. The Lord Jesus died on the Cross for *you*. He paid the cost. He paid the price!"

Let Him In

Some one left an almanac at the door of a little cottage. In the center of the almanac was a picture of the Lord Jesus knocking at the door of the heart. The mother hung the almanac on the kitchen wall. When the little boy came home from school, he looked at it. He wanted to know about the picture. His mother was busy preparing dinner, and would not answer his questions. Presently, Father came in from work. "Who is the Man, Daddy? Why is He knocking at the door?" the little fellow asked. The father did not answer the question, but the little boy kept asking it. At last the father said: "It is the Lord Jesus knocking at the door. He wants to get in!" "Then, why don't they let Him in?" asked the little boy. Dinner came just then. The father changed the subject.

Again and again, during the following days, the little boy kept asking the question, "Why don't they let Him in?" Soon, the question was ringing in the father's ears, and in the father's heart. At last, one day, he fell on his knees, and cried, "Lord Jesus, I know You are knocking at the door of my heart. Please forgive me for keeping You waiting so long. Lord Jesus, the door is open now. Won't You come right in?" The Lord Jesus heard the prayer of the man. He came into the man's heart, and washed his sins away!

In the Bible, we read: "Behold, I stand at the door, and knock: if *any man* hear My voice, and open the door, I will come in to him, and will sup with him, and he with Me" (*Rev. 3:20*).

He Is Enough

A lady, visiting in a hospital ward, found a little Irish boy. His white, thin face and emaciated form roused her deepest sympathy. He was, perhaps, fifteen years of age, but he was so small that he looked to be twelve. The lady was very kind to the lad. She visited him time and again, bringing gifts and flowers and fruit. She soon found him willing and even eager to hear about the Lord Jesus, the sinner's Saviour.

Gradually, the lady brought the boy to think upon his *own need* of a Saviour. When he began to realize that he was a sinner and needed a Saviour, he spoke of the religious rites of his church. But he never wholly left out Jesus Christ, and His death on the Cross.

One morning, the lady called and found his face aglow with joy. She asked him why he was so happy, and he replied, "Oh, Missis, I always knew that Jesus was necessary, but I never knew until yesterday that He was *enough!*"

What an important discovery the boy had made! Jesus is *necessary* for our soul's salvation, and He is *enough*,

"There is none other name under Heaven given among men, whereby we *must* be saved" (*Acts 4:12*)

"None Other Name"

In London, England, there lived a man who was worried about his sins. He wanted to be saved. He thought that he could be saved by being good and kind. One day, on his way home, he passed a corner where there sat a blind man. The blind man was reading out loud from a Bible written in Braille. The blind man could read this Bible, because the letters were raised, and he could feel them with his fingers. He could not read with his eyes. But he could read with his fingers. The blind man was reading from the Bible these words: "Neither is there salvation in any other: for there is none other name under Heaven given among men, whereby we must be saved." The blind man came to the words, "There is none other name." Then, he lost his place. He kept saying, over and over, "None other name"; "none other name"; "none other name." Some of the people, who were passing by, laughed. The man who was worried about his sins, passed on. But he kept hearing the words, "None other name." Finally, he said, "Thank You, Lord, for that blind man. Thank you for his mistake. I see now that there is none other name but Jesus. He *alone* can save me."

"Look Unto Me"

The snow was falling. A young man named Charles Spurgeon was on his way to church. He stopped in a little chapel. Only a few people were present, because of the heavy snow storm. The minister did not arrive. A working man stood up to preach. He quoted this Bible verse: "Look unto Me, and be ye saved, all the ends of the earth." He said, "My dear friends, it's no trouble to look. You don't have to lift your foot or your finger. You just *look*. You do not look at yourselves. You look at the Lord Jesus. He is the One who says, 'Look unto Me.' Do you not see Him hanging on the Cross and dying for *you?* He says, 'Look unto Me.' O poor sinner, look unto Him!" When the man had talked about ten minutes, he pointed his finger at Charles Spurgeon, and said, "Young man, you look very miserable. You will always be miserable unless you obey my text. But if you will look in faith to the Lord Jesus *this minute, you will be saved!*" Spurgeon obeyed the invitation. He looked in faith to Jesus, and was saved. Afterwards he said, "I looked at Him, and He looked at me, and we became *one* forever!"

Salvation Is for Everyone

Down in the State of Georgia there lived a young man who was a great sinner. He came to the altar during a revival meeting. At the altar he wept. How greatly did he feel the burden of his sins! The preacher asked, "Won't you take Jesus Christ as your Saviour?"

The young man said, "I am a big sinner. I don't know whether God wants anyone like me."

The preacher said, "I can show you from the Bible that God loves you and wants to save you."

The young man said, "Even if I saw my name, James Green, written in the Bible, I would not know whether God wants me. There might be another man named James Green. I am a great sinner!"

The preacher said, "My friend, God has put a word in the Bible that surely means *you*. Listen to John 3:16, 'For God *so* loved *the world,* that He gave His only begotten Son, that *whosoever* believeth in Him should not perish, but have everlasting life.' That word *whosoever* includes *every* James Green in the world. It includes *every* John Brown in the world. It includes every one, no matter what his name may be."

The poor fellow jumped up. With a smile on his face, he said, "I *know* that word *whosoever* means me, and *right now,* I will believe in the Lord Jesus as my Saviour!"

"He Lifted Me"

A little lame dog was trying to climb up the curbstone from the street to the sidewalk. The poor dog could not quite reach the top. He always fell back. Many people passed by. They watched the little dog, and laughed at him. No one offered to help him. After awhile, a workman came by. He saw the little dog and pitied him. He went over and lifted the little dog up to the sidewalk. Then, he went on his way.

That is what the Lord Jesus did for us. He left Heaven and came down to earth to lift us from sin and its ruin. He even gave His life for us upon the Cross. Then He went back up in Heaven. How we thank Him for His loving-kindness!

The Irish Landlord

In Ireland, there was a landlord on whose vast estate dwelt a number of needy tenants. The landlord was converted. He was anxious to make God's provision for salvation clear and plain to his people. So, he had posted in prominent places notices to the effect that on a given day he would be in his office from ten o'clock in the morning until twelve noon. During that time, he would pay the debts of all who brought their unpaid bills to him. The notices caused much excitement. The tenants talked much of the strange offer. Some declared it was a hoax. Others said, "There must be a 'catch' somewhere." A few said, "The landlord must be going out of his mind!"

When the announced day came, many people were seen making their way to the office. By ten o'clock, a crowd had gathered about the door. Promptly at ten, the landlord and his secretary arrived. Without saying a word to any one, they entered the office and closed the door. A great discussion began among the crowd. Was there anything to the offer? Did the landlord really mean it? Would he only make a fool out of any one who carried his bills to him? An hour passed by, and no one had gone in to present his claim. If one suggested that some one venture in first, he would be met by the angry response, "I don't owe so much. Let somebody else try it first, some one who owes more than I do!" So the precious moments passed by.

Finally, when it was nearly twelve o'clock, an aged couple, who lived at the edge of the estate, came hobbling along. In one hand, the old man had a bundle of bills clutched tightly. In quavering tones he asked, "Is it true that the landlord is paying the debts of all who come today?" "He ain't paid none yet," said one. "We think it is just a cruel joke," said another. The old couple's eyes filled with tears. "Is it all a mistake? We hoped it was true. We thought how good it would be to die free of debt!" They were turning sadly away when some one said, "Well, no one has tried him yet. Why don't you go in? If he pays your bills, come out quickly, and tell us, and then we will go in, too."

The old folks agreed. Timidly, they approached the office and opened the door. A cordial welcome awaited them. The bills were presented, and a check was made out to cover all of them. They started to leave the office, but the secretary said, "Just be seated. You must remain until the office is closed at noon." They explained that the crowd outside was waiting to hear what had happened. But the landlord said, "No, you must not tell them. You took me at my word. Your debts are paid. If they had believed me, their debts would have been paid, too!" The minutes passed by. Outside the people moved about restlessly, watching the closed door. But no one entered the office.

At exactly noon, the office door opened and the old couple came out. "Did the landlord keep his word?" the throng asked. "Yes, neighbors, here is his check, and it is as good as gold!" "Why did you not come out and tell us?" angrily asked the crowd. "He said that we must wait inside. He said that you must come as we did, taking him at his word."

A moment later, the landlord and his secretary appeared. The crowd pressed around them, holding in their hands their personal bills and crying, "Won't you do for us as you did for this couple?" The landlord said, "It is TOO LATE NOW. I gave you the opportunity. I invited you to come, but you did not believe me. If you had come, I would have paid every cent for you!" Then the landlord told them how God has offered to pay the debt of every sinner. He has invited ALL sinners to come to Him, but many do not believe. They will not accept the salvation which God offers them. Solemnly, he warned his tenants and neighbors of the folly of passing up God's offer of salvation until it was TOO LATE to be saved!

Bought with Blood

Some years ago, an Englishman was traveling in Africa with many wagons and servants. One day, a native boy came running towards him. A lot of men were chasing him. The boy ran up to the white man's wagon to find protection. Those who followed him came close, and their leader, a chief, tried hard to reach the lad, "Let me get at him. He has bewitched my son!" You know, boys and girls, that the poor natives believe in evil spirits, and cruel gods.

The Englishman tried to shield the poor native boy. He said, "I will buy him. How much do you want for him?"

The native chief, in rage, said, "I don't want money for him. I do not want to sell him. I want blood. I will kill him." Then he fitted an arrow to his bow, and shot at the poor boy.

Quick as a flash, the white man threw his arm in front of the boy, and the sharp arrow struck his arm, making a deep gash in it! When the chief saw it, his face fell. He was afraid of what might happen because he had wounded an Englishman!

The white man said, as he drew out the arrow, "You did not want gold. You wanted blood. See, here it flows before your eyes! But you *must* give account for it!"

"Oh," said the chief, "my heart is sad. White man, I did not mean to hurt you."

"But you have," said the white man. "I have bought your slave with my own blood. Give him to me, and there will be peace between the white man and the black man!"

The chief was glad to escape so easily, and readily consented to the plan. Then the poor boy came up to his new master, and kissed his feet, saying, "Gara, whom you have bought with your own blood, will be your faithful slave forever." "Oh no," said the white man, "Englishmen don't have slaves. You are *free!*" "Free?" asked the poor boy. "Then, let Gara serve his master, for you have bought me with your blood!"

A White Heart

A Negro woman was disturbed by a racket in the kitchen. She went in and discovered her little boy wallowing in the flour barrel. "Land sakes, Sonny," she said, "what am the matter wid you?" She listened to his tale of woe. He did not like to be black. He wanted to be white. His mother took him on her knee and said, "My boy, you will never be white, even though you use all the flour in that barrel. Your skin will always be black. But, listen Sonny, you can have a *white heart.* The Lord Jesus shed His Blood on the Cross so you and I could have hearts washed white in His precious Blood. It is better to have a black skin and a white heart, than to have a white skin and a black heart. Sonny, remember Jesus' Blood can wash you and make you whiter than snow!"

"Twice Mine"

A little boy made a toy sailboat. He worked many days upon it. When he had finished it, he painted it with red and white paint. After it was dry, he carefully fastened the sails upon the boat. Then, he carried it to the river, and placed it near the edge of the water. Suddenly, the wind swept the little boat out into the river. The little boy tried to catch it, but he could not reach it. Away down the river it went.

Several weeks later, the little boy was walking down the street of a little town. He saw his little sailboat in a shop window. He rushed in, and demanded that the storekeeper give him his boat. The storekeeper said, "No, you can't have this boat unless you pay for it," and he named a price.

With a sad heart, the little boy walked away. For many days he worked, doing odd jobs. He wanted to make enough money to buy his boat. Finally, he had enough money. He went back to the little town. He went to the store, and laid the money down on the counter. He demanded his boat. This time, he received it. As he walked down the street with his little boat, he said, "You are *mine,* little boat. You are twice mine. Once because I made you, and twice because I bought you!"

The Song of Heaven

A minister was talking to a man about Heaven. The man said, "Oh yes, I want to go to Heaven, and I think I will. I have always been kind to my wife and children, and I have never tried to harm my fellowmen."

The minister said, "It is nice that you have been a kind man, but what kind of a place do you think Heaven is? What do you think we will do there?"

"Oh," answered the man, "I think it is a happy place, and we will sing a good deal there."

"Yes," answered the minister, "they do sing there! I want to read you one of the songs they sing!"

Opening his Bible, the minister read, "Unto Him that loved us, and washed us from our sins in His own Blood" (*Rev. 1:5 l. c.*). Then, the minister asked, "Could you join in that song of praise? Have you been washed from your sins in His own Blood?"

The man was silent for a moment, and then he said, "No, I couldn't sing that song! Oh, won't you pray for me? I want to be washed from my sins in His Blood!"

Handkerchief Pool

There are many interesting things to see in Yellowstone Park. One thing is, "The Handkerchief Pool." If you drop your dirty handkerchief on the top of this pool of water, it will disappear. In a little while, it will come back to the top of the water, clean and white. Then you can take it out on a stick. The pool has cleansed the soiled handkerchief!

Cleansed from All Sin

A boy, named Joe, lay wounded on a field of battle. The guns were roaring; the machine guns were incessantly beating out rat-tat-tat! Joe lay in the mud, the filth, and the blood of battle. He was dying far from home, and loved ones. As he lay there, he tried to think of something that would help him. He was a sinner. He was not ready to die. He remembered that his old grandfather used to say something about the Blood. He prayer earnestly that God would help him remember. Then, he seemed to hear his grandfather's deep voice saying, "The Blood of Jesus Christ His Son

cleanseth us from *all* sin!" As Joe thought of the words, peace came into his heart. He was no longer afraid. The Blood of Jesus had cleansed him from *all* sin!

Whiter than Snow

A woman one day hung her washing out on the line. She was proud of its whiteness. A snowstorm came, and covered all the ground with a mantle of white. When the woman came out and looked at her washing, she saw that it no longer looked white. Beside the whiteness of the snow, the clothes looked gray and dingy! Nothing is as white as snow, except a poor sinner who has been washed in the Blood of the Lamb.

Will you not today come to Jesus, the Saviour, and ask Him to wash your sins away and make you one of His children?

The Wordless Book

A missionary explained to a man in Morocco how to be saved. He used the Wordless Book. The first page of the book is black, representing sin. The second page is red, representing the Blood of Jesus Christ. The third page is white, representing one who has been cleansed of his sin. The fourth page is gold, representing beautiful Heaven. The man understood the story. He knew that he was a sinner, black like the first page. He trusted in the Lord Jesus who had shed His Blood for him, red like the second page. He knew that his sins were forgiven, and cleansed. So he was now white like the third page. How happy the man was! He looked forward to the time when he would go to Heaven, gold like the fourth page.

Some months passed by. The man became sick and lay dying. His wife, who was not a Christian, came to his bedside. She knew that he had not long to live. She told him to call upon Mohammed to help him. The man refused. He said that his trust was in the Lord Jesus Christ, the *only* Saviour.

Then his wife brought him the little Wordless Book that the missionary had given him. She said, "Lay your head on the white page while you die. Tell God that your life has been as clean as that white page. Perhaps God will accept you in Heaven."

The husband replied, "No, I will not do that. It is not true. Open the book to the red page. That stands for the Blood of Jesus. Let my head rest on that!" So the man died, resting upon the shed Blood of Jesus Christ. Surely, God took that man into Heaven.

We have forgiveness of sin through the Blood of Jesus. We have peace with God through the Blood of Jesus.

I Know It Does

A preacher was speaking from the text, "The Blood of Jesus Christ His Son cleanseth us from all sin." Suddenly, he was interrupted by one who asked, "How can blood cleanse sin?" The preacher asked, "How can water quench thirst?" "I do not know," replied the unbeliever, "but I know it does." "Neither do I know how the Blood of Jesus cleanses from sin, but I *know* that it does!" answered the preacher.

Around, Within, Up

It was wintertide. The earth was covered with freshly fallen snow. The whole country was beautiful in its white robe.

A little girl was crossing a field, with a milk can in her hand. She was on her way to the neighboring farmhouse to buy some milk. About the middle of the field she stopped and took three looks. She looked *around*. All was pure and white. The hedges, the trees, the ground, the house were covered with snow! She looked *within*. She thought of her sin; of how many wrong words she had spoken; of how many wrong things she had done. She knew that her heart was black with sin, and not at all like the snow around her. She looked *up*, and thought of Jesus, the Saviour of sinners. Then the little girl cried, "Lord, wash me, and I shall be whiter than the snow." Did Jesus hear that cry? Indeed He did. He answered at once. The little girl knew that the precious Blood of Jesus had cleansed her from *all* sin and that she was whiter than snow in His sight.

Though They Be as Scarlet

A man once came to a missionary in India. He had heard the missionary speak on the love of Christ, and on the death of Christ for the sin of the world. Said the man, "Can this Man whom you told us about save us from sin?"

"Yes! 'The Blood of Jesus Christ His Son cleanseth us from *all* sin.'"

"Can He save us from the sin of murder?"

The missionary replied, quoting from the Bible, "Though your sins be as scarlet, they shall be as white as snow.'"

"Can He save from the sin of *two* murders?" asked the man.

Again, the missionary quoted, " 'Though your sins be as scarlet, they shall be as white as snow.' "

The number of sins which the man had committed was great, but he found that

Christ's love and Christ's forgiveness were *larger!* He deeply repented of his sins. He accepted the *gift* of God's love, and his sins were washed away with the Blood of Christ.

All Through the Blood

One day, there came to Mr. G. Campbell Morgan at the close of a service, a rag picker. The rag picker was an old man who had served sin and Satan for many years. Mr. Morgan knelt by him and told him how the Blood of Jesus Christ cleanses from *all* sin. Then, he looked around and saw kneeling next to him, the *mayor* of the city, a man of culture and refinement. Mr. Morgan began to tell him how God can forgive sin, how the Blood of Jesus Christ, His Son, cleanses from *all* sin. Presently the light of the Gospel broke on the mayor. He too, saw the Lord Jesus as *his only Saviour.* With joy in their hearts, Mr. Morgan and the rag picker and the mayor rose to their feet. *Both* were *saved* and *satisfied* through the precious Blood of Jesus!

A Clean Heart

Over in India, a Hindu shopkeeper found a piece of paper in his wastebasket. On the paper were printed these words: "Blessed are the pure in heart: for they shall see God." When he read these words, the shopkeeper said, "How beautiful are these words!" He learned the words by heart. Each day, he thought about the words.

One day, someone told the shopkeeper that the words he had learned came from the Gospel of Matthew. So he bought a copy of the Gospel from a missionary and read it through. Then he found that there were other books similar to the Gospel of Matthew. So, he bought a New Testament, and read it through. Then he asked, "Are there any people who live like this book?" He found the answer: *True* Christians live like the Book! So, the shopkeeper became a believer in, and follower of Jesus. He did much Christian work, and then he decided to become a preacher of the Gospel. When he was ordained, he used as the text of his sermon, "Blessed are the pure in heart: for they shall see God!" He told the Hindus, who listened to his message, that *only* God can give us a clean heart. He told them that a heart is made clean when it is cleansed in the Blood of Jesus Christ.

The Sand and the Waves

A woman came to a minister carrying a quantity of wet sand. "Sir," said she, "my sins are like this sand. They cannot be numbered!" Then she began to weep greatly.

The minister asked her where she had gotten the sand. She replied, "At the Beacon." Said the minister, "Go back to the Beacon. Take a spade with you. Dig in the sand until you have made a mound of sand. Shovel it as high as you can. Then stand back on the shore and watch the waves come in."

The woman understood what the minister meant. The Blood of Jesus Christ could wash *all* her sins away! God's Word says, "In that day there shall be a fountain opened to the House of David and to the inhabitants of Jerusalem for *sin* and for *uncleanness.*" (*Zech. 13:1*).

SECOND COMING

"You May Have My House"

A Christian man said to the boy who worked for him, "When the Lord comes, you may have my house and my automobile." The man had been talking to the boy about the Second Coming of Jesus. He had explained to him how "the Lord shall descend from heaven with a shout" (*1 Thes. 4:16*). The boy looked surprised when he heard the man say, "You may have my house and my automobile." He was more surprised when he heard the man add, "Oh, yes, you may have my furniture and money, too." The boy gasped and said, "Oh, thank you, sir."

That night when he was alone in bed, the boy began to think, "If the Lord comes, and my master goes to heaven, what will I do with his house, his furniture, his automobile, and his money? Where will I be?" The boy became greatly troubled. He dressed hurriedly and went to his master's house and wakened him. He cried out, "Oh, please, sir, tell me how to get ready for the Lord's coming. I do not want to be left behind when you go to meet the Lord."

"Be ye also ready."

Faithful Service Rewarded

The noble preacher, R. E. Neighbour, had not been preaching long when he went to a little town in Kansas to hold revival services. One night, tired and discouraged, he retired to his room. He thought it was time to "give up the battle." He fell asleep and had a dream. He saw clouds gathering in the sky. At first, he thought a cyclone was coming, as it often does in the State of Kansas.

As he looked at the clouds more closely, he saw that they were very unusual. They began to glow with great brilliance and beautiful colors! Suddenly, the thought came, "These are the glory clouds in which the Lord will return to earth!" His heart was filled with awe and gladness! Then he awakened, with the thought of the Lord's Coming in great power and glory. He said, "I will be true and faithful to the Lord. I will preach for Him and serve Him with *all* of my might. Some day soon, He is going to return in power and great glory to *reward* His faithful ones!"

"Be Ye Ready"

A man visiting a certain school said that he would give a prize to the pupil whose desk he found in the best order when he returned. "When will you return?" someone asked. "That, I cannot tell," was the answer.

A little girl, who always had an untidy desk, announced that she meant to win the prize. "You!" her schoolmates jeered. "Why your desk is always out of order."

"Oh, but I will clean it the first of every week."

"But suppose he comes at the end of the week?"

The little girl was silent for a moment, and then she said decidedly, "I know what I will do: *I'll just keep it clean all the time*. Then, I will be *ready!*"

So it should be with us. The Lord's Coming may be at midnight, at the dawn, or in the morning. The Bible does not say, "Get ye ready." It says, "Be ye ready."

Lord Cecil's Warning

Lord Cecil, a first cousin of Queen Victoria, spent much time in Canada, preaching the Gospel. He preached in the cities, in the backwoods, and in the lumber camps. One Sunday morning, he was on his way to church, when he passed the house of a certain Christian man. This man had once been a faithful witness for his Saviour. But he had become so occupied with his business that he had grown cold in his love for Christ. He neglected the church. He neglected his Bible reading, and prayer. The man was in his back yard, at his wood pile, chopping wood to cook the Sunday dinner. Lord Cecil stopped and shouted at him: "The Lord is coming, brother; the Lord is coming!" Then he went on his way.

The words that Lord Cecil spoke reminded the neglectful man of the Lord's Return. The words entered his heart and smote his conscience. He *knew* that he, God's servant, should be busily occupied serving the Lord. From that moment, he changed his ways.

How changed will be your ways and my ways, if we will always remember that we must live, ready for His Coming.

Loving Christ's Appearing

Dr. George E. Gill once asked Pastor William Anderson, Jr., of Dallas, Texas, what his attitude was on the Lord's Second Coming. Pastor Anderson replied that he did not have any attitude on the subject, that he was not interested. He said that he had been so busy preaching the first coming that he had not had time to think about the Second Coming. "Well," said Dr. Gill, "I only wanted to know whether you 'love His Appearing.'"

Alone in his study, Pastor Anderson sat by his desk, asking himself over and over again, "Do I love His Appearing?" Then he took up his Bible and read *many* verses about the Lord's Return. Before he left his study, he was able to *say with a glowing heart,* that *he did love Christ's Appearing!*

From that time, Dr. Bill Anderson's ministry was transformed. His pastorate became so fruitful, that great glory was brought to the Name of the Lord.

He May Come Today

A traveler in Switzerland came upon a beautiful villa on the shores of a lake, far from the beaten track of tourists. An aged gardener cared for the beautiful villa. He seemed glad to have a visitor. He had lived alone at the villa for twenty-four years.

"How often does the owner of the villa come to see you?" asked the traveler.

"He does not come often," replied the old gardener; "indeed, it has been twelve years since his last visit."

"But," exclaimed the traveler, "you have everything in such perfect order. Everything is so clean and beautiful and flourishing. It looks as if you were expecting your master to come tomorrow!"

"Oh, no," said the old man, "I am expecting him to come *today,* sir! He may come *today,* and I *must* have *everything* in *order!*"

One Shall Be Taken

Two sisters lay down to sleep one night in the same bed. One was a Christian; the other, a scoffer. The Christian sister had come home that night from a church service in which the preacher had quoted the words, "One shall be taken, and the other left," and had solemnly warned his hearers to be ready for the Coming of the Lord. Her heart was so filled with concern for her unsaved sister that she could not sleep. She told her of the sermon, and earnestly pleaded with her to accept Christ as her Saviour, and make certain her soul's salvation. The unsaved girl jested and rebuffed her and soon fell fast asleep! The Christian girl could only weep and pray. At last, she rose from her bed, and went into a room near by where she knelt and poured out her heart in prayer for the salvation of her sister.

After awhile, the unsaved girl awoke, and missed her sister from her side. Suddenly, she remembered the conversation of the earlier part of the night. With alarm, she thought, "What if the Lord has come! What if I am left alone!" With alarm, she arose from her bed, and called for her sister. When she found her sister on her knees, sobbing and crying unto God for her salvation, the unsaved girl threw herself down on her knees, and began to pray, too. She found the Saviour, and a little later they lay down together, joyful with the thought that if Christ should come that night He would find them both ready for His Return. One would not be taken and the other left. They would both go *together* to be "forever with the Lord!"

"I Washed Myself"

A little girl heard her mother and some friends speaking about the near Return of the Lord Jesus. Some hours later, the little girl was missed. She was found at a window, near the top of the house. She said, "Oh, Mother, I heard you say that Jesus may come today. I wanted to be the *first* to see Him. See, I washed myself, and put on a clean dress."

If we daily look for the *soon* Return of Jesus, we will try to keep ourselves clean, and "unspotted from the world." God's Word says, "And every man that hath this hope in Him *purifieth* himself, even as He is pure" (*I John 3:3*).

If We Had Known

Some years ago, the Prince of Wales, on a visit to the Midlands, went into the home of a certain working man. The next day the working man sadly told his friends, "I never expected him, nor did my wife. The house was untidy and I hadn't washed. We shall never forgive ourselves. If we had known he was coming, we would have been *ready* for him!"

Boys and girls, the Lord Jesus, who is the "Prince of Peace," *is* coming soon. We do not know the day nor the hour of His Coming, but we *can be ready* for His Coming. The question for each one of us is this: "Are *you* ready to meet him?"

Messiah Is Coming

A Chinese lady in Java was wonderfully saved. She knew Christ as Saviour, but she knew nothing of Him as coming King. One day, in her home, she heard a voice say clearly in her own language: "Messiah is coming!" She did not know the meaning of the word "Messiah." She thought a visitor was coming to call on her. She wondered how she would entertain the coming guest. Again, came the voice, saying, "Messiah is coming soon!" Perplexed, she went to a Christian friend, and asked who Messiah is. She found that Jesus

Christ is the Messiah; that He is the coming King. How happy she was over the news. How different became her daily life. Each day, she lived in *readiness* for the coming of Messiah.

Why Bobby Was Thankful

Not long ago, we were having a testimony meeting in our church. Little Bobby stood up and said, "I thank the Lord for all that He has done for me. But today I am especially thankful that my mother is coming home. She has been in California. Yesterday, she wrote, saying that she is coming home in a few days." Bobby loves his mother, and that is why he was glad she was coming home. He missed her while she was away, and longed for her return. How greatly do we long for the Return of the Lord Jesus!

Queen Victoria's Crown

One day Queen Victoria heard her court minister give a message on the Second Coming of Christ, with all its attendant glories and blessedness for our needy world. It thrilled her heart and stirred her soul. She was seen to be weeping quietly in her royal box. Afterward, the court minister asked the Queen why she wept. With tears in her eyes, the Queen said, "Oh, that I would be here when He returns! I would like to place my crown at His feet!"

SELFISHNESS

Self Hides Jesus

A little girl and her mother were staying overnight in the home of a friend. On the bedroom wall, just over the head of the bed in which they were to sleep, there was a picture of the Lord Jesus. This picture was reflected in the large mirror of the dressing table at the foot of the bed. The little girl saw the picture in the mirror while she lay in bed. She exclaimed, "Oh, Mummy, I can see Jesus in the mirror!" Then she quickly got up and kneeled to get a better look at the picture in the mirror. When she did so, her body got between the picture and the mirror, so she could no longer see Jesus in the mirror. She saw only herself. When she lay down again, she saw Jesus. When she got up again, she saw only herself. Finally, she said, "Oh, Mummy, when I can't see myself, I can see Jesus. But every time I see myself, I can't see Him!"

How true it is that when SELF fills our vision, we cannot see Jesus!

Pleasing Self

One morning, Harry sat at the breakfast table with his parents. He was in deep thought, Finally, he exclaimed, "Father, I have made up my mind not to eat any more salt mackerel."

"Why have you decided that?" asked his father.

"Because, my Sunday school teacher said we ought to give up something, so that we might have money to put into the missionary box."

"What has induced my boy to choose salt mackerel as the thing he will give up?" asked the Father.

"Why?" answered Harry. "Because we don't have salt mackerel often, and I don't like it much anyhow!"

The Spoiled Child

A spoiled child was in a dreadful fit of temper because his nurse would not let him have a valuable vase which was on the top of a cabinet. The mother, hearing him cry loudly, went into the room and asked, "What do you want, darling?" Said the naughty little boy, "I want that vase!" Very unwisely, the mother answered, "Yes, darling, you shall have it." She took the vase and put it before him. Then the child lifted his voice and began to yell again. "Why, what do you want now?" asked the mother. Between his sobs, the little boy answered, "I want to have something that I mustn't!"

Selfish Bobby

Little Bobby was giving his wee neighbor a ride in his wagon. He looked up smiling when his aunt appeared in the doorway. "Aunt Mary," he called, "I am trying to make Janie happy!"

"What a beautiful spirit Bobby has!" exclaimed the admiring aunt. But presently the aunt heard Janie crying. Janie was evidently afraid to ride, and she was trying to climb out of the wagon. "Janie doesn't like to ride," said the aunt. Then Bobby answered, "Janie wants to pull the wagon, but I want to do that myself. I want to make her happy by doing the things I like to do."

Who Was Selfish?

A father said, "Tommy, I think you should be able to find some boy to play with you. What's the matter with Johnny Jenkins and the little Drake boy?" Tommy replied contemptuously, "Pooh! They are a whole year younger than I am. I wouldn't play with them."

Then the father said, "Well, there are Jack Spear and Willie Hanson. Can't you play with them?" Tommy replied wistfully, "I would like to play with them, but they are a year older than I am, and the mean things will not play with me!" Tommy failed to realize that he himself was just as selfish and mean as those two boys.

How greatly do boys and girls need to have the spirit of Jesus! "The Son of Man came not to be ministered unto, but to minister, and to give His life a ransom for many." God wants His children to forget self. He wants us to think of others and to live for others. The Bible says, "look not every man on his own things, but every man also on the things of *others*" (*Phil. 2:4*); "Let no man seek his own, but every man another's wealth" (*I Cor. 10:24*); "For whosoever will save his life shall lose it: and whosoever will lose his life for My sake shall find it" (*Matt. 16:25*).

An Unselfish Boy

One day, on the way to Sunday School, John saw some ragged boys. He invited them to go to Sunday School with him. One said he would go but he had no coat. John took off his coat and gave it to him. The two went to Sunday School, the ragged boy with a coat, John without a coat.

Years passed by. That ragged boy became the teacher of a Bible class. One day, he told the incident to his Bible class, and then he said, "Friends, I was that ragged boy, and Dr. John G. Paton, the now famous missionary, gave me his coat!"

Not Excusable

Some years ago, in the city of Chicago, a terrible fire raged. The Iroquois

Theater burned. Many were trampled to death, as a maddened crowd fought for the exit. One of those who got out was a young woman. She was carried along in the stampede, passing over many who had fallen. On her way home, she was nervous and agitated. A fellow traveler noticed her distress, and spoke to her, desiring to be of help if possible.

The young woman told of her escape from the terrible fire. Said the fellow traveler, "You ought to be thankful that you escaped such a frightful death."

"Yes, I know that, but I didn't save anyone!"

"Yes, but under the circumstances, you were perfectly excusable in trying to save yourself!"

"But, oh, I didn't even try to help any one else," sobbed the young woman.

What's Wrong with the World

Selfishness is like a disease that is eating the heart out of this world! Nations go to war because of selfishness. Individuals fight because of selfishness. There is discord in the home because of selfishness.

Abraham Lincoln was walking down the street between his two sons. Both were crying lustily. "What is the matter with the boys?" asked a friend. "Oh, just what is the matter with the *whole world*," replied Mr. Lincoln. "I have three walnuts and each boy wants two of them!" Selfishness always brings sorrow, and trouble.

SHEEP AND THE SHEPHERD

"The Wolf Prefers Lambs!"

A minister went to spend a brief vacation with a Scottish sheep herder. His host met him at the station. In the long drive to the ranch, the host did not talk much. There seemed to be a heavy burden on his heart. The minister finally asked him what had happened. The old shepherd began to weep. He said, "I lost sixty-five of my best lambs last night. The wolves got in!" The minister expressed his own sorrow over the great loss of the shepherd. Then he asked, "And how many sheep did the wolves kill beside the lambs?" The shepherd looked surprised. "Don't you know that a wolf will never take an old sheep as long as he can get a LAMB?" he asked.

Satan likes to get the lambs. How careful we should be to keep the little children from Satan. The Lord Jesus loves them. The Lord Jesus wants them to come to Him.

Only Sick Sheep Will Follow a Stranger

A man, travelling in the East, heard that there was a shepherd who called his sheep by name. He found the shepherd and said to him, "Let me put on your clothes and take your crook. Then I will call your sheep by name and see if they will follow me." The shepherd let the man put on his clothes and take his crook. Then the man called one sheep, "Mina, Mina." The whole flock, including Mina, ran away from him.

"Will none of the sheep follow me if I call them?" asked the man.

The shepherd replied, "Some of them will. The sick sheep will follow anybody."

Following the Others

One day Joe came home with his clothes wringing wet. "I just knew the ice was not strong enough," he grumbled. "Then why did you slide on it?" asked his aunt. "Because all the other boys did. I had to or they would have laughed at me. I knew it wasn't strong enough and it broke and I fell through into the water."

His aunt gave him some dry clothes and had him sit down near the kitchen stove where it was warm. Then she told him a story.

"When I was a little girl my father had a lot of sheep. They were so queer. Where one went, all of the rest followed. One day the big ram found a hole in the fence. He jumped through it without looking where he was going. Down he tumbled to the bottom of an old dry well where Father used to throw stones and rubbish. The next sheep never stopped to see what had become of him. He jumped right after him and landed in the well, and so did the next and the next. Father tried to drive the sheep back and Watch, the old shepherd dog, barked his loudest, but the sheep kept on coming, one after the other, until the well was full. Then Father had to pull them out and the sheep at the bottom were almost smothered to death."

"My! How silly those sheep were," exclaimed Joe. Then he began to laugh. He too had been silly.

The Seeking Shepherd

General Garibaldi once met a shepherd who had lost a lamb from his flock. The shepherd was greatly distressed because he could not find it. Garibaldi became deeply interested. He proposed to the soldiers of his staff that they all search through the mountains for the lost lamb. The search was started. At a late hour in the night, the soldiers returned one by one, empty-handed.

The next morning, the General slept long after his usual rising hour. Finally, his servant went in and aroused him. The General rubbed his eyes. Then he took from under his covering the lost lamb. He had kept on searching through the night until he had found the lost lamb!

"I was lost, but Jesus found me,
  Found the sheep that went astray;
Threw His loving arms around me,
  Drew me back into His way!"

The Hole in the Fence

A father took his boy on his knee and told him the story of the lost sheep; how it found a hole in the fence and crawled through; how glad it was to get away; how it skipped and played in the sunshine until it wandered so far that it could not find its way back home. And then he told him of the *wolf* that chased the sheep, and how, finally, the good shepherd came and rescued it and carried it back to the fold.

The little boy was greatly interested and when the story was over, he surprised his father by asking, *"Did they nail up the hole in the fence?"*

What Happens Without a Shepherd

A man was a guest at a large sheep ranch in the west. One day, he was riding with the rancher along a ridge, bordering a deep canyon. Three sheep appeared among the boulders. The sheep stood for a moment with their heads up, eyes frightened, one front foot up, poised to run. Then, they crashed into the canyon, and disappeared!

The man expressed surprise that there were still *wild sheep* to be found on this ranch. "Not so," replied the ranchman. "Those are not wild sheep. Those are the sheep that my herder failed to count in with the others three nights ago!" The man turned and looked at three thousand gentle sheep, grazing in the valley below. Then, he thought, "What a *difference three nights without a shepherd has made!*"

Straying Sheep

It was a dark, wintry night. The rain was falling fast. The warm glow of the fire was inviting. Suddenly, there was a knock at the door! The farmer was told that all of his sheep were missing from the field where they had been placed. The farmer put on his raincoat and got a lantern and went forth into the darkness. The field where the sheep had been left was surrounded by hedges. The farmer discovered "a bolting hole" in the hedge. A strong sheep had worked its way through the hedge at that point. He had been followed by the others.

The farmer began to search through field after field for his straying sheep. In the fourth pasture, he found them. No two of them were together. They were scattered through the pasture, each following its own course, each choosing for itself. Finally, the farmer succeeded in rounding them all up, and leading them back to the field where they belonged.

How like sheep are we, "All we like sheep have gone astray; we have turned every one to his *own* way."

The Disobedient Sheep

A lady was visiting in Switzerland. In the mountains she came upon a shep-

herd's fold. She walked to the door and looked in. There sat the shepherd with his sheep about him. On a pile of straw, near at hand, there lay a sheep that had a broken leg. The lady asked, "How did it happen?"

The shepherd answered, "Madam, I broke the sheep's leg! Of all the sheep in my flock, this sheep was the most wayward. It would never obey my voice. It wandered to the verge of many a perilous cliff. It would never follow in the pathway in which I was leading the flock. Often, it led other sheep in my flock astray. So, I broke its leg. The first day, I carried food to it, it tried to bite me. I left it alone for a couple of days. Then I went back. It took the food and licked my hand. Now, let me tell you something, when this sheep is well, and it soon will be, it will be the model sheep of my flock! It will hear my voice quickly. It will follow closely at my side. It will be an example and guide for the wayward ones, leading them in the path of obedience. That sheep has learned obedience through its sufferings!"

The Door

A visitor in the Bible Land was interested in the shepherds. He often went out and talked with them as they cared for the sheep. One evening, he watched a shepherd take his sheep to the sheepfold. One by one, the sheep passed into the fold as the shepherd stood counting them. When the last one had entered, the visitor asked, "Where is the door?" The shepherd replied, "I am the door," and then, he lay down across the opening to the sheepfold. Nothing could pass in or out of the fold without going over his body.

"My Shepherd!"

A Scotch minister was teaching a small boy, in the home of one of his parishioners, to read the Twenty-Third Psalm. The little boy began, "The Lord is my Shepherd." The old minister interrupted him. He said, "No, no, you don't read it right!" Again, the little boy began. Slowly and earnestly, he said, "The Lord is my shepherd." "No, you don't read it right," said the old minister. "Now watch me." The minister held up his left hand. He placed the forefinger of his right hand on the thumb of the left hand and said, "The!" Then he placed the forefinger of the right hand on the next finger and said, "Lord!" Then, he placed it on the third finger and said, "Is!" And then, grasping hold of the fourth finger of his left hand, he said, "MY! You take hold of that fourth finger and say, 'My!'" "Oh," cried the little boy; "I see. It's 'The Lord is MY Shepherd.'"

Not long afterwards, the little boy took the sheep out to pasture one morning. Later, his broken body was found at the foot of a steep cliff where he had fallen by accident. The life was going from his body. But the parents saw one thing which cheered their heart! The little boy's right hand was clasped firmly around the fourth finger of his left hand. They KNEW that he had been saying, "The Lord is MY Shepherd!" They KNEW that their laddie was SAFE in the arms of his Shepherd, the Lord Jesus!

The Shepherd's Voice

During the first World War, some Turkish soldiers saw some sheep on a hillside near Jerusalem. They saw that the shepherd was sleeping. The soldiers started to drive the sheep away. Suddenly, the shepherd aroused. He saw his sheep being driven off by the soldiers. This shepherd did not want the Turkish soldiers to get his sheep. Suddenly, he had an idea. Standing on the side of the ravine, he gave his own peculiar call to gather his sheep. The sheep heard the call. They listened. Then, they heard the call again. Turning, they rushed down one side of the ravine, and up the other side to where their shepherd stood! The Turkish soldiers could not stop the sheep. Before they could follow the sheep, the shepherd had led them away to a place of safety.

Jesus said, "My sheep hear My voice." When we are followers of Jesus, we will listen to the voice of Jesus, and obey His call. Nothing will stop us from following Jesus.

"Follow, follow, I will follow Jesus,
Anywhere, everywhere, I will follow on!"

SIN

The Tragedy of Little Sins

A mountain eagle in Colorado was accustomed to feasting on rabbits. The rabbits were found in abundance in a nearby valley. The rabbits were such a nuisance to the ranchers in the vicinity that they imported ferrets to kill them. One day the eagle swooped down upon a ferret. The tiny ferret, quick as a flash, caught the eagle by the throat. The eagle flew far into the air. But in a few moments it came tumbling down. A ranchman saw the eagle fall. He ran to the fallen bird and found it dead. The tiny ferret had bitten through the eagle's throat and was still clinging to it.

Sometimes a man takes into his life a secret sin. He thinks that it is so small and easily hidden that there can be no danger from it. But sin, like a ferret, has sharp teeth. To cherish sin, means certain disaster.

The Poison of Sin

A lady caught a cute little creature which she thought was a chameleon. A chameleon is a harmless little reptile. It can change its color from gray to green or red. It is considered very beautiful by some people. The lady fastened the little creature by a chain to her collar. Instead of being a chameleon, however, the little creature was a poisonous lizard. One day it bit the lady, causing her death.

What a terrible mistake the lady made! And yet there are many who are taking sin into their lives. They think that sin is a beautiful and pleasant thing. They do not know that it is a deadly poison which may some day bring eternal death.

The Scars Remain

When Jim was a little boy, he and his father were great chums. They lived on a farm. Jim went around with his father and helped him in all of his tasks. As Jim grew older, he became mean and disagreeable. Often he disobeyed father. Often he told lies. Often he lost his temper. Father was sad. He wanted to help Jim overcome his bad ways. One day, he went with Jim out to the barn. He got a can of nails and a hammer and he said, "Jim, every time

you disobey me, every time you tell a lie, every time you get angry, I want you to take a nail and hammer it into the barn door."

Jim laughed. He thought there would not be very many nails in the barn door; but soon he saw that he was wrong. The barn door was almost covered with nails in a very short time. Then Jim realized what a bad boy he was. He went to his father and said, "Dad, I didn't know I was such a bad boy. I want to change my ways. I want to get rid of those nails in the barn door. I don't like to look at them."

Dad told Jim that he could win the victory over sin by trusting in Jesus to save him. He told Jim to pray each day and ask Jesus to help him. Then Dad said, "Jim, I have another plan. Every time you do good, pull a nail out of the barn door. Every time you are tempted to tell a lie but you tell the truth, pull a nail out. Every time you win the victory over anger, pull a nail out."

From that time on, there was a change in Jim's life. Every day nails were pulled out of the barn door. Soon there was not one nail left, but to Jim's dismay, he saw that the barn door was filled with holes. Those holes reminded him every time he looked at them of his past sinful life.

The Lord Jesus saves us from sin. He gives us the victory over sin. Let us seek his help early in our lives before our lives are scarred by sin. Let us remember that the scars of sin remain.

The Strong Chain

A tyrant one day sent for one of his subjects and asked, "What is your work?"

He replied, "I'm a blacksmith."

"Go home," said the tyrant, "and make a chain of such a length."

The blacksmith went home. He worked hard on the chain. He made it as strong as possible. He spent several months working on the chain and received no wages during that time. Finally, he finished the chain and took it to the monarch.

The monarch said, "Go home and make it twice as long."

Again the blacksmith labored hard. He returned to the monarch with the chain. Again the monarch said, "Go and make it longer still." Finally the blacksmith returned with the long, strong chain. Then the monarch said, "Take the chain and bind the blacksmith hand and foot and cast him into the dungeon."

The devil is the tyrant who commands his subjects to make a chain, a strong chain, a long chain. This chain is made of evil deeds, of wicked thoughts. For years many work for their master, the devil, making the chain of sin longer. Then one day they discover that the devil has used this chain to bind them hand and foot. How helpless is the sinner. Let us remember that only the Lord Jesus Christ can break the chain of sin which binds so many hand and foot.

Don't Let Sin Enter

In Hampton Court Gardens there are many great and stately oaks. These oaks are almost overcome by the monstrous coils of ivy which have entwined themselves around the trunks of the trees like huge serpents. There was a time when the ivy was a tiny plant, asking only a little aid in its upward climb. Had the ivy been denied then, the oaks would have never become the victims of the ivy. Now, there is no way to untwist the great coils of ivy from the oaks. Every hour, the life of the oaks is being sapped out!

Beware of the first lie; the first dishonest act; the first cigarette; the first taste of strong drink. Never let sin enter your lives.

The Tiger Converted from Sin

Pastor Gih was preaching in Shanghai, China. He preached on sin. As he was leaving the church, a giant of a man stopped him, and told him openly that he would beat him up if he preached on sin again.

But for three nights, Pastor Gih continued to preach on sin. The crowds increased. Each night Pastor Gih was threatened by the giant of a man. The next night, another preacher gave the message. He, too, preached on sin.

Suddenly, a great cry of despair rang through the building, and the giant, known throughout the province as "Tiger, the bandit leader," fell on his knees and began to cry, "O God, my sin, my sin!" God heard the cry. That night, the man was wonderfully saved. The following day, the converted bandit started out at daybreak to talk with others about the Saviour. He was no longer "Tiger, the bandit." He was "Tiger, the Christian!"

From the East to the West

A man asked an old Christian woman, "Does the devil ever trouble you about your sins?"

"Oh, yes," she replied.

"What do you do?"

"Oh," said the woman, I just send him to the east. And if he comes back, I send him to the west. I keep him going from the east to the west, and he can never find my sins!"

The Bible says, "As far as the east is from the west, so far hath He removed our transgressions [sins] from us" (*Ps. 103:12*); "I have blotted out, as a thick cloud, thy transgressions, and, as a cloud, thy sins"(*Is. 44:22*).

> "God has blotted them out,
> I'm happy and glad and *free!*"

Sin Brings Death

A colony of American eagles made its home near the shores of Chautauqua Lake, N. Y. One day, one of them was noticed hovering over the lake. Suddenly, like the lightning, it darted toward the water. It caught in its talons a large fish, two feet or more in length, weighing probably ten pounds. There was a clash, and a splashing of fins and feathers. Then, the bird slowly arose into the air, with its captive dangling and wriggling below! When the eagle had gone up about a thousand feet, it began to sink slowly toward the lake. Its descent gained speed. Finally, it fell with a splash into the water.

Later, the bird and the fish were found fastened together, dead! The eagle had found the fish too heavy to carry, but had been unable to drop it because its talons were so firmly fastened in the flesh of the fish. The strength of the eagle gave way, and he sank into the water, and was drowned!

What a picture this is of the man or woman, boy or girl, who loves sin and plays with sin. Sin will surely bring death and ruin, for the "wages of sin is death."

Sin Destroys

A strong eagle flew up into the sky. He was a beautiful bird. A man stood watching him. Suddenly, he saw the eagle stop flying. A moment later, the great bird fell to the earth, near the man's feet. The man saw that the eagle was dead. He looked closely, and he saw that a small weasel had dug its claws into the stomach of the bird. When the bird was high in the sky, the weasel had sucked its life's blood away. Then, the eagle had plunged to its death!

You Can't Deceive God

When Charles was a little boy, he one day tried to deceive his mother. There had been pancakes for breakfast. Charles liked pancakes and ate a lot of them. Then his mother told him that he could not have more to eat. She was afraid that he would get sick. Mother went into the next room to sew. Little Charles filled both hands with pancakes and hid them behind his back. Then, he walked through the room where Mother was sewing. He had both eyes shut tight. He had his hands filled with pancakes behind his back. Mother said, "Charles, what do you have?" Charles replied, "You can't see me." But Mother could see Charles! Mother *knew* that Charles had disobeyed her.

The Floating Tobacco

One day a revenue cutter headed for a ship on which was a cargo of tobacco. The men on the ship were trying to smuggle the tobacco into our country without paying duty. They knew that if they were caught, every man on the ship would go to jail, the ship would be sunk, and the tobacco seized. So, the men pitched the tobacco overboard as rapidly as they could. They did not want the government men to find it.

A cabin boy went up on deck to report on the approach of the revenue cutter. In an instant, he ran downstairs. His face was as white as a sheet, as he said, "The tobacco is overboard, but it will not sink! It is floating all around our ship!" The government men on the revenue cutter caught the smugglers, put them in jail, sunk the ship, and confiscated the tobacco.

We can *never* hide our sin from God! "Thou God seest *me*"; "Be *sure* your sin will find *you* out."

Sin Like Icebergs

A London preacher once said, "When you are tempted to judge sin leniently, excusing it, and saying that it does not matter, *remember* that sins are like icebergs — the greater part of them is out of sight!" Scientists say that only one-tenth or one-eighth of an iceberg is seen above the water. The rest of it is hidden from sight.

Remember God sees the hidden sin.

Fooled

Some wild ducks had a feeding place among the reeds, growing on the edge of a river in Africa. Some boys discovered the regular visits of the ducks and planned to catch them. They placed pumpkins on the river among the reeds. At first, the ducks were nervous when they saw the pumpkins and flew away. Soon, they decided there was no harm in the pumpkins, and returned to their feeding place among the reeds.

A few days later, the boys took pumpkins, scooped the inside out, made two small holes through which to see, and then placed the pumpkins over their heads. Quietly they slipped into the river with only the pumpkins showing above the water. Slowly, they moved toward the ducks. The ducks were not alarmed when they saw the pumpkins. They had seen pumpkins before. Soon, the boys were among the ducks. They caught them by their legs under the water and killed them.

How many boys and girls are led into the way of sin, because they do not see the harm in it. They are accustomed to the sin. They see people sinning all around them. They forget that the wages of sin is *death*. Never become accustomed to sin. Always shun it and avoid it. Always hate sin as God hates it.

Afraid of Sin

Chrysostom was a great Christian who lived hundreds of years ago. The emperor of Constantinople had Chrysostom arrested, hoping to make him recant, or deny his faith in God. Chrysostom refused to recant. So the emperor said to his attendants, "Put him in prison." One of them replied, "He will be glad to go to prison, for he delights in the presence of his God in quiet!" "Well, then," said the emperor, "let us kill him." "He will be glad to die," said the attendant, "for he wants to go to Heaven. I heard him say so the other day. There is only *one thing* that can give Chrysostom pain, and that is to make him sin. He has said that he is afraid of nothing but sin. If you can make him sin, you can make him unhappy."

SINGING

The Songs of Heaven

A man was saved when he was old. He had been a great singer, and had sung many of the world's great songs. He had been applauded and honored by the world. A few days before his death, his daughter saw him weeping as he lay in his bed. She asked why the tears were running down his cheeks. "Oh," said he, "I just dreamed I was in heaven. Everywhere I went in heaven, people were singing. They wanted me to sing with them, but I couldn't sing the songs of heaven, because I did not know them! I cried so hard that I awakened crying. Just think, daughter, I have been singing all my life, but I have never learned any of HEAVEN'S SONGS!"

Scowling or Singing, Which?

A great earthquake hit Japan. After the earthquake two little Japanese girls in Tokyo were comparing experiences. One said, "As soon as the earthquake was over, I went with my parents to the Buddhist Temple. There were great throngs there. They were all silent and hopeless as they passed before the idol. My parents just looked at the 'god' and scowled."

The other little girl said, "As soon as the earthquake was over, I went with my parents to a service held by a Christian missionary. The people there just looked up to God, and SANG! They sang,

"How firm a foundation, ye saints of the Lord,
Is laid for your faith in His excellent Word!"

The Song the Lepers Loved

A native pastor in Africa took a foreign friend to visit a large leper colony. When they entered the colony, they had to put on sterile robes and medicated boots. They walked past the little homes and gardens to the great temple. Permission had been given to hold a service there for the Christians. One by one, the sufferers came limping into the temple. Their swollen faces wore happy smiles! When the lepers had all gathered, the leader asked, "What shall we sing? What is your MOST LOVED hymn? The foreigner thought these lepers would call for, "I must tell Jesus all of my troubles." To his surprise, the request was very different. The song the lepers loved best was this:

"Singing I go along life's road,
 Praising the Lord, praising the Lord;
 Singing I go along life's road,
 For Jesus has lifted my load!"

Song in the Heart

One day, a little girl was rocking her dolly to sleep. She was singing the song, "Jesus Loves Me." Her father sat in a chair nearby. He was reading the newpaper. He did not like the song the little girl was singing. He was not a Christian. Roughly, he said to the little girl, "Be still!"

The little girl was quiet while she rocked her dolly. Then suddenly, she began to sing again, "Jesus loves me, this I know." The father was angry, and he said, "Didn't I tell you to be still? Why do you disobey me? Why do you keep singing that song?" The little girl said, "Daddy, I can't help but sing. The song just sings itself. It's down in my heart! I did not mean to disobey you."

How beautiful it is to have the hymns that we sing down in our hearts!

Singing Helps Us

A little boy was hit by a car one day. He was carried to the hospital. A surgeon was examining him to find out what was wrong. Suddenly, the little boy said, "I wish I could sing! I think I would feel better then!" The doctor said, "All right, laddie. You may sing if you will sing something nice!"

In a high, clear voice, the little boy began to sing, "Nearer, My God to Thee!" The song rang out. The doctors, the nurses, the patients in different parts of the hospital heard the words! Every one who heard the song was blessed. The little boy was singing from his heart.

When the doctor had finished examining the boy, he said, "Well, little man, you seem to be all right. I can't find any broken bones." The little boy replied, "It was the singing that fixed me. I always sing when I feel bad, and then God helps me!"

"Saviour Like a Shepherd"

It was Christmas Eve. Mr. Sankey, the sweet singer of Gospel songs, was traveling up the Delaware River on a steamboat. Many passengers had gathered on the deck. They asked Mr. Sankey to sing. He asked God what song to sing. Then he raised his eyes to the starry heaven and began to sing:

"Saviour, like a Shepherd lead us,
Much we need Thy tender care!"

There was deep silence as the words floated out over the deck and the quiet river. Every heart was touched!

When the song was ended, a man came up to Mr. Sankey and asked, "Did you ever serve in the Union Army?"

Mr. Sankey said, "Yes."

Then the man asked, "Do you remember doing guard duty on a bright, moonlight night in 1862?"

"Yes," replied Mr. Sankey.

"Well," said the stranger, "I was serving in the Confederate Army. I, too, was out doing guard duty that night. I saw you standing at your post. I raised my gun and took aim at you. I was hidden in the shadows. You were standing with the full light of the moon falling on you. I was ready to pull the trigger when you raised your eyes to heaven, and began to sing:

"Saviour, like a Shepherd lead us,
Much we need Thy tender care!"

When I heard that song, I couldn't shoot you!"

SOWING

Watch Your Sowing

An English traveller loved the wild flowers that grew along the lanes and fields of England. Whenever he went abroad, he would fill his pocket with the seed of the wild flowers and scatter them everywhere.

Every day, we have opportunities to sow good seed in some hearts. It may be some simple, encouraging word, or some kindly act. It may be a line written in a letter, or a Bible text which is quoted. When we sow good seed, lives are blessed.

Barley or Oats?

A man asked his servant to sow barley. The servant sowed oats. The man asked why he sowed oats. The servant replied, "Well, I hope to grow barley!" The man said, "What a foolish idea. Whoever heard the like? You sow oats, and you hope to grow barley!"

The servant replied, "Sir, you yourself sow in such a fashion. You are constantly sowing evil seed and yet you hope to reap the fruit of virtue!" God has said, "Whatsoever a man soweth, that shall he also reap."

A Splendid Inheritance

A young man lay on a hospital bed recovering from a serious operation. His skillful surgeon was paying his daily visit. The surgeon inquired about the young man's family. He was greatly interested in knowing what kind of ancestors lay behind this young man. The patient said, "My folks are all religious. In fact, all the family way back have been religious, but I don't take much stock in that sort of thing myself." The Christian surgeon answered, "Young man, you may not take stock in having a religious background, but you have inherited very valuable stock from your God-fearing ancestors! People who fear and serve God live clean and upright lives. The reason you are recovering so rapidly is because those ancestors of yours bequeathed to you good, clean blood and a sound body. Never speak lightly of them! And remember, it is your responsibility to pass on the good inheritance to your own children."

"Slightly Soiled"

Two students were walking along a street in London. They were passing by an "Old Clothes" store. In the window, there hung a suit of clothes on which was a sign, which read, "Slightly soiled. Greatly reduced in price." One of the students said, "That sign is exactly right. We young people get soiled, maybe it is just slightly soiled, by seeing a vulgar show, or reading a coarse book, or listening to an unclean joke. We think that it makes no difference, but we should remember that when the time comes for our manhood to be judged, we are 'SLIGHTLY SOILED. GREATLY REDUCED IN PRICE'!"

Evil Sowing

A tenant farmer renewed the lease on his farm from time to time. He had worked long hours, year after year, and had made the farm a model of its kind.

One day, the agent who collected the rent told the tenant farmer that the owner wanted the farm for his son who was about to be married. The farmer was greatly upset. He made a number of offers, hoping that the owner would change his mind, and renew the lease. All were in vain.

The day drew near when the farmer was to leave the farm. Then he did something which he should not have done. He gathered seed of all the weeds and pests of the farm. When it was dark, he moved up and down over the clean, fertile soil, casting the evil seed everywhere!

Early the next morning, the agent rode up to the door and told the tenant farmer that the owner had changed his mind, and that the owner would be glad to renew the lease. Then, the tenant farmer, remembering his evil sowing, and knowing of the evil harvest to come, cried out, "My God, what a fool I have been!"

The Bible says, "Even as I have seen, they that plow iniquity, and sow wickedness, reap the *same*" (*Job 4:8*) ; "He that soweth iniquity shall reap vanity" (*Prov. 22:8*) ; "For they have sown the wind, and they shall reap the whirlwind" (*Hos. 8:7*).

Sowing the Word

Night was coming on. A young man, tired and hungry, stopped at a farmhouse in Brazil. He asked for a place to sleep. The farmer invited him in. When he learned that the stranger was a Protestant, he said, "I dare not let you sleep in our house. The priest has forbidden our entertaining Protestants. But you are tired, and I will let you sleep in the barn; only let no one know you had shelter here."

The farmer gave the stranger a good supper. Then, the young man knelt in the kitchen and prayed, thanking God for His goodness, and asking God to bless the family. He went to the barn and slept on the hay.

The next morning, after breakfast, the farmer said, "Will you pray for us again? We never heard a prayer until last night!" The young man prayed again. Before leaving, he gave the farmer a copy of the Word of God.

Eagerly, the farmer read the Word. He read it to his family. He read it to his neighbors. God blessed the sowing of the Word in that little community. A short time later, a missionary came to the community and found over *fifty converts* awaiting baptism! This was the precious harvest from the Word which was sown!

Watch the Beginnings

Two Scotchmen left the Old Country and emigrated to California. They wanted to take to their new home some reminder of their homeland. One took with him a thistle. The thistle is the national emblem of Scotland. The other took with him a swarm of honey bees.

Years passed by. For miles the fields near the home of the first Scotchman were filled with thistles which the farmers could not get rid of. For miles, the forests and fields near the home of the second Scotchman were filled with honey bees and honey! Little did those two men think of what would come from the thistle and honey bees when they brought them from Scotland.

How careful we should be to watch the little things, the little deeds, in our lives. These deeds may bring burdens or blessings. We must watch the little beginnings.

Reaping

During the days of prohibition, a certain millionaire was engaged in the "bootlegging business." He sold intoxicating liquors "under cover." He thought it an easy way to increase his wealth. But one day he was arrested. He was tried, and placed in prison for breaking the law. A friend called on him within the prison walls, and found him working with a big needle and ball of twine, sewing burlap bags. The friend said, "Sewing, eh?" Looking up, the man replied, "No, I am reaping!" He was right, for he was reaping what he had sown.

Sowing in Africa

Two missionaries were forced to leave their station in Africa because of bad health. They returned to America for two years. They left behind them six believers. They dared not hope, on their return to Africa, to find any Christians. How could six young converts stand alone for God in an African village?

How happy the missionaries were when they discovered that the six had met several times each week for Bible study and prayer. They had witnessed for Christ so faithfully that all their village and all the neighboring villages knew that they were "Jesus men!" The sowing of the two missionaries — their faithful preaching and living for Christ in the African village — had not been in vain. Even in their absence, it had brought forth great fruit. Is it any wonder that the church at that mission station grew so large that on the twenty-fifth anniversary, seven thousand people assembled for a communion service? In the service were three African ministers and twenty-four African elders.

SUFFERING

"It Came to Pass"

A poor, uneducated negro loved his Bible although he could read it only with great effort. Often he had to spell out the words. Often he could not grasp the meaning of the verses he tried to read. One time he rose in a testimony meeting to give his favorite verse from the Bible. He said, "Brethren and sisters, I gets the most help from these blessed words: 'And it came to pass.' These are the most blessed words in the Bible."

The leader of the meeting asked the brother what he meant, and he explained, "When I'm upset with trouble, and pestered with trials, I go to the Bible and begins to read, and I never goes far before I come to the words, 'It came to pass.' Then I stop and praise the Lord that it didn't come to *stay*. It came to pass!"

Surely all of us can praise the Lord that our troubles will pass, and not stay. "Our light affliction, which is but for a moment" (*II Cor. 4:17*).

Men, Not Peaches

A young man had a peach orchard. It was blooming bountifully, when a killing frost came. His heart was filled with sorrow and disappointment. He did not go to church the next Sunday, nor the next, nor the next. His pastor called on him. He asked the reason for his absence from church. The discouraged young man said, "I am not coming to church any more. Do you think I can worship a God who loves me so little, that He will let a frost kill all my peaches?"

The minister replied, "Young man, God loves *you more* than He loves your peaches. He knows that peaches do better without frost, but that it is impossible to grow the *best men* without frost. His object is to grow the *best men*, and not peaches!"

We *all* need to remember that God knows what is best for us. Sometimes, He allows sorrow and trouble to come to us to bring us back to Himself. Sometimes, He allows them to come to refine us as silver.

Knocked Down

A gang was repairing lines for a power company. Some of the new poles they were setting up were green and water-soaked. Such poles conduct electricity. The gang was placing a new pole into position. The street was wet; the pole was green and wet. Overhead, was a high voltage line. They were hoisting the new pole up through the maze of wires to a place where it could be dropped into the hole dug for it. One of the men thoughtlessly seized the end of the new pole as it swung clear of the ground to help guide it into its place. Suddenly, one of his comrades ran toward him and knocked him sprawling upon the wet, muddy, sloppy street! The man knocked down was *mad* and *ready* for a fight! The comrade pointed up high to where the new pole had hit a high voltage wire! Instantly, the man who had been knocked down *knew* that his life had been saved by his comrade. Electricity from the high voltage wire would have passed through the water-soaked pole and killed him instantly.

Sometimes God sees His children headed toward great danger. They are wayward and disobedient. Then, God in mercy, "knocks us down." He sends chastening in the form of sorrow or trouble upon us in order to halt us in our ways.

Blessings In Disguise

What blessings come to us in disguise! What blessings come through sorrow and chastening! Charlotte Elliott, the author of the *Invalid's Hymn Book,* lived to be eighty-two years old. She never knew a well day. Her sweet hymns were the outpouring of a heart that knew what it was to suffer. She learned in suffering what she taught in song.

"I walked a mile with *pleasure,*
  She chattered all the way,
But left me none the wiser,
  For all she had to say!

"I walked a mile with *sorrow,*
  And never a word said she,
But, oh, the things I learned from her,
  When sorrow walked with me!"

Dead to Self

When James Calvert went as a missionary to cannibal tribes in Fiji, he was warned that it would be at the risk of his life. Friends said, "You will risk your life and the lives of all those with you if you go among such savages!" The young missionary replied, "We died before we came here!" He meant, little ones, that he had died to self, and to self-pleasing, and self-seeking.

He Knows What Is Best

Some years ago, a magnificent diamond was found in a mine in Africa. It was presented to the king of England to blaze in his crown. The king sent it to Amsterdam to be cut by an expert lapidary. The lapidary took the priceless gem. He cut a notch in it. Then, he struck it a hard blow, and, lo, the precious jewel lay in his hand cut in twain!

You say, "What recklessness! What wastefulness!" But that is not so. For days and weeks, the lapidary had *planned* and *studied* that blow! He had studied the gem with greatest care. He *knew* its qualities; its defects. When he struck that blow, he did the *one* thing which would bring the gem to its most *perfect* radiance and splendor! The blow which seemed to ruin the precious stone brought it to *perfection.* From the two halves, two magnificent gems were brought forth for the king's crown!

In the Fire

A Christian blacksmith was suffering great affliction. An unbeliever asked him why God was allowing him to suffer so much. The blacksmith said: "I don't think I can account for these things to your satisfaction, but I can to my own.

I am a blacksmith. I often take a piece of iron and bring it to white heat. Then, I put it on the anvil and strike it once or twice, to see if it will take temper. If I think it will, I plunge it into the water. Then I put it back into the fire again. I repeat the operation several times. Then, I put the iron on my anvil and hammer it and make some useful article out of it which will do service for years. If, however, when I first strike it on the anvil, I think it will not take temper, I throw it into the scrap heap. It can never be of service. I believe that my Heavenly Father has been testing me to see if He can make of me what He wants, to see if He can use me. I have tried to bear my suffering patiently. I have daily prayed, 'Lord, put me in the fire if Thou wilt. Put me in the water if I need it. Do anything you please, dear Lord, but don't throw me in the scrap heap. Make me and use me in Thy service!' "

Let the prayer of our hearts be:

"Have Thine own way, Lord!
Have Thine own way!
Thou art the Potter; I am the clay.
Mold me and make me after Thy will,
While I am waiting, yielded and still."

Suffering Worthwhile

A missionary in Africa wrote, "For four years I have lived alone in Africa. Thirty times I have been stricken with fever. I have been attacked by rhinoceri and lions; have been ambushed by natives; have eaten everything from ants to rhinoceri; but I would gladly go through it *all* again for the joy of teaching these people to know the Saviour who gave His life a ransom for them!"

"Betty, Lie Still"

Old Betty loved the Lord Jesus. She was very poor. But she worked hard to serve Jesus. She visited the sick. She gave money to those who were poorer than she was. She visited the sorrowing ones, and told them of Jesus. At last, Old Betty caught a cold. Then she got rheumatism. For months, she lay helpless in her bed. A Christian man went to see her. He asked Betty if it was hard for her to lie on the bed, suffering month after month. She replied, "No, sir, not at all. When I was well, I used to hear the Lord say, 'Betty, go here; Betty, go there,' and I used to do it as best I could. Now, I hear him say, 'Betty, lie still.' "

Betty could suffer without complaining because she loved Jesus with all her heart.

His Image in Us

A visitor was watching a silversmith. The silversmith heated some silver in a crucible over a hot fire. Hotter and hotter grew the fire. The silversmith was closely watching the molten silver in the crucible. The visitor asked, "Why are you watching the silver so closely? What are you looking for?"

The silversmith replied, "I am looking for my face in the silver. When I see my image reflected in it, then I stop. The work is done!"

God sometimes allows sorrow and suffering to come into our lives. But He will watch over us, and when He sees the image of Christ reflected in our lives, He will be satisfied. In the midst of his suffering, Job said, "But He knoweth the way that I take: when He hath tried me, I shall come forth as gold" (*Job 23:10*).

A Privilege

David Livingstone, a great missionary to Africa, said, "People talk of the sacrifice I have made in spending so much of my life in Africa. Is that a sacrifice which brings peace to heart and mind, and a bright hope of a glorious destiny hereafter? Away with such a thought! Say rather, 'It is a *privilege.*' Anxiety, sickness, suffering, and danger may cause the spirit to waver, but this is only for a moment. All these are nothing when compared with the glory which shall hereafter be revealed! We ought not to talk of sacrifice, when we remember the great sacrifice He made when He left His Father's home on high, and gave Himself for us!"

Saved by a Stone

In the City of Pottsville, Pa., the broken end of a high voltage wire was lying upon the pavement. A man, walking by, did not know of this fact. A friend of his saw the danger. He yelled a warning, but his voice was drowned by the noise around. He picked up a stone and threw it, and hit the man on the chest. The man looked up, and saw the dangerous, broken wire, just as he was about to step upon it! With tears streaming down his face, he thanked his friend for throwing the stone and saving his life.

Let us remember that sometimes God uses the chastening rod to save us from some terrible sin or calamity.

"I Must Go"

A patient in a mission hospital in India asked the doctor how long she would live. He replied, "Three months if you stay in the hospital." She inquired how long she would live if she did not stay. The answer was, "Two or three weeks, and you will suffer much." Immediately, the patient said, "I am going home. I *must* go and tell my people about Jesus!" That woman was willing to suffer for Christ's sake, and for the sake of her lost loved ones.

TEMPERANCE

Tad's Promise

One afternoon, Tad Lincoln was in the office, waiting for his father, President Lincoln. A sobbing mother came into the office to implore the President to save her son's life. Said the mother, "My boy used to be the *best* boy till he got to drinking." After the mother had gone out, sobbing and brokenhearted, President Lincoln bowed his head on his desk and wept. It was some time before he was able to control his emotions. At last he sat erect, clasped his hands, and repeated these words of Shakespeare, "O God, that men should put an enemy in their mouths to steal away their brains!"

Deeply moved, the President turned to his son and said, "Taddie, lad, promise me that you will never drink! Did you see how that poor woman was suffering?" Tad nodded. Then the President said, "I want you to promise me that you will *never drink.* Give me your word of honor." Tad put his small hand into his father's hand, and said, "Papa, I won't drink anything but *cold water!*" Then the two repeated for a pledge these words: "The Lord watch between me and thee, while we are absent one from another!"

Tad Lincoln never forgot the pledge he made to his father. He kept the pledge until the day of his death!

A Wonderful Change

A British soldier was wonderfully saved from the sin of drunkenness. Four weeks later, he gave this testimony: "If you had told me some months ago that feeling very thirsty and hot, as I rode my bicycle, I would refrain from calling at a tavern to enjoy a few whiskies, I would not have believed you. But it has happened! As I was riding to this service at Soldiers' Welcome, I passed by the public taverns and came on here for a cup of tea. *Only* the Lord Jesus could make this change in me!"

The Red Flag

A little girl loved her father very much. The father was an engineer on the railroad. The little girl noticed that every morning, her father went to the closet shelf and took down a bottle of strong drink. He drank from it before he went to work. She noticed that her mother looked sad and afraid when the father did this.

One day, the father told the little girl about the red flag used on railroads. When there was danger, the red flag was put out. A few days later, the little girl found a red flag that her father had brought home. Climbing upon a chair, she placed the red flag beside the *bottle* on the closet shelf. She put it there to warn him about the danger of using strong drink.

When the father saw the red flag, he knew what it meant. His heart was

touched. He was sorry that he had been using that which would finally ruin him, and cause him to lose his job. He asked the Lord Jesus to deliver him from this great sin. His life was saved, and his home was made happy!

Not the Place for Our Uniform

One day a group of young soldiers arrived in Washington. They marched through the city, while great crowds of people cheered them. Then they were given time to see the city before they went to camp.

Two of the young soldiers came to a saloon. They were just about to go into the saloon, when a hand was laid upon the arm of one of them. Turning, they looked up into the kind eyes of *President Lincoln*! President Lincoln shook hands with the young soldiers, and smiled upon them. Then he said, "Boys, I don't like to see our uniform going into these places!" Turning, he walked away.

The young soldiers passed on. Said they, "We would not have gone into that saloon for all the wealth of Washington!"

Lincoln's Promise

One day, President Abraham Lincoln was riding in a coach with a colonel from Kentucky. The colonel took a bottle of whisky out of his pocket. He offered Mr. Lincoln a drink. Mr. Lincoln said, "No, thank you, Colonel. I never drink whisky." In a little while, the colonel took some cigars out of his pocket and offered one to Mr. Lincoln. Again, Mr. Lincoln said, "No, thank you, Colonel."

Then Mr. Lincoln said, "I want to tell you a story." Then he told this story:

TEMPERANCE

"One day, when I was about nine years old, my mother called me to her bed. She was very sick. She said, 'Abey, the doctor tells me that I am not going to get well. I want you to be a good boy. I want you to promise me before I go that you will *never* use whisky or tobacco as long as you live.' I promised my mother that I never would, and up to this hour, I have kept this promise! Would you advise me to break that promise?"

The colonel put his hand on Mr. Lincoln's shoulder and said, "Mr. Lincoln, I would not have you break that promise for the world! It is one of the best promises you ever made. I would give a thousand dollars today if I had made my mother a promise like that and had kept it like you have done. I would be a much better man than I am!"

The Saloon a Bar

The following poem was written by a life-time convict in Joliet Prison:

"The saloon is sometimes called a bar,
That's true:
A bar to Heaven, a door to hell,
Whoever named it, named it well.
A bar to manliness and wealth,
A door to want and broken health,
A bar to honor, pride and fame;
A door to grief and sin and shame,
A bar to hope, a bar to prayer,
A door to darkness and despair,
A bar to honored, useful life,
A door to brawling, senseless strife,
A bar to all that's true and brave,
A door to every drunkard's grave,
A bar to joys that home imparts,
A door to tears and aching hearts,
A bar to Heaven, a door to hell,
Whoever named it, named it well!"

"Don't Trust Strong Drink"

Some years ago, there lived in Atlanta, Georgia, a great writer named Henry W. Grady. The people were going to vote and decide about bringing back saloons in Georgia. Henry Grady wrote in the newspaper, saying, "Don't trust strong drink. It enters a humble home to take the roses from a woman's cheek. It strikes a crust of bread from the lips of a starving child. It is the enemy of peace and order. It is the terror of women. It brings a cloud to the face of children. It digs graves, and sends souls to hell. It brings gray-haired mothers in sorrow to their graves. It turns the wife's love into despair. It takes away the laughter of little children. It takes music from the home, and fills it with sorrow. It ruins the body and mind. It wrecks the home. Don't vote it back!" (Words of Henry W. Grady, simplified).

Tommy and Grandfather

Tommy was nine years old. He *loved* Jesus with his whole heart. He loved his Bible, and tried to follow its teachings. One day, Tommy and his father and mother were invited to the home of a relative for dinner. Grandfather was present. Grandfather was getting old and had many aches and pains. A friend had told him to take a bottle of beer to "pep" him up a little. Grandfather brought a bottle of beer to the table with him.

When the family was seated, Tommy was asked to say the blessing. Tommy had never "said grace" over a beer bottle before. He was troubled. All bowed their heads. Tommy could not say a word. Finally, he raised his head and, looking over to his mother, said, "Mom, I *can't* ask God to bless us, or the food on this table, with that beer bottle setting there!"

Grandfather grabbed the bottle and started for the back door. He put the bottle in the garbage can and returned to the table. Then Tommy said grace, and the meal was eaten. Grandfather never again touched any strong drink.

No Whisky Here

Some policemen were looking over the wreckage of an automobile to determine whether strong drink had been the cause of the accident. One of them found a Bible. He turned to his companion, saying, "No use to look for whisky here."

Why did the policeman make this remark? It was because he knew that those who read their Bible and *follow* its teachings never use strong drink. In the Bible, we find many warnings against the use of strong drink. Listen to some of the verses: "Wine is a mocker, strong drink is raging: and whosoever is deceived thereby is not wise" (*Prov. 20:1*); "Hear thou, my son, and be wise. . . . Be not among winebibbers; among riotous eaters of flesh: for the drunkard and the glutton shall come to *poverty*" (*Prov. 23:19-21 f. c.*); "Who hath woe? who hath sorrow? who hath contentions? who hath babbling? who hath wounds without cause? who hath redness of eyes? They

that tarry long at the wine; they that go to seek mixed wine. Look not *thou* upon the wine when it is red, when it giveth his colour in the cup, when it moveth itself aright. At the *last* it biteth like a serpent, and stingeth like an adder" (*Prov. 23:29-32*).

Just the Man Wanted

A businessman needed someone to fill an important position. He advertised and received a large number of applications for the position. From these, he chose twenty men, and asked them to meet him on a certain day. The twenty men arrived on the day he appointed. Said he, "Men, before we get on with the business, I think we will go over to the hotel nearby, and have a little drink together." The men quickly got up and followed him to the door, that is, all *except one*.

"Hurry up there," the businessman shouted, "are you not coming for a drink?"

"No, thanks," said the man, "I am a Christian, and I never touch strong drink of any kind!"

"Good for you," said the employer, "you are just the man I want for this position!" Then, he turned and told the other men that they could go home.

TEMPTATION

Jesus Stronger Than Satan

A little boy came to his father. Looking very much in earnest, he asked, "Father, is Satan bigger and stronger than I am?" "Yes, my boy," said the father.

"Is he bigger and stronger than you, father?"

"Yes, my boy, he's bigger than your father."

The little boy looked surprised. Then he thought again and asked, "Is he bigger and stronger than Jesus?"

"No, my boy," answered the father. "Jesus is bigger and stronger than he is."

The little boy was satisfied. A smile came to his face and he said, "Then I am not afraid of him."

God Can Deliver

Years ago, there lived in St. Louis, a lawyer who was a drunkard. One day he was wonderfully saved by Jesus. But he was afraid to go near a saloon. When he saw one, he would go across the street.

One day, the lawyer saw a picture of Daniel in the lions' den. He saw the lions all around Daniel. Then he looked at Daniel. Daniel was not afraid. He was looking up toward Heaven. The lions were not hurting Daniel. Suddenly, the lawyer said to himself, "God shut the lions' mouths. They could not hurt Daniel. Today, I am surrounded by 'lions.' My old habits, my old sins are around me. But God can shut their 'mouths.' The God who delivered Daniel can deliver me. I will no longer be afraid!"

Let Jesus Go to the Door

A little girl was a "problem child." She was always getting into mischief. Many predicted that she would come to an early ruin in life. Then, someone took an interest in her, and invited her to go to Sunday School. The girl went, and there she heard about the Lord Jesus Christ. Soon, she trusted Christ as her Saviour. A great change came into her life. She was as full of "pep" as ever. But instead of injuring others, she helped others. She seemed to be always kind and thoughtful.

One day a neighbor said to her, "How is it that you have changed so much? I know they say you have been converted, but doesn't the devil ever come to you with temptation?"

"Oh, yes," replied the girl. "The devil comes to my heart every day. He knocks on the door with temptation the way he always did. Before I became a Christian, I used to go and answer the door, and I always got into trouble. But now, I let Jesus go to the door for me, and when the devil sees Him, he leaves right away!"

Able to Bear the Test

In New York State, a bridge was being built across a great chasm in a mountain. The chasm was hundreds of feet deep. Everyone watched the building of the bridge with great interest. On the day that it was completed, the people gathered to watch the testing of the bridge.

Two huge locomotives drew up on the bridge. For half a day, they remained on the bridge with their great tons of iron quivering and beating. The bridge beneath them looked like a great spider's web supporting them. But the bridge was strong. It was able to bear up under the great test put on it. It was worthy of trust on the part of man.

When the Lord Jesus was met by the devil in the wilderness, He was tempted, sorely tempted. But He withstood the test. He could not sin, for He is God. The Bible says of Him, that He knew no sin; that in Him there was no sin; and that He was without sin. Are you not glad that you have such an One to help you in time of trouble and testing?

Saying "No" to Satan

A man saw a little boy stop in front of a fruit store. Suddenly, the little boy reached out and grabbed an apple from a basket. The little boy hid the apple in his hat, and started to run down the street. The man felt very sorry when he saw the little boy steal the apple. As he stood watching, he saw the little boy run back to the store. He took the apple out of his hat, and put it back on the basket. Then, in a loud voice, the little boy said, "Get thee behind me, Satan!" Turning, he ran back down the street.

The little boy had won the victory over Satan. He had said, "No" to Satan. It was Jesus who had given him the power to say "No" to Satan. It was Jesus who kept him from falling into Satan's trap in the hour of temptation.

The Rock Never Shook

Some years ago, a terrific storm swept down on the northwest coast of America. The cities on the coast were buffeted by the storm. In one city, the report got out that the lighthouse near the shore had gone down.

Three days later, the keeper of the lighthouse was seen on the street of the city. One of his friends said to him, "We heard that the lighthouse went down in the storm." The old keeper was amazed. He said, "Gone down? It is true that the storm was the fiercest I have ever known, but all the time the rock, upon which the lighthouse was built, never shook once. All the time the lighthouse stood firm and unmoved!"

When our house of life is built on the sure *Rock*, Christ Jesus, we will stand firm and secure during every time of testing and trial and temptation. No storms will shake us, for our Rock, Jesus, will stand firm and secure.

Satan's Power

Charles Finney, the great evangelist, once preached on the subject, "Satan and His Power." A man came to him and said, "Mr. Finney, I don't believe in the devil." Finney looked at him and replied, "Don't you? Well, if you would really resist him for awhile, you would soon change your mind."

When we are trying to live lives pleasing to God, then Satan tries to hinder us. Then we realize his power and know that we *must* have God's power to successfully resist him. In times of temptation, let us remember:

"Greater is He that is in you,
Than he that is in the world."

A New Master

A young man, from a Christian family, got into ways of sin. His family was very sad. His family prayed for him. One day, the young man gave his heart and life to Jesus. After that, things were different. When the young man was tempted to go into the ways of sin, he would simply say, "Lord Jesus, You are my Master now. You lead me out of this temptation!" Jesus never failed him. Jesus always helps those who call upon Him.

Victory Over Satan

A little girl was forbidden by her mother to take some oranges. Later, while the mother was in the kitchen, the little girl slipped into the dining room, and took an orange from the dish on the table. The mother heard the noise, and, looking into the dining room, she saw what the little girl had done. Her heart was very sad.

Just as the little girl neared the door, she turned around, went back to the table, and put the orange back in the dish. Then she said out loud, "That's one time you didn't get me, Satan!" How glad the mother was that her little girl won the victory over Satan!

Held by Christ

A minister, traveling on a train, sat in a compartment with a young man who was reading a newspaper. When the young man looked up, the minister began to talk to him. He asked, "Are you a Christian?" The young man said, "Yes, I am a Christian, but I am not a very good Christian! I am often tempted to do wrong, and I am not very strong. I often yield to temptation and fail miserably." The minister took a pocket knife from his coat. He opened the knife and, reaching for a book, he said, "Young man, watch. I will make this knife stand up on the cover of this book in spite of the rocking of the train." The young man said, "I am afraid that will not be very easy to do, sir." "But," said the minister, "I am doing it now!" "Oh, but you are holding it," said the young man. "Why, of course I am holding it. Did you ever hear of a knife standing up on its end without being held up?" "No," said the young man. "Well," said the minister, "I have never heard of a young man who could stand up in the time of temptation unless Christ was holding him up." "Thank you," said the young man, "I see what you mean. I cannot stand in the time of temptation unless Christ holds me."

The Master of the Devil

A poor man was a helpless slave to drink. He tried to get free from this great evil. Others, too, tried to help him, but the chain of sin held him fast. Then, one day, he came to Jesus, the Saviour. Jesus set him free from strong drink. A wonderful change came into his life. Someone said, "I hear you have got the mastery of the devil at last!" "Oh, no," was the answer, "but I have got *the Master of the devil!*" The Lord Jesus is the *Master* of the devil.

"Change Your Hitching Post"

A young man who had been a drunkard was wonderfully saved from sin by the Lord Jesus. One day an old deacon saw that when the young man came to town, he still tied his horse to the old hitching post in front of a saloon. The deacon went to the young man and said, "Young man, change your hitching post! If your life is changed, you *must* change your hitching post!" Many Christians today need to change their parking place; they need to stay away from the places of temptation and sin.

"Please Hold My Hand"

Some years ago, a minister had a dear little boy, four years old. The little boy was given a new overcoat. The overcoat had a new kind of pockets, which went in "sideways.' The little boy wanted to wear his new overcoat, and waited for a cold day to come.

One night, it snowed! Then it rained. The sidewalks and streets were covered over with a sheet of ice. The next morning, the minister started to go out to make a call. The little boy said, "Oh, Daddy, please let me go with you. I want to wear my new overcoat!" The father said, "All right, son."

The little boy hurriedly put on his new overcoat and went out with his father. Father said, "Son, let me hold your hand. The walk is very slippery, and you may fall." The little boy said, "Oh, no, Daddy, I want to put my hands in my pockets." The little boy put his hands in his pockets, and the two walked along together.

In a moment, the little fellow's feet slipped, and he fell down and got a bump on his head! The father helped the little boy get up, and then said, "Son, let me hold your hand so you will not fall again." The little boy replied, "Oh, no, Daddy. Please let me put my hands in my pockets." The two walked along together.

In a few moments, the little boy's feet went out from under him, and he received another bump on his head. The father helped his son up, but said nothing.

Then the little boy looked up at his father, and said, "Daddy, I think you had better hold my hand!" The father put his strong hand around the boy's little hand, and they walked along together.

Soon, the boy's feet slipped again, but this time he did not fall. Father was holding his hand!

Tempted Like As We Are

A man in a responsible position was intrusted with a large sum of money.

One day, he was tempted to put some of the money in his own pocket. He knew that it would be a long time before his theft would be discovered. He resisted the temptation, and then he felt that he must tell somebody about the anguish of mind through which he had passed. He went to the man who had occupied the position before him. He told him all about the temptation, and how he had almost fallen. The man did not rebuke him. He put his hand on his shoulder in a fatherly sort of way, and said, "I *know* exactly how you felt. I went all through that myself when I occupied your position!"

How good it is to know that we have *One* who was "in all points tempted like as we are, yet without sin"! and that this *one* is *able* and *ready* to help us in the hour of temptation!

Jesus' Property

A Negro had accepted the Lord Jesus as His Saviour. He realized that he belonged to Jesus, because he had been bought with a price, the precious Blood of Jesus. When he was tempted to do wrong, he said, "Massa, Jesus, I'm your property. Your property is in danger. Please come and look after Your property!" Thus trusting in Jesus, he was able to resist temptation.

THANKSGIVING

Thanksgiving Street

In a mid-week prayer service, a good brother related a long, complaining list of experiences. He told about the trials and difficulties which he was meeting on the way to heaven. At the end of his

talk, another brother arose and said, "The brother who just sat down lives on Grumbling Street I see. I lived there myself for a while, but I never enjoyed good health there. The air is bad on Grumbling Street. The houses are bad.

The water is bad. The birds never sing on that street. I was gloomy and sad while I lived there. Finally, I moved to Thanksgiving Street. Since then I have had good health and so have my family. The air is pure. The water is good. The sun shines all day. The birds are always singing. I am as happy as I can be. I suggest that our brother and others, too, who are gloomy and sad, move from Grumbling Street to Thanksgiving Street. There are plenty of houses 'To Let' on Thanksgiving Street."

Asking the Blessing

Christians should always bow their heads and give thanks before they eat. Surely our hearts are thankful for God's many blessings, including the blessing of good food.

A Christian man went into a restaurant one day. He quietly bowed his head and gave thanks for the food before he began eating. A waitress came over to his table and said, "Pardon me, but I see you must be a Christian! I have been watching for three months for a Christian to come in here, because I want to become a Christian myself!" How astonished the Christian man was! He knew at least fifteen professing Christians who regularly ate in that restaurant, but apparently not one of them had bowed his head before eating, and said, "Thank you, Lord!" In a few moments, this Christian man explained to the waitress how to be saved.

The Ones Who Never Gave Thanks

A farmer was asked to dine with a gentleman. The farmer did, as he was accustomed to do at home: He asked the blessing at the table. When he had finished, his host said, "You are very old-fashioned. It is not customary now-a-days for well-educated people to pray at the table!" The farmer replied that it was customary for him, but that some of his household never prayed over their food. "Ah!" said the gentleman, "they are sensible and enlightened. Who are they?" The farmer answered, "THEY ARE MY PIGS!"

Billy Bray Gave Thanks

Billy Bray was a Cornish miner. He was known far and wide for his simple faith in God. One year, Billy's potato crop was almost a failure. As he was digging his potatoes, Satan seemed to say to him, "There, Billy, isn't that poor pay for serving your Heavenly Father the way you have all this year? Just look at those small potatoes!" Billy replied, "Ah, Satan, there you go again talking against my Father, bless His Name! Why when I served you, I didn't have any potatoes at all. I thank my dear Father for these small potatoes."

What He Liked Most

Nancy's father was a good man in many ways. But he was always grumbling and complaining. One night, Nancy's family and a guest were sitting in the parlor talking about food. Nancy told in a very clever way what each member of the household liked to eat. Finally, it was the father's turn to be described. "What do I like best?" the father asked laughing. The little girl answered slowly and truthfully, "Well, father, you like almost anything that we HAVEN'T GOT!"

Benefits Without Number!

A father and his little girl were walking along one winter's night, hurrying toward home. It was a clear, bright starlight night. The little girl said, "Father, I am going to count the stars." "Very well," said father, "go on." By and by he heard her counting: "Two hundred and twenty-three, two hundred and twenty-four, two hundred and twenty-five." Then the little girl gave a sigh, and said, "O, dear, I had no idea there were so many stars. I don't believe I can ever count all of them!" The father answered, "My dear, the stars are just like God's benefits. God showers us with His blessings and benefits day by day. There are so many of them that we can never count them all!"

"Count Your Blessings"

One night during the Chapman-Alexander Meetings a poor man who was paralyzed was brought down the aisle in a wheelchair. His chair was placed near the platform. During the song service, Mr. Alexander caught sight of him and asked, "What is your favorite hymn?" He immediately answered, "Count Your Blessings!" That poor cripple had the real thanksgiving spirit. He did not wail, or complain. He just thanked God for His goodness!

Tell Him

A kind uncle gave his little niece a beautiful doll. Her mother asked, "Did you thank Uncle for the doll?" "Oh, yes, Mamma, I thanked him in my heart, but I didn't tell him about it." The mother said, "You *must* be sure and *tell* him about it." If we are thankful to God for His many blessings; if we love Him; then we must say so with our lips.

"Praise God from whom *all* blessings flow;
Praise Him, all creatures here below;
Praise Him above, ye Heavenly host;
Praise Father, Son, and Holy Ghost!"

The Ungrateful Farmer

A farmer in Texas said to a minister, "I don't owe the Lord anything. What I have, I made myself. I worked hard for it. I made my money myself. I don't owe God anything."

The minister said, "You made your money by wheat farming. How can you say you don't owe God anything? Who made the seed you planted? Who sent the sunshine? Who sent the rain? Who put the life in the little seed so it could sprout into grain? Who took care of you and kept your heart beating, so you could do your work? Who gave you breath while you were sleeping? It was God! Every step you take, the Lord is in it! Everything you do, God is in it!"

The farmer turned red in the face. He was ashamed, because he was so unthankful, so ungrateful.

The Grumbling Farmer

A farmer at the morning meal thanked God as usual for His bountiful provision. Then he began to eat his breakfast. As he ate, he grumbled. He grumbled about the hard times. He grumbled about the food he had to eat. He grumbled about the way it was cooked.

His little girl asked, "Father, do you suppose God heard you thank Him a little while ago?"

"Certainly," he answered.

"Well, does He hear what you say about the weather and the crops and the bacon and the coffee?"

"Of course," the father said.

"Then, Father, what does He believe? Does He believe what you pray or what you say?"

Like Mule and Ox

Are *you* thankful for the common, ordinary blessings of life? Are *you* thankful for your home, food, raiment? A man asked a minister whether it was according to the rules of etiquette to say thanks, or "grace," at a banquet table. The minister answered, "I do not know much about etiquette, but I remember a picture I saw on the wall of a farmer's home. It showed mules and oxen eating at a crib. They were devouring the fodder, and scattering some beneath their feet. The picture had this little verse inscribed on it:

'Who without prayer sits down to eat,
  And without thanks then leaves the table,
Tramples the gifts so good with feet,
  And is like mule and ox in stable.'

Like His Dog

A little boy, six years old, was invited to lunch in a neighbor's home. As soon as all were seated at the table, the food was served. The little boy was puzzled. He asked, "Don't you say a prayer before you eat?" The host was uncomfortable and mumbled, "No, we don't take time for that." The little boy was silent for a moment, and then he said, "You are just like my dog. You start right in!"

Forgetting to Be Thankful

Little Ben had the habit of grumbling. He grumbled all the time. He complained about the weather. He found fault with his friends, and his family. He wanted to stop, but he kept right on grumbling. Then, one day, he read this verse:

"When thou hast truly thanked thy God,
  For every blessing sent,
But little time will then remain,
  For murmur or lament."

"Oh," said Ben, "I see what the trouble has been. I have grumbled so much that I have forgotten to be thankful for the things I have. Every time, I find myself starting to complain, I am going to thank God for something He has given me." Ben's plan worked. He began to thank God for the things which he had. The Bible says, "Do all things without murmurings (complaining)" (*Phil. 2:14*).

TONGUE

Why She Was Odd

The ladies were having a meeting at the minister's house. As he entered the room, he heard them talking about an ABSENT friend. "She's very odd," said one. "Do you know she often does so and so?" said another. Then a third mentioned something against her. The minister stopped them. He asked who it was. When he was told, he said, "Oh, yes, I agree with you. She is very odd. Why, would you believe it? She has never been known to speak ill of any ABSENT friend!" The ladies present felt rebuked and stopped their gossiping for that day.

Daily News

In a small town there lived a woman who was a gossiper. She always carried the "News!" from door to door. One day, she was in the office of "The Daily News." She chanced to lean up against the wall where there were several copies of back editions of the paper on display. It was warm. Her dress was white, and some of the print came off onto the back of her dress. She did not know this. As she walked down the street, on her way home, she was conscious of giggling, and whispering whenever folks came up behind her. Finally, she reached home. She turned around before her husband and said, "What is there on my back?" He read there, in black print, the words, "Daily News!" Very meekly, he replied, "Madam, there is nothing there that doesn't belong there!" Was she not "The Daily News" in the little village? Did she not carry the gossip from door to door?

Gather Your Gossip

A peasant, with a troubled conscience, went to a monk for advice. He said he had circulated a vile story about a friend, only to find out that the story was not true. The monk said, "If you want to make peace with your conscience, fill a bag with goose down. Go to every door in the village, and drop one fluffy feather!" The peasant did as he was told. Finally, he came back to the monk and announced that he had finished doing penance for his folly.

The monk said, "You have not finished yet. You must now take your bag and go the rounds again. Gather up every feather you have dropped." Greatly dismayed, the peasant said, "But I cannot gather up the feathers. The wind must have blown them all away!" "My son," said the monk, "so it is with GOSSIP! Words, good and evil, are easily dropped. But no matter how hard you try, you can never get them back again!"

Saying Kind Things

"I wonder how Vera ever got such a fine disposition,' said Eva. "She never seems to say anything that hurts any one or makes any trouble."

"I think she does it by watching," said Alice. "Vera told me once that she used to have a terrible habit of saying sharp, unkind things. One day, she hurt someone terribly. After that, she decided she would overcome the habit of saying sharp things. Every night after that, she asked herself if she had said anything harsh or unkind to any one that day, and if she had, she would sit down and write a note of apology. Now, she is always saying only kind things!

The Best and the Worst

An old fable is told about Xanthus and Aesop. Xanthus wanted to give a banquet for some friends. He sent Aesop to the market to purchase the *best* things to be had, nothing but the *best*. Aesop bought tongues, nothing but tongues. Every course at the banquet was tongues prepared in one way or another. Xanthus questioned Aesop about the tongues. Aesop replied, "Is there anything as good as the tongue? Great and noble truths are uttered by the tongue. The tongue makes friends. The tongue can comfort the sorrowing. It can give instruction. With the tongue we can praise God!"

Xanthus was not angry. He planned another banquet for the following day.

He told Aesop to go to the market, and purchase nothing but the *worst* of things, the very *worst*. He thought that this command would bring to his table many different dishes. But at the banquet the next day, nothing but tongues was served. Again Xanthus questioned Aesop. Aesop replied, "Is there anything *worse* than the tongue? The tongue brings strife. The tongues causes lawsuits and wars. The tongue spreads lies. It brings sorrow, and even *death!*"

Kind Words

Some years ago, there sat in the station in New York City a poor German immigrant woman. She had just arrived in this country, and was on her way to the Midwest to start a new life among strangers. Her husband had died and been buried at sea. Her heart was filled with sadness and loneliness. A kind Christian lady noticed the sadness on the poor woman's face. She went to her, and spoke a few comforting words. Said she, "God loves you. The Lord Jesus loves you, and He will never forsake you." Then, she pressed some money into the poor woman's hand.

The kind words and deed of the Christian lady gave the poor woman the strength and courage she needed. May we always be quick to speak kind, loving, comforting words. Long ago, Isaiah said, "The Lord God hath given me the tongue of the learned, that I should know how to speak a word in season to him that is weary: He wakeneth morning by morning, He wakeneth mine ear to hear as the learned" (*Is. 50:4*).

Helpful Words

When John Bunyan was young, he chanced to hear three or four women, sitting in the doorway in the sun, talking about the things of God. If those women had been talking about their neighbors, repeating scandals, they would have never helped John Bunyan. But what he heard them talking about was God. They told how God saves and changes lives. They told how they were comforted and refreshed by the love of Christ. And as John Bunyan went about his work, as a tinker, mending the pots and pans of that neighborhood, their talk went with him and helped him.

The Bible says, "Then they that feared the Lord spake often one to another: and the Lord hearkened, and heard it, and a book of remembrance was written before Him for them that feared the Lord, and that thought upon His Name" (*Mal. 3:16*).

Words of Praise

Some time ago, a young man lay on the operating table in a hospital. He was being prepared for an operation. A skilled surgeon stood nearby, and a group of medical students round about him. The doctor said to the patient, who had cancer of the tongue, "My friend, if you wish to say anything, you *now* have the opportunity. But I must warn you that your words will be the *last* words which you will ever utter. Think well, therefore, what you wish to say." After a moment's thought, the young man exclaimed, *"Thank God for Jesus Christ!"* Tears came to the eyes of all those who heard the words.

The Best and the Worst of the Sacrifice

A certain king in Egypt sent a sacrifice to a wise man, asking him to return the best part and the worst. The wise man sent back the *tongue*. For good or for evil, there is no mightier instrument on earth than the tongue. The tongue sends forth words of kindness or curses. It spreads blessing or blight. Long ago, David prayed, "Keep the door of my lips." How important it is for every Christian to daily pray this prayer.

WILL OF GOD

God's Will is Best

A wasp got into a little girl's buggy. The little girl tried to catch the wasp. The maid kept saying, "No, no!" The little girl began to cry. The Mother, hearing the crying, called out, "What's that child crying for? Let her have it." A few minutes later, the Mother heard an awful scream and asked in alarm, "What's the matter?"

"She got it," said the maid. "She got the wasp. That was what she wanted." Sometimes we cry for things that will bring us only sorrow and trouble. God knows it. If we keep crying, sometimes God allows us to have what we cry for and then we learn through pain that God's will is best for us.

Resignation

A gentleman visited a school where he saw a deaf and dumb boy. He asked, "Who made the world?" The boy wrote on the blackboard the answer, " 'In the beginning God created the Heaven and the earth.' "

The man asked, "How do you hope to be saved?" The boy wrote, " 'This is a faithful saying, and worthy of all acceptation, that Christ Jesus came into the world to save sinners.' "

For a last question the man asked, "Why did God make you deaf and dumb while most people can hear and speak?" For a moment the poor boy seemed puzzled and then he wrote, " 'Even so, Father, for so it seemed good in Thy sight.' "

It is wonderful to be resigned to God's will. He knows what is best for us.

Pleasing the One Higher Up

One cold, wintry night some people in a railway station were passing through a gate, going to their train. The man at the gate had to look at their tickets before they could pass through the gate. Many were grumbling at him because they had to open their overcoats and reach in their pockets for their tickets. Someone remarked to him, "You are not very popular with this crowd this night." The man replied, "I don't want to please this crowd. The man I want to please is up there," and he pointed to a window, high up in the station, where his boss could be seen. We want to please God, rather than men.

God's Plan Missed

A man captured two baby eaglets. He placed them in a cage. They grew to be fine, big eagles. One day, their cage door was left open. The eagles escaped. One was killed by a hunter. The other fell into the river and drowned. These eagles had missed God's plan for their lives. They were created to live in high places and to fly high in the sky. Instead, they lived on the ground, and did not learn to fly. And so, they met an early death. How wise we will be to follow God's plan for our lives.

The Way to Blessedness

The great poet, Wordsworth, in one of his poems tells about a bird that was carried from Norway by a storm. The bird fought against the wind, trying to wing its way to Norway. But all of its effort was in vain. At last, the bird yielded to the wind. It was borne along by the wind, and instead of being carried to destruction, it was carried to the warm shores of England, to the green meadows and forests. If we go against God's will, our efforts will come to nought, and we will do ourselves injury and harm. If we will gladly accept His will and *do* it, we will be borne on to blessedness and joy and peace.

Just Like the Plan

A great suspension bridge was being built over the Hudson River in New York City. The engineer, who drew the plans for the bridge, was confined to his bed. How interested he was to hear reports of the work! Months passed, and finally the bridge was completed. Four men carried the engineer to a place where he could view the bridge, spanning the great river. In his hands, he held the blueprint which he had drawn. Carefully he looked from the bridge to the blueprint. He looked at every detail. Then tears filled his eyes as he cried out, "It's just like the plan! It's just like the plan!"

We Can Trust God

A lady once said, "I am afraid to pray, 'Thy will be done.' I am afraid God will send me some sorrow, or trouble."

Her Christian friend replied, "Suppose your child should come to you and say, 'I want to be and do just what you desire today.' Would you try to make it hard for the child? Would you say to yourself, 'I will make my child do all the disagreeable things I want done. I will cut off all his pleasure and give him only hard discipline?'"

"Oh, no," said the lady, "I would give my child the *best* day I could possibly plan!"

"Well," said the friend, "do you think God is *less* kind and loving than you? You can trust Him! If you will pray, 'Thy will be done', He will give you *only* those things which are *best* for you!"

God's Will Is Best

A little girl came to her father and said, "Father, I want a nickel." The father drew out his pocketbook, and offered her a neat five dollar bill! The little girl, not knowing what it was, would not take it. "I don't want it; I want a nickel." How like the little girl are we!

We ask, or demand, some small favor from God, and refuse His offer that would bring blessings a hundred times more valuable to us. God's will is always best for us.

Helping the Lepers

In a mission orphanage in India there lived a Christian girl who was soon to be married. She was attractive and capable. One day, some sores appeared on her hand. It was soon discovered that she had leprosy. She was sent from the orphanage to the leper asylum. She put on her beautiful white flowing garment and walked with her brother to the asylum. The women in the leper asylum were dirty and filthy. Their faces were sad and hopeless. When the girl saw them, she put her head on her brother's shoulder and wept and said, "Am I going to become as they are?"

The missionaries in the leper asylum asked the girl if she would like to help the poor women there. Then a ray of hope came to her and she caught the vision of what she could do for God and others in that horrible place. She started a school and taught the women to read and write and sing. She could play. So, the missionaries got her a folding organ. Music entered the lives of the poor, desolate women. Gradually, a change came into the place. The houses were made clean, neat, and tidy. The women washed their clothes and combed their hair.

After she had been there for some time, the Christian girl said, "When I first came to this asylum, I was hopeless. Now, I know that God has a work for me to do here for Him. If I had not become a leper, I never would have discovered my work. Every day I live, I thank Him for having sent me here, and for the work He has given me to do!"

For years, the girl worked in this asylum. Her fingers wasted away, but her face was shining and radiant. She never uttered a word of complaint. She always had a word of cheer for the sad and weary ones. Most of the women in the asylum were brought to the Lord Jesus through her ministry.

God has a plan for the lives of His children. It is our part to present ourselves unto Him: "A living sacrifice, holy, acceptable unto God" (*Rom. 12:1*). It is His part to show us what is His "good, and acceptable, and perfect, will." How happy we will be if we will seek God's perfect will for our lives, and gladly go in the way which He has chosen for us.

Safe in the Will of God

Someone asked Sam Higginbottom of India, "Is it safe to work among the lepers?" The answer was, "It is *safer* to work among the lepers, if it's my job, than to work anywhere else. The *only* safe place for God's children is in the *center* of God's will." The great missionary, David Livingstone, said, "I had rather be in Africa in the will of God than upon the throne of England out of the will of God!"

We Can't Have Our Own Way

Two little boys were walking down the street. One of them was crying as if his heart would break. A man asked, "What is the matter?" The answer came, "Nothing, except he wants to have his own way and can't."

The man walked on, saying to himself, "That is just the matter with me. For forty years I have been trying to have my own way, and blubbering because I could not have it!"

Happiness can come to us only when we want God's way and NOT our own way.

WITNESSING

Bringing Them In

A missionary doctor in a hospital in China operated on a man who was blind with cataracts. The man was cured of his blindness. A few weeks later the man came back to the hospital. He brought forty-eight blind men from one of China's interior provinces to the doctor. Each one of the blind men held on to a rope and walked behind the man who had been cured. Thus, in a chain they had come to the doctor, having walked two hundred and fifty miles. Nearly all of them were cured of their blindness.

The first blind man came to the doctor, put his trust in him, and received his sight. Then he went out and led forty-eight others to him. Have you who have been healed of spiritual blindness by the Savior brought others to Him?

Grandpa Won By A Four-Year-Old!

One day, a little girl four years old, climbed upon her grandpa's knee. She looked up into his face and stroked it. She said, "Grandpa, do you know the A B C of the Gospel?" Grandpa asked, "What do you know about it?" She replied, "I will tell you what I have learned in Sunday school: A means, 'All have sinned.' Grandpa, that means you, too. B means, 'Believe on the Lord Jesus Christ and thou shalt be saved.' Grandpa, have you ever done that? C means, 'Come unto Me'. Grandpa, have you ever come to Jesus?" God's Word in the mouth of the little girl led Grandpa to the Lord!

Eternal Doom

The world is filled with *lost, needy* souls! How greatly do these souls need the healing touch of the Great Physician, *Jesus!* How miserably we fail if we do not bring these needy souls to Jesus. A man dreamed that he went to Heaven. He was thrilled and delighted with the glory-world! All at once, an angel said to him, "Come! I want to show you something!" The angel took him to the battlements (of heaven) and said, "Look down yonder. What do you see?" The man replied, "I see a very dark world." "What else do you see?" asked the angel. "Why, I see men who are blindfolded. Many of them are going over a precipice to their destruction and eternal doom!" Said the angel, "Will you stay here and enjoy Heaven, or will you go back to earth, and spend a little more time there, telling men, women, and children about the Saviour?" The man awakened from his sleep. From that time on, he was an *earnest soul winner.* He did *all* that he could to bring lost, perishing sinners to Jesus, the Saviour!

Before It Is too Late

A Punjab brother in India was sobbing as if his heart would break. The missionary went up to him and put his arms about him and said, "Brother, the Blood of Jesus Christ cleanseth us from *all* sin." A smile lighted up the face of the Punjab brother. Said he, "Thank God, Sahib, but, oh, what an awful vision I had. Thousands of souls in this land of India are being carried away by the dark river of sin! They are going into *hell!* Oh, if I could only snatch them before it is *too late!*" Let *us* "rescue the perishing," and bring them to Jesus, the Saviour.

He Went after His Man

A lady was deeply burdened for her husband's salvation. The minister wanted to make an appointment to see him, and speak to him about Christ. But Jim left word with his wife that if the minister wanted him to see him, he must call upon him at his place of business. The minister found out that Jim was a steeple jack, and that he was working on the steeple of a new church.

When the minister went to the scene, he found that Jim was working at the very top of the church steeple. The foreman suggested that they call Jim down, but the minister said, "No." Then the minister climbed ladder after ladder until he was nearly two hundred feet above the sidewalk. There, high in the air, the minister talked to Jim about his soul. In five minutes, Jim was brought to the Saviour.

The next Sunday, Jim was at church. There he confessed before others his faith in the Saviour. Friends wondered at the change in Jim's life. Jim said, "The preacher who climbs two hundred feet of ladders to call on me can get me every time!"

We should let nothing discourage us as we bring others to Jesus. Remember, "He that winneth souls is wise!"

A Beautiful Sight

How happy are the boys and girls who bring their loved ones to Jesus! A minister once said, "The most beautiful thing I ever saw was in Orleans, a town of southern Indiana. I was helping in a revival meeting. Many people were saved. Among the first converts were two children, a boy and a girl. As soon as they were saved, they went to the door and brought in their father. He was a railway engineer. He had just gotten off his engine. They brought him to the altar and knelt beside him, and pointed him to Christ. He was wonderfully saved. That was the most beautiful thing I ever saw!"

Only One Interested in Souls

A pastor once went into a large department store, and talked to the owner of the store about his soul's salvation. As he spoke to the man about the Lord Jesus, the tears began to roll down his cheeks. The business man said, "I am seventy years old. I was born in this city. I have known many ministers and church members. I have done business with them. But you are the *only* man who ever spoke to me about my soul!"

The Work of Every Christian

A man was seriously hurt in an automobile accident. A crowd gathered around the injured man. A minister happened to pass by. Some of the bystanders were members of his church, and they cried, "Make way! Here's the minister." The crowd made way for the minister. The minister talked to the injured man about the Saviour, who alone can give life eternal. As the minister left the scene of the accident, he asked himself, "Why didn't some one from my congregation try to help that poor soul to God? That is the work of *every* Christian."

A Young Chinaman

A young Chinaman was converted in Atlanta, Georgia. He was given a copy of the New Testament, and told, "You are now a Christian. Read the Christian's Bible, and follow its teaching." The Chinaman began to read carefully and seriously the New Testament. When he came to John's Gospel and read about the two disciples who found Jesus, and then went out and found their own brothers and brought them to Christ, he was troubled. In far away China, he had an unsaved father, mother, brother, and sister. He felt that it was his duty to personally bring them to Christ. He wrote letters telling them about the Saviour and about His Gospel. But he could not make them understand. He decided that he *must* go and bring them to Jesus. He worked hard, and saved his money and went back to China. After many weeks, he won his loved ones to Christ. Again, he worked and saved his money until he could come back to America, his adopted home.

God wants *us* to take this business of winning others to Jesus seriously. Each one of us must tell another personally about Jesus. We must tell our loved ones and schoolmates about the Saviour.

No One Cared

Billy Sunday once talked with a young man about his soul. He used every Scripture and every argument to get him to promise to give his heart to the Lord. But he did not succeed. Finally, Mr. Sunday asked, "Are your father and mother Christians?" The young man replied, "I don't know. Father has been an officer in the church for several years, and mother has been superintendent of the Sunday School for some time, but I don't know whether they are Christians or not." "Have you a sister?" asked Mr. Sunday. "Yes, sir," replied the young man, "but I don't know whether she is a Christian or not. She has the primary department in the Sunday School." "Do your father and mother ever ask grace at the table?" "No." "Have your father, mother, or sister ever asked you to become a Christian?" "Mr. Sunday," replied the man, "as long as I can remember none of them has ever said a word to me about my soul! Do you believe they think I am *lost?*"

Golden Opportunities

One morning, Dr. O. P. Gifford of Boston was preaching in his church.

He said, "*Every* Christian can win somebody to Jesus." At the close of the service, a poor seamstress came to the pastor. She was greatly distressed. She said, "Pastor, you seemed to be unfair this morning. You kept saying that *every* Christian could win somebody to Jesus. You made *no* exceptions. Surely, I am an exception. How could I win anyone to Jesus? How can I go out and witness for Jesus? I sew early and late to keep the wolf from my door and to provide for my fatherless children. I have no education, and I have no opportunity to win somebody to Jesus." The pastor looked at her a moment, and then he asked, "Doesn't anybody ever come to your house?" She replied, "Why, certainly, a few people come there." "Does the milkman ever come?" "To be sure. He comes every morning." "Does the bread man come?" "He comes every day." "Does the meat man come?" "Yes, he, too, comes." The pastor waited for a moment, and then he said, "A word to the wise is sufficient!"

The little seamstress went her way. That night, as she lay in bed, she pondered long upon what the pastor had said to her. She had never even *tried* to win anybody to Christ. She had never told anyone about Jesus. She claimed to be a Christian. She claimed to be Jesus' friend, and yet she had *never* opened her lips for Him at all. She decided that she would begin in the morning with the coming of the milkman.

Before daybreak, the seamstress was up. Soon, she heard the milkman coming. She met him on the porch. She tried to speak to him about Christ, but her tongue seemed to be tied. He left and went toward the gate. Suddenly, she called him back! "Just a minute," she said; "I want to say something to you." Then, with a rush of words, she asked,

"Do you know Christ as your Saviour? Are you a Christian?" The milkman nearly dropped his bottles. He looked into her face with anguish on his. He said, "Little woman, what on earth has happened to make you talk to me like this? For two nights, I have been unable to sleep. I am so burdened about my sins, that I cannot sleep. If you know how to help me find the *light*, please tell me."

In just a few moments, the little seamstress had told the milkman how the Lord Jesus came to this earth to die for all sinners. She told him how he could be saved from his sins by simply trusting Jesus. The milkman was the *first* man the little woman won to Jesus. She *continued* to witness for Jesus, and before a year had passed, she had won *seven to Christ!*

You, too, can win somebody to Jesus if you will just witness for Jesus to your neighbors and friends, and to the strangers who come to your door.

Why He Was Happy

William Gladstone, the great statesman of England, was working late one night, preparing an important message to be given before Parliament the next day. Some one came and called him to the bedside of a dying boy. William Gladstone left his work. He went to tell the dying boy of Jesus. The boy was wonderfully saved! As day broke, William Gladstone returned to his study. Said he, "I am the happiest man in London, England today!" The throne and kingdoms of this world will crumble into dust. The poor dying boy had found life eternal in Jesus, the Saviour. The Bible says, "And they that be wise shall shine as the brightness of the firmament; and they that turn many to righteousness as the stars for ever and ever" (*Dan. 12:3*).

He Won One Hundred

Some time ago, an old man gave his heart to the Lord Jesus, becoming a Christian. He had a great many friends, many of whom were sinful, lost men. He wanted them to become Christians, too. He made a list of the names of his old associates. There were one hundred and sixteen names on the list. Some of them were infidels; some were drunkards; some were among the worst men in the town where he lived. He began to pray *earnestly* for these people. He talked to them about Christ. He gave them tracts and good Christian books to read. Some refused to listen to him. Others made fun of him. But he kept on praying and working for their salvation. Within two years, *one hundred* of the persons whose names were on his list had become Christians.

The Layman's Example

Three preachers and a Christian layman were riding together on a train. They talked about the things of the Lord, and had real fellowship together. When the subject of personal work came up, the preachers admitted to each other that it was not easy for them to approach another individual about Jesus Christ. While they were discussing their difficulty, the *layman* quietly left them. He went down the aisle, and sat down beside a soldier. He began to talk to the soldier and soon led the conversation toward the matter of the soldier's salvation. In just a few moments, the *layman* had won that soldier to the Lord Jesus! The three preachers got red in the face. They were filled with shame. One of them said, "May the Lord forgive us! We three preachers have been sitting here *talking* about soul winning while that *layman* has done it!"

His Dead Level Best

Some years ago, a rescue crew was organized in Northwestern University, near Chicago. The purpose of the crew was to rescue drowning people from Lake Michigan. Early one cold November morning, word came to the campus that the *Lady Elgin* had been caught in a violent storm and was rapidly going to pieces near the shore. On the *Lady Elgin* were many passengers. The college youths hurried to the scene of the wreck. The life-saving group rushed into the cold, angry waters, but were soon driven back.

One fine, athletic youth, Ed Spencer, would not give up hope of rescuing the drowning. He threw off most of his clothes, tied a rope about his waist, and threw himself into the choppy, chilly waters! He swam out to the wrecked vessel, got hold of a drowning man, and then signaled to be pulled to shore. Time and again, he leaped into the chilly waters until he had rescued *ten people!* Then, he was utterly spent. He went and stood by the fire which had been built on the beach. He was blue, trembling, and hardly able to stand.

As Ed stood there, he looked again toward the sinking *Lady Elgin*. There, he saw men, women, and children struggling in the water. He said, "Boys, I'm going in again!" "No, no, Ed, it is utterly vain to try. You have used up all your strength. You can't save any more!" But Ed said, "They are *going down. I must* try again!" Into the bleak, cold waters, he leaped again, and he brought safely back to shore five

more persons! Now, he could hardly get to the fire on the beach. As he stood there, he saw a spar of the wrecked ship floating up and down on the waves. Then, he noticed a man's head just above the spar. He said, "Boys, there is a man out there trying to save himself. I'm going to help him!" "No, no, Ed, you can't help him," they said. "I'll *try* anyway," said Ed, and into the waters he leaped.

Ed rescued his man. Just as he reached the shore with him, he gave way utterly. He was carried to his room. He was delirious. During the day and night, whenever his mind cleared, Ed would ask, "Boys, did I do my best, my dead level best?" "Why, yes, Ed," they would reply, "you saved sixteen!" Then Ed would say, "Yes, I know that; but did I do my *best*, my *dead level best?*"

The Unanswered Question

A minister was asked to conduct the funeral services of a young girl. The minister called at the home, and asked the father if Mary was a Christian. The father said, "I do not know. I don't take as much interest in those things as I ought. Her mother will know. Ask her." When the mother came in, the minister asked, "Was Mary a Christian?" The mother replied, "I do not know, but she went to Sunday School. Maybe her Sunday School teacher will know!" The minister asked the Sunday School teacher, "Was Mary a Christian?" Sorrowfully, the teacher said, "I do not know. I had long intended to speak to Mary about the Saviour, but somehow, I neglected to do it, and now she is *gone* from us!"

How sad it was: A soul had gone out to meet God without an earnest effort from *any one* to bring her to the Saviour!

> "Rescue the perishing,
> Care for the dying,
> Snatch them in pity,
> From sin and the grave.

"Thank You, John"

John A. Broadus was saved when he was a boy. The *next day*, he went to one of his schoolmates, Sandy Jones, and said to him, "I wish you would be a Christian. Won't you?" Sandy was a red-haired, awkward boy. Sandy replied, "Well, I don't know. Perhaps, I will." Not long afterwards, one night in the little church, Sandy Jones accepted Christ. He then walked across that little meeting house, held out his hand, and said, "I thank you, John!"

Dr. Broadus went forth from that little town and became a great scholar, and the president of a great school where ministers are trained to preach the Gospel. Every summer, when Dr. Broadus went home, an awkward, red-haired old farmer, in plain clothes, with red mud on his boots, would come up. He would stick out his big hand and say, "Howdy, John. Thank you, John! Thank you, John. I never forget, John!"

It is said that when Dr. Broadus lay dying, his family gathered around him. He said to them, "The sweetest sound to my ears when I get to Heaven, next to the welcome of Jesus, whom I have tried to love and serve, will be the welcome of Sandy Jones. He will thrust out his great hand and say, "Howdy, John! Thank you, John! Thank you, John!"

The Pull Heavenward

One day, a man said to Dr. Wilbur Chapman, "Listen to my story: Once I was a big businessman in this city. I had a lovely home, a wonderful wife, and a dear little boy. Strong drink became my master. I soon fell low. One day, I was helplessly lying in the gutter, drunk, when some one came and said, 'If you want to see your boy alive, hurry home.' The words aroused me from my drunken stupor. I arose and quickly went home. I went to the dark room where my sin had forced my wife and boy to live. We had lost our beautiful home. I found that a truck had passed over my boy and seriously hurt him. He was dying. My boy took me by the hand, and pulled me down by his side and said, "Father, I love you. Even though you get drunk, I love you. I will not let you go until you promise to meet me in Heaven!' Still holding my hand, he died. From that day, I have felt him pulling me Heavenward. I am now a saved man. The Lord Jesus is my precious Saviour. How I thank God for my little boy who loved me and would not let me go until I promised to meet him in Heaven!"

Get Busy!

A man told Mr. Moody that he had spent five years on the mountain top since he had trusted in Christ as his Saviour. Mr. Moody asked, "How many souls have you led to Christ in those five years?" The man hesitated, and finally said, "I can't recall any.' "Well," said Mr. Moody, 'we don't want that kind of mountain-top experience. Souls are perishing, and we must go out and win them for the Saviour!"

Someone to Care

For many nights, between the hours of ten and twelve, a poor woman was seen making her way through the streets of a certain section of London. She was searching for her only daughter who had left home one year before and had gone to the great city to enter a life of shame and sin. The mother had learned that the daughter might be seen every night in a certain part of the city. So she went to the city and searched for the missing girl. After many nights of watching, she was about to despair, when she saw a figure resembling her daughter approaching. Eagerly she ran forward with outstretched arms. She was about to embrace the girl, when the light of a lamp showed her that this was not her child. In great grief, she cried out, "Ah, it is not you. I was looking for my daughter, but you are not my child!" The poor girl burst into tears, saying, "I have no mother. I wish I had one. I wish I had someone who would *look for me!*"

Today, we seem to hear the bitter cry from many, "*I wish I had someone to look for me!*" Christless, they are going their darkened way. Their spirits cry out, "*No man careth for my soul!*" Will you not seek for these lost ones every day?

Rabbi Abraham

Long ago, Count Zinzendorf, a great Christian, met an aged Jew Rabbi Abraham. The Count took the hand of the aged Jew and said, "Gray hairs are a crown of glory! I can see that you have had much experience. In the Name of the God of Abraham, Isaac, and Jacob, let us be *friends!*"

The aged Jew had never heard such words from a Christian before. Often he had ben badly treated. He had heard people say, "Be gone, Jew!" The aged Rabbi Abraham was surprised. His lips

trembled. His voice shook. Tears ran down his cheeks upon his beard. Count Zinzendorf said, "Father, we understand each other!"

From that moment the two were friends! Often, the Count visited Rabbi Abraham, and ate black bread at his table.

One day, the aged Rabbi said, "My heart is longing for light!" Then, Count Zizendorf told him about the Lord Jesus who died upon the Cross. He told him how the Lord Jesus died to save lost sinners. The old man wept. Zinzendorf said, "Believe on Him whose Blood was shed for you and me. Find in Him your salvation." So be it,' said old Rabbi Abraham, and his heart was filled with light! He was won to Jesus because Count Zinzendorf showed him kindness and friendship, and then told him of Jesus.

Tracks

How easy it is to witness for the Lord by passing out tracts. A minister gave a Negro a tract. Some time later he asked the Negro what he thought of it. This was the reply, "Ah, Massa, it done my soul good. I never knew before why they called them 'tracks.' But I read that little book you gave me and it tracked me this way and it tracked me that way. When I go out in the barn, it tracks me there. When I come in the house it tracks me there. It tracks me everywhere I go. Then I know why they call them tracks."

Baby Lips

A Christian mother taught her little three-year-old girl to say, "Jesus loves me, even me." Some special revival meetings were being held in town. Mother tried to get the father to go to the meetings with her, but father refused. He did not love Jesus. One evening the little girl met her father at the door when he came home from work. She smiled up at him, so he picked her up and kissed her. As he put her down, the little girl said, "Pa, Jesus loves me, even me. And Jesus loves even 'ou." The father's heart was touched. Tears came to his eyes. That night he went to the meeting to hear more about the love of Jesus.

A Ready Answer

We should always be ready to speak God's Word. A Christian Hindu was on his way to church. He passed some British soldiers who thought that they would joke him. "How is Jesus this morning?" they called. The Hindu stopped and said, "You ask how Jesus is this morning? Jesus Christ is the same yesterday, and today, and forever!" The words from the Bible, which the Hindu quoted troubled the two soldiers. All night, they kept thinking, "Jesus Christ the same yesterday, and today, and for ever!" The next day, they went to the Hindu Christian and said, "We can find no rest. We want to give ourselves to Jesus! You brought us to Jesus!"

Don't Hesitate

A minister, somewhat fearfully approached a great man, and asked him if he were a Christian. The man answered courteously and allowed him to continue the conversation. At the close, the minister said, "I hope you do not consider me rude in speaking so abruptly on this subject!"

The great man grasped the minister's hand. Tears were in his eyes as he answered: "Don't ever hesitate to speak to any man about his soul. For twenty years, I have been longing to have someone speak to me. I believe there are thousands of men in this city who are like me. They are carrying an uneasy conscience and a great burden of sin. But they are not courageous enough to seek instruction. But they would willingly receive it if only someone would speak to them!"

Not Afraid

It was almost noon. The pupils in the fifth grade were tired. They would be glad when the bell rang for recess. Now, they had their geography books out. As Alice sat studying her geography, a Voice seemed to say to her, "Alice, you like your school friends. Alice, if you do not tell them about Jesus, many of them will be lost." Alice could not study her geography any longer. She raised her hand and asked the teacher to let her say something to the class.

Bravely, Alice went up and stood by the teacher's desk. She told all her class about Jesus, her Saviour. She told them that she was praying that they would know Jesus as their Saviour, too.

Many of the boys and girls hid behind their geography books and laughed. But some of the boys and girls listened carefully. In their hearts, they longed to become Christians. After the class was over, some of them asked Alice to talk to them and tell them *more* about Jesus. Alice won many of her friends to Jesus, because she was not afraid to speak about Him.

Keep On Witnessing

Some years ago, there lived in a southern town a business girl who was having a hard time among her friends. She was a Christian, and she suffered much persecution for her Christian testimony. She came to a minister who was holding some special services in the town. She told him she was afraid she must give up trying to witness for Christ among her worldly friends and associates.

The minister said, "We put lights in the darkness." The girl saw his meaning. She realized that the Lord had put her in a dark place that she might shine for Jesus in the midst of darkness. She went back determined to be *more* courageous than ever in her witnessing for Jesus.

A few weeks later, at the close of a service, the girl came to the minister with a group of other girls. All their faces were beaming with joy! Said she, "Oh, I am *so* glad I have *kept on* witnessing for Jesus! Thirteen girls from our business house have decided for Christ!"

The Stammering Tongue

When Dr. Fred Moffit, the greatly used preacher, was a boy, he lived in Scotland. He stammered so terribly that the neighbors laughed at him. Soon after his conversion, he attended a testimony meeting. He wanted to testify about what the Lord had done for him. He held back because of his stammering tongue. The call to testify became so insistent that he promised the Lord that if a girl sitting near him would testify, he would too. Soon, the girl arose and gave her testimony. Then, Fred Moffit kept his promise. The Lord helped him to give his testimony, so that the people understood what he said! And miracle of miracles, after that day, his stammering tongue gave him no more trouble!

A Dummy Christian

In a meeting in the city of Nankin, a Chinaman arose and said, amidst tears and groans, "Oh, God, forgive me! I have been a *dummy Christian*. When I was converted, the devil said to me, 'There are preachers to do the preaching. You need not bother about it!' I listened to the devil's lie, and all these years, I have been a dummy Christian. I have been living in *ease* while souls have been *lost!*"

Witness Where You Are

A man in an elevator said to the operator, "I hope to meet you in Heaven!" Those few words led the girl to Jesus.

A man in prison wrote on the wall the words of John 3:16. The verse led one of the other prisoners to Jesus.

A lady in a garden spoke about Jesus to a workman repairing the wall. Her words led the man to the Saviour.

A little, old lady gave a tract to an actor going into a theater. Later, the man read the tract and was saved.

A little girl wrote a letter to a friend, telling about Jesus. The friend read the letter and was saved.

If we will witness for Jesus every day, *where we are,* we, too, will win souls for Jesus. The Bible says, "He that winneth souls is *wise.*"

Witnessing to Little Sister

A little boy trusted Jesus as his Saviour. He was very happy when Jesus forgave his sins. One day, he asked a friend who was visiting in his home, "Hadn't I better tell my sister about Jesus?" The sister, who was younger than the boy, was asleep upstairs.

The friend asked the little boy why he wanted to tell his sister about Jesus. He replied, "Father never told me. My mother never told me. My teacher at school never said anything. I would never have given my heart to Jesus if my Sunday School teacher had not told me about Him last Sunday! Maybe no one will tell sister about Him. Don't you think I'd better tell her?"

The friend said, "Yes, you should tell her about Jesus!" How happy the little boy was when he told his little sister about Jesus, and won her for the Saviour!

A Chinese Girl

A twelve-year-old Chinese girl was a pupil in a mission school. One day, her parents came to get her. They said she must now earn her living, that she must go to a city thirty miles away to work in a heathen home. The girl came to the room of the missionary to say good-bye. Quietly, she said, "I shall be the *only* Christian in that city." "Yes," replied the missionary, "but you know who is going with you, don't you?" "Oh, yes," said the girl, her face lighting up with joy, "the Lord Jesus Christ is going with me!"

In the heathen city, the Chinese girl remained true to the Lord Jesus. She told others about Jesus. She refused to worship idols, or to do reverence to the household gods. Sometimes, she was persecuted, but she showed no anger. She was always true and kind, no matter what others said or did.

Several months later, two men walked the thirty miles to the mission school. They told the missionary that they had been sent to ask that some one come to their city to teach them about Jesus and to start a school. Several times missionaries had tried to get permission to work in that city, but always they had been denied. Now, the missionary asked, "Why do they want us to come to the city?" The reply was, "A little girl, twelve years old has come to our city. She says that she is a Christian. Every one who visits the home where she works has noticed her happy face, and her kind, gentle manner. When they question her, she always replies, 'It is because I love Jesus, and Jesus loves me, and is always with me.' " Then the man said further to the missionary, "We want the other girls in our city to be like that Christian girl. Won't you send somebody to our city to tell us about Jesus and start a school?"

A hostile city in China was opened to the Gospel message, because *one* twelve-year-old girl witnessed for Jesus with her *lips* and with her *life!*

Not a Wooden Christian

Sophie, the scrubwoman, was constantly talking about the Lord Jesus Christ. One day, she was seen talking about Christ to a *wooden Indian,* standing in front of a cigar store. Some one joked her about it. She replied, "Perhaps I did talk to a wooden Indian about Christ, for my eyesight is very bad. But talking to a wooden Indian about Christ is no so bad as being a *wooden Christian* and never talking to anybody about the Lord Jesus!" Sophie was right!

"You talk about your business,
    Your bonds and stock and gold;
And in all worldly matters
    You are so brave and bold.
But why are *you* so *silent*
    About salvation's plan?
Why don't you speak for Jesus
    And speak out like a man?

"You talk about the weather,
  And crops of corn and wheat;
You speak with friends and neighbors
  That pass along the street;
You call yourself a Christian
  And like the Gospel plan
Then why not speak for Jesus
  And speak out like a man?"

"Are You Saved?"

A little girl said to a man, who later became a great preacher, "Are you saved?" "Go away," was the rough answer the man gave to the little girl's question. "No, I can't go away!" was the little girl's reply. Again she asked, "Are you saved?" The man's heart became tender. He trusted Jesus as his Saviour, and began to bring others to Jesus. Will you not talk to your neighbors about Jesus?

In an Elevator

Peter Stam had the habit of witnessing for Jesus wherever he went. One day, he was in an elevator in a large building. Everyone left the elevator except Mr. Stam and the operator. He said to the elevator operator: "I hope when you make your *last* trip, it will be *up* and not *down!*" The girl was so surprised, she swallowed her gum. Then, he said, "My dear girl, I am seventy years old. One of these days, I am going to leave this earth. I am going to meet my Lord and Saviour Jesus Christ. I hope I shall meet you there!" The elevator girl never forgot the words of Peter Stam. She became a Christian, and a true follower of the Lord Jesus!

WORKING FOR GOD

Forever Delaying

An angel passing over the earth one day saw a little boy in a sunny field. "Do you love Jesus?" the angel asked.

The boy looked up with bright eyes and said, "Oh yes, I am one of His children."

"Then," said the angel, "I have work for you to do for Jesus. Will you do it?"

"Yes, after awhile," said the boy. "I want to play a few hours first."

Away went the boy to play among the butterflies and flowers. The day was ended, and the little boy had not done the work for Jesus.

Years passed by, and the little boy had become a young man. One day the angel visited him again. The angel said, "Young man, the day is fast passing. I have work for you to do for Jesus. Will you do it?"

The young man said, "Yes, but there is plenty of time. I am busy right now." The night came and the work was not done."

The young man became an old man. One day the angel came again. He asked, "Have you done the work for Jesus which I gave you to do?"

The old man said tearfully, "No. I meant to do it, but I thought I had plenty of time. Now the night has come, and I fear it is too late for me to begin."

This is the sad story of many who profess to love Jesus, but always put their own selfish interests first in their lives. They find out too late that they have failed to serve Jesus, and have failed to lay up treasures in heaven.

God and Hudson Taylor

Hudson Taylor said, "One day, God said to me: 'I am going to evangelize inland China. If you will walk with me, I will do it through you." When Hudson Taylor went to China, God worked in and through Hudson Taylor, and thousands of Chinese were won for the Lord Jesus.

Cripple Tom

Cripple Tom loved the Lord Jesus. He wanted to serve Him. But there seemed little to do. All day, Cripple Tom lay on a cot near the window. He looked down below and saw the people passing by. He longed to tell them of Jesus, His Saviour. One day, he had an idea. He asked his mother to give him a tablet and a pencil. Then he copied verses from the Bible on the paper. He began to drop these verses down on the passers-by. Soon, he became quite expert. He could drop the little pieces of paper, with the verses on them, so that they would fall at the very feet of those passing by.

One day, Cripple Tom dropped one of the papers in front of an elderly man. The man picked up the paper. He read the Bible verse. He looked up to see where the paper had come from. He inquired from the storekeeper below about the family that lived upstairs. He heard about Cripple Tom.

Presently, Tom heard foosteps coming up the stairs! Then, the door opened and the man walked in. He walked over to the bed, and, looking down at Tom, he asked, "Did you drop this paper down to the sidewalk?" Tom replied, "Yes!" "Why did you do it?" asked the man. Tom was a little frightened, but told the truth. He said, "The Lord Jesus is my Saviour and my Friend. To know Him, sir, is to love Him, and to love Him is to serve Him! It wouldn't be loving Him without serving Him!" Tears came to the man's eyes. From that day, he became Cripple Tom's friend, and did much to help him.

Don't Be Lazy

God wants His people to have a mind to work. He does not want us to be lazy and indifferent when there is work to be done. Too many of us are willing to let others do the work.

The laziest man in the village was seen running one day. His hat was off and his coat was flying in the wind. He kept on running until he collided with the minister. "What on earth has happened to make you run like this?" asked the minister. "I just heard of some work, and I'm going to see about it," said the man. "Well, I hope you get the job. What kind of work is it?" Sam had already started to run again, but he called back, "Oh, it's some washing for my wife to do."

The Fruit Peddler

A quiet little man had a cart which he pushed about on the streets. In the carts were fruits and vegetables. He sold the fruits and vegetables from house to house. One day a little notebook dropped from the cart. A man picked up the notebook. On the first page were written the words, "For Jesus' sake." On the next page was written a list of names. The list was followed by the words, "These were absent from Bible school last Sunday. Be sure to visit them." On other pages were written, "Ask about the sick baby"; "Leave fruit for the blind lady"; "Speak a word of cheer to the old cripple man"; "Invite the new family to church services."

The next day, the man handed the notebook back to the quiet, little fruit peddler. The fruit peddler thanked the man and said, "That is my book of reminders. Thank you for returning it!" The man expressed surprise at the things which the fruit peddler had written in the book. He replied, "Well, the reason I want to do these things for *others* is for *Jesus' sake*. You see, I love Jesus."

The Spirit of Washing

A minister, calling on an old Negress, found her bending over the wash tub. She was scrubbing with all her might. "Aunt Dinah," said he, "don't you get very tired doing that hard work?" "Oh, yes, sir," she replied, "I haven't got much strength, and I ask the Lord, and He gives me the *spirit of washing*."

Humble Instruments

A converted Hindu, addressing some of his countrymen said, "By birth, I am of a low contemptible caste. I am so low that if a Brahman chanced to touch me, he must go and bathe. And yet God has chosen me to preach His Gospel; My friends, I will tell you why God did this: If God had chosen one of you, high and learned Brahmans, and made you a preacher, and you won souls for Him, people would say that it was your great name that made you successful. When God uses me to win souls, no one thinks of praising me. They give God *all* of the glory."

How glad we are that God can and does use humble people in His service. We like the little poem which says,

"Oh, to be nothing, nothing
Only to lie at His feet;
A broken and *empty* vessel.
For the Master's use made meet!"
Broken that so unhindered,
His life through me might flow;
Emptied that He might fill me,
As forth to His service I go!"

The Strength We Need

A Korean was once asked. "Can you do it?" with reference to some church work. With quiet confidence, he replied, "We ask questions, such as, 'Can you do it?' about men's work. We never ask them about God's work. God gives us the strength we need for His work!"

Done Unto Jesus

A little girl was left motherless at the age of eight. Her father was poor. There were four children younger than she was. This little girl tried to care for all of them. She tried to take her mother's place. She got up early every morning, and worked all day until late at night. She cooked. She scrubbed the house. Her little fingers became hard and scarred. Her little body became thin.

When the girl was thirteen, her strength was all gone. She became sick. She said to a neighbor, "I think I am going to die. I am not afraid to die, but I am ashamed!"

"Why are you ashamed?" the neighbor asked.

"Since Mamma left us, I have been so busy. I haven't had time to do anything for Jesus. When I get to Heaven and meet Him, I shall be ashamed. What can I tell Him?"

The neighbor took the little girl's hands in hers. She looked at the scars and callouses. She said, "My dear, you will not need to tell Him anything. Just show Him *your hands!* You have been living for Him every day, doing the work He has given you to do. You have been a little mother to your brothers and sisters!"

Coöperation with God

A friend saw Uncle Dan working in his garden. He asked, "Uncle Dan, did you not ask the Lord to give you a good garden? Why are you working so hard?" Uncle Dan replied, "Yes, I asked the Lord to give me a good garden. But I never pray for a good garden unless I have a hoe in my hand. I say, 'Lord, You send the sunshine and rain, and I will keep down these weeds.'" Uncle Dan believed in working together with God. How glad we are that we can work with God! God is our never-failing Helper.

John Wanamaker

A country boy went to church one night. He heard an old man tell how God was blessing him. He heard a young man tell how God had saved him, and was blessing him. The country boy said, "Being a Christian helps you in your old age. Being a Christian helps you in your youth. *I will be a Christian!*" He accepted Christ as *his Saviour that night.*

God blessed the boy greatly. He grew to be a great business man, owning two big stores, one in New York and one in Philadelphia. He became Postmaster General of the United States. He was also superintendent of a large Sunday School.

Some one once asked, "How can you find time to work in a Sunday School when you have so many other things to do?" His reply was, "All the other things are *just things.* The Sunday School is my *real work!*"

This is the story of John Wanamaker who was called of God to work for Him when he was just a country boy!

A Chinese Boy

A little Chinese boy was working on a naval vessel. He soon won the hearts of the Captain and the crew. Young Soong loved Captain Jones. C a p t a i n Jones became his "hero." One day the Captain told Soong about the Lord Jesus, and the little Chinese boy placed his faith in Jesus. He became a Christian, and received his education in America.

Then the boy went back to China to tell the good news of what Christ had done in his life. He began to print the Gospel in the Chinese language. Soong married a Chinese girl, and they had six children. One girl became Mrs. Sun Yat Sen, the wife of China's liberator. Another girl became the wife of the minister of finance. Another girl became Madame Chiang Kai-shek, a leader not only in China but throughout the world. A son became the member of the cabinet. This is the account of a Chinese boy who was called of God to do His work.

God's Finger

A man was praying in prayer meeting. He prayed that God would "touch" a certain sinner with His finger. Suddenly, he stopped praying! A brother asked, "Why have you stopped your prayer?" He replied, "Because the Lord said to me, '*You are My finger!*' Now, I must leave this service. I must go and find that man and bring him to God. God wants to use me as His finger!"

Don't Lose the Taste for Work!

A woman in Philadelphia used to employ occasionally an old Negress, known as Aunt Cecelia. She lost sight of her for some time. Then, one morning, she met her. She said, "Good morning, Aunt Cecelia. Why aren't you washing nowadays?" "It's this way, Miss Ann. I've been out of work so long that now when I could work, I find I've lost my taste for it."

"Done for Jesus Christ"

In a little town a group of young people had a mission band. It was a small band, but much work was done for Christ. At each business meeting, every one turned in reports, telling how many sick had been visited; how many lost ones had been told about Christ; how much money had been given to the missionaries. At the end of each report, this sentence was written: "This work was done for Jesus Christ." If nothing had been done, this sentence was written: "Nothing done for Jesus Christ." The little sentence at the end of the report had a profound effect on each one of the members! Work for Christ *must* be done well.

God Needs Instruments

Once there was a terrible train wreck in Britain. People, writhing in pain, lay all along the track. Presently, a man came up and recognized a doctor who did not seem to be hurt at all. He asked, "Why don't you do something for these poor people? Can't you see they are in agony?" With tears coursing down his face, the doctor replied, "I would, but I have no instruments!"

Today, the world is bruised and dying. We cry to God, "Why don't *You* do something?" God seems to reply, "I would, but I have no instruments!" God needs human instruments. He needs *you* and *me* to do His work here on earth. Are *you* ready and willing to be an instrument in God's hands?

Working for the Lord

A Moslem teacher from a government school in India was visiting a teacher in a mission school. Asked the Moslem, "What do they pay you?" "Two shillings (about fifty cents a week)," was the quiet answer.

"Two shillings?" said the Moslem, "Man, don't you realize you could get ten times that amount in a government school?"

"I am not teaching for the money I receive. I am working for the Lord," answered the mission teacher.

"And is that what you wear?" softly asked the Moslem, as he indicated the neat, white shirt and trousers of home-spun material.

"Yes," said the missionary.

"But you have a big robe at home, surely?" The Moslem could not imagine otherwise.

"No," said the mission teacher, "I do not need a big robe. This is sufficient."

The Moslem gazed at him in silence, and finally said, as he turned to go, "I never thought there was anything to this Jesus way, but there must be, for a man to be willing to work for two shillings a week and not even to have a big robe to wear!"

Serving Jesus

A preacher went to see an old Scotch lady. She began to weep. Then she dried her eyes with her apron. The preacher asked what troubled her. She confessed, "I have done so little for Jesus. When I was just a wee girl, the Lord spoke to my heart. I did so want to live for Him. I did so want to serve Him!" "Well, haven't you served Him?" asked the minister. "Well, I have tried to live for Him, but I have done so little. I have been busy, caring for my family. I have washed dishes, cooked three meals a day, mopped the floor, and mended the clothes. That is what I have done all my life, and I did so want to serve Jesus."

The preacher looked at the little Scotch woman and smiled, "Where are your boys?" he asked. She had four sons, and had given them *all* Bible names.

"Oh," said she, "Mark is in China, preaching for the Lord. Luke was sent out from your own church. He is in Africa, preaching the Gospel. I had a letter from him the other day. A revival has broken out. He is having a wonderful time serving the Lord! Matthew is in China with his brother, Mark. They are working together for God. I am so happy about that. And the other night, John, the youngest of my boys, came and said to me, 'Mother, I have been praying, and tonight in my room, the Lord spoke to my heart, and told me that He wants me to go to my brother in Africa and help him preach the Gospel.'"

The minister looked at the little Scotch woman and said, "You say your life has been wasted in mopping floors, darning socks, and washing dishes. But, sister, you have *truly been serving Jesus!* Surely, the mansion which the Lord has prepared for you will be very close to His throne!"

God's Work First

Some time ago, the Standard Oil Company wanted two extra men in China. Mr. Li was one of the two chosen. He was housemaster in a boys' boarding school of the China Inland Mission. The Standard Oil Company offered him double the wages he was earning in the mission. When Mr. Li found that he would have to work on Sundays, he gave up the new job. He was offered three times his former wages, and excused from Sunday work. He returned to the job, but soon he was very unhappy. Finally, he wrote this letter to the Company, "I am sorry I cannot work for your Company. I have decided to work for God. I *must* win the boys for Jesus Christ." The manager of the Standard Oil remarked, "I thought I did well to hire a Christian, but I see they put Christ *first*."

Hard Work in a Hard World

A student asked a minister: "What can I do that will be *easy?*" The preacher said: "Young man, you can't be a writer; you can't be a preacher; you can't be a merchant; you can't be a doctor; you can't be a farmer; you can't be a soldier or a sailor. You can't study, or you can't think, if you want something easy to do. Young man, you have come into a *hard* world. There is hard work for each one to do. The *only* easy place I know of is the *grave*. When you die and are buried, then there will be no work for you to do!"

God needs willing workers in His service. Won't you be a willing worker for Jesus, doing day by day what Jesus wants you to do?

The Great and Powerful God

Richard was a brave king. He was often called, "Richard the Lion-Hearted." He did mighty deeds. With him, he carried his sword. Some one looked at the sword. It was just an ordinary, common sword. He said, "I don't see how such a sword can do such mighty deeds." King Richard replied, "It is not the sword that does those deeds. It is the arm of the king." God often does great and mighty things through His weak servants. It is not the servant of the Lord who does these mighty things. It is the great and powerful God!

A Rich Reward

A friend spent a few hours in the operating room of a medical missionary. He saw the missionary perform a difficult operation. When the operation was over, the missionary's face was pale, and he was wet with perspiration. Said the friend, "Doctor, how can you stand this? Surely, every day is not like this." The doctor merely smiled.

Asked the friend, "How much money would you receive in the United States for an operation like this?" "Oh, about six hundred dollars," said the medical missionary. "How much *will* you receive for this operaton?" A light came into the tired eyes. The missionary replied, "My fee for this operation will be this man's *gratitude*. There can be no richer reward than that!"

Asleep

God wants us to help those who are working for Him. We must not be one of the many who are lying down and sleeping on the job. Sam and Joe were sent to the basement of a factory to do some work together. During the morning, the superintendent of the factory went down to the basement to see how their work was coming along. He could not find them. A search was made. He found Sam asleep and Joe loafing. "What have you been doing, Joe?" the superintendent asked. "Oh," said Joe, "I've been helping Sam."

Too many of us are helping the Sams, when we should be wide-awake and busy doing the work God has given us to do. More than nineteen hundred years ago, Christ told His followers to go into all the world and preach the Gospel to every creature; and still there are millions who have never heard the Gospel message. Are *you* asleep on the job?

Jesus' Sunday School

A Canadian Sunday School superintendent felt that the parents, teachers, and officers of the School were not helping in the work as they should. They were not sharing in the burden of the work. He decided to talk to them in Sunday School. He wanted them to feel that the Sunday School was *theirs*, and not *his* alone. He started his talk by asking, "Whose Sunday School is this?"

For a moment, there was silence. Then a little blue mitten was raised. The superintendent said, as he smiled at the wee owner, "All right, Penelope, you tell us." The child raised her blue eyes and said softly, "It's Jesus' Sunday School!"

Penelope's answer made every one present think. If it were Jesus' Sunday School, then each one of them must work with God to build up His work. The entire Sunday School received new life, because each one realized that it was Jesus' Sunday School.

Up and At It

At a revival meeting one day, a minister turned to Henry Heinz, of the "fifty-seven varieties" fame, and said, "You are a Christian. Why are you not up and at it?" Heinz went home in anger and went to bed. But he could not sleep. At four o'clock in the morning, he prayed that God would make him a power in His work. Then he went to sleep.

At the next meeting of bank presidents which he attended, Mr. Heinz turned to the man next to him, and spoke to him of Christ. The man looked at Mr. Heinz in amazement, and said, "I have wondered many times why you never spoke to me if you really believed in Him!"

From that time on, Mr. Heinz kept busy bringing others to Jesus. The bank president was the first of two hundred and sixty-seven souls whom Mr. Heinz won to the Lord Jesus!

Do Your Part

When Sir Michael Costa was having a rehearsal in which a choir of many voices was singing, accompanied by the music of many instruments, *one* man who played the piccolo ceased to play. The piccolo is a very *small* instrument. Perhaps, the player thought that his little instrument would never be missed. Suddenly, the great conductor threw up his hands. All became still! Then the conductor cried out, "Where is the piccolo?" God has given to each one of us, big and small, a part in His service. Do not fail to do *your* part. God expects you and me to do the work which He has given to us.

Pray and Work

Martin Luther had a dear friend named Myconius. When Martin Luther spent hours working for Christ, Myconius expressed sympathy. Said Myconius, "I can help best where I am. I will remain here and pray while you toil."

Day by day, Myconius prayed for Luther. But as he prayed, he began to feel uncomfortable. One night, he had a dream. The Saviour showed him His hands and His feet. Then, He showed him the fountain in which he had been cleansed from sin. Then, the Saviour said, "Follow Me." The Lord took him to a lofty mountain and pointed eastward. Myconius saw a plain stretching far away to the horizon. It was dotted with white sheep — thousands and thousands of them. One lone man, Martin Luther, was trying to shepherd them all. Then, the Saviour pointed westward. Myconius saw a great field of corn. One reaper was trying to harvest it all. The lonely laborer was exhausted, but still he persisted in his task. Myconius recognized in the lonely reaper his old friend, Martin Luther.

When Myconius wakened from his sleep, he said, "It is not enough that I remain here and pray while Martin Luther labors for the Lord. The sheep must be shepherded; the fields must be reaped. Here am I, Lord; send me!" And Myconius went out and shared his old friend's labors.

How He Rested

A Christian man worked hard all week on the street railway system. He would get down on his knees with a shield over his eyes, and weld the steel rails. When Saturday noon came, his work was over for the week. He was just "worn out."

Then the man would go home, and get a bundle of tracts and books and start out, hunting up poor, needy souls. Maybe, he would find them in the county hospitals, or in the jail; maybe, he would find them in the slum district. Whenever he heard of somebody lying sick, and miserable, he would go to see that one. He would sit by the bed, and give them the Gospel. Often, when he found that there was no money to pay the bills, he would lay a five dollar bill on the table near the bed.

When Sunday came, the man would say, "My, I was tired, and worn out yesterday. But I had a wonderful time in the afternoon, and now, I am all rested up!"

Do Your Best for God

A beautiful story is told of a king going into his garden. To his surprise, he found his trees dying, his shrubs and flowers wilted. He asked the oak why it was dying, and the oak replied, "Because I cannot be tall like the pine." He asked the pine why it was drooping, and it replied, "Because I cannot bear grapes like the vine." He asked the vine why it was wilting, and it replied, "Because I cannot blossom like the rose."

Then, the king came upon the heartsease, blooming as fresh as ever. He asked why it was not wilting like the other things around it, and the heartsease replied, "I took it for granted that when you planted me here you wanted heartsease. If you had desired an oak or a vine or a rose here, you would have planted such. Since you put me here, I decided to do the *best* I can to be what you want me to be. I am trying to be the *best* heartsease for you." The king was greatly pleased with the heartsease.

Many people in the Lord's garden want to be something else than what the Lord intended them to be. They are not satisfied to do what the Lord wants them to do, and are unhappy and drooping, when they should be happy and serving. Let us *gladly* obey every command and wish of the Lord for *our* lives.

The Doctor Who Worked with God

A great surgeon in a large city hospital always insists upon having a moment alone before he enters the operating room. Because of his great skill, many of the younger doctors wondered if his success were related to this unusual habit.

One day, one of the interns asked him if there was any connection between his success and his moment *alone* before his operations. The great surgeon replied, "There is very close connection between the two. Before every operation, I am alone for a moment. In that moment, I ask the Great Physician to be with me and to guide my hands in their work. There have been times during an operation when I didn't know what to do next. Then, there came a power to go on, a power which *I know* comes from God. I would not think of performing any operation without asking God's help!"

Soon, the surgeon's story spread through the country round about. One day, a father brought his little daughter to the hospital, insisting that the doctor who *worked with God* should operate on his child.

"The Night Is Coming"

Some years ago, a man passed by a humble cottage. Near the window of the cottage sat a lady busy sewing. She was sewing by the light of a candle. As she glanced at the candle, she saw that it was burning low. Then she said, "I *must* hasten and finish my work. This is the only candle I have and the light will soon be gone." When the man heard the words of the lady he said, "I, too, must hasten. I must do the work of God, for the night is coming when no man can work."

WORLDLINESS

Animals or Fowl

The story is told of a battle between the animals and the fowls. A bat was among them. When the animals rushed upon the fowls, the bat drew in his wings, and said, "I am an animal." When the fowls turned upon the bat, he stretched out his wings, and said, "I am a fowl!" Alas, that is the way with some professing Christians. They are always like the crowd they are in.

The Senator's Opinion

A distinguished Christian lady was spending a few weeks at a hotel at Long Branch. An attempt was made to induce her to attend a dance. She declined. Finally, a senator tried to persuade her to attend the dance. Said the lady, "Senator, I cannot do it. I am a Christian. I never do anything during my summer vacation, or wherever I go, that will injure my influence over the girls of my Sunday School class!" The senator bowed and said, "I honor you. If there were more Christians like you, more men like myself would become Christians!"

The Bible says, "Be ye not unequally yoked together with unbelievers: for what fellowship hath righteousness with unrighteousness? and what communion hath light with darkness" (*II Cor. 6:14*). When we love the world, we do not love Christ fully. The Bible says, "Ye cannot serve God and mammon." If we love the world and serve the world, then our love for Christ will wane, and our service for Him come to nought.

A Different Wife

On their fourth wedding anniversary, a young wife said to her husband, "I have been a very happy woman for four years! Only *one* thing is lacking to make me the happiest woman in the world." "What is that?" he asked. She replied, "If you were only a Christian!" He asked, "Are you a Christian?" She answered, "Yes." "Well," he said, "I didn't know it. You do not swear, neither do I. You do not gamble, neither do I. You do not get drunk, neither do I. But we both drink wine at receptions out of courtesy to the hostess. We both go to the theater. We both play cards. We both dance. If you will show me the difference between the kind of life which you are living and the kind I am living, I will become a Christian!"

The young wife stood speechless! She knew every word her husband spoke was *true*. She had been living for the world. Later, when her husband unexpectedly returned from an errand, he found her on her knees, with her face buried in her hands and weeping. He asked if he had hurt her feelings. "No," she answered, "I want to ask your forgiveness. With God's help, you shall have a different wife from this time on!" Many months later, that young husband stood in a large meeting, and said, "For four months, I have been a Christian. I was won to Christ by the earnest, sincere, consistent, beautiful Christian life of my devoted wife!"

Dead Unto Sin

In a little western town there lived a young woman who was prominent in all the social activities. She was a favorite with all. An evangelist came to town. The young woman refused to attend the meetings. Finally, on the last night she went, and was saved. Her life was completely and wonderfully changed. She could not be persuaded to attend the social gatherings. Instead she sought the fellowship of Christians. Her worldly friends missed her presence, for she had always been "the life of the party." They decided on a scheme to get her back. On the evening of her birthday, they went by her home and said, "Lucy, we have reserved seats at the theatre for tonight in honor of your birthday. We want you to go with us." Lucy promptly refused saying, "I cannot go. I am very sorry that you have done this. Really, I have never attended the theatre in my life and would be entirely out of place." The friends replied, "Why, Lucy, you know you have often attended our theatre parties. Indeed, not long ago you were the very life of them." Lucy looked at them earnestly and said, "It was not I, the new Lucy, who went to the theatre parties. It was

the old Lucy who was dead in sin. I have buried the old Lucy."

Evil Companions

Some boys roaming through the woods found a linnet's nest. In the nest were two fledglings which the boys managed to capture. They carried the little birds home and placed them in two wooden cages. They hung the cages on either side of a canary, explaining to their mother that they hoped the young linnets would learn to sing like a canary and forget to cheep like linnets ordinarily do. She was not sure that the plan would work, but she agreed that the boys could try it and see what would happen.

A few days later the boys said, "Mother, our CANARY is cheeping like a linnet." It was so. The canary had to be separated from the wood birds and kept under cover for some time before he regained his beautiful song. Here is a lesson for all Christians. When Christians fellowship with the world, it does not mean that the godless will take up the way of the Lord. It generally means that the Christians lose their joyous song, and take on the manners and speech of the world.

Doubtful Things

Sandy was a thrifty Scot. Because he objected to any unnecessary laundry expense, whenever he wore a dress shirt to a banquet, he would carefully put it away in a drawer for future use. One time he was dressing for a big dinner. He took a used shirt out of the drawer, hoping to be able to wear it that evening. He was not sure the shirt was clean enough, so he carried it over to the window where the light was better to look at it. His wife glanced over and saw him scowling as he looked at the shirt.

"Remember, Sandy," she said, "if it's doubtful, it is dirty."

That settled the question. The used shirt went in with the dirty clothes, and a clean one came out of the drawer. If you, as a Christian, have any doubt about whether something is right or wrong for you to do, settle the question by remembering, "If it's doubtful, it's dirty."

Keeping Clean

A group of young ladies wanted to go down into a coal mine. One of them had on a white dress. Her friends told her she should not wear the white dress into the mine. The young lady questioned the old miner, who was to guide the party. Asked she, "Can I wear a white dress down into the mine?" "Sure, Ma'am," replied the old miner. "There is nothing to keep you from wearing a white dress down into the mine, but there will be plenty to keep you from wearing one back!" The old miner knew that the white dress would become soiled and dirty down in the mine.

When we accept the Lord Jesus as our Saviour, He gives us new hearts, new lives. He wants us to keep our lives clean. He wants us to be unspotted by the sins of the world.

You Can't Eat Mud

A young man wanted to become a Christian. But he did not want to give up the sinful amusements of this world. Said he, "There are many things that I do now that I will have to give up if I

become a Christian. I like to dance. I like to play cards. I like to go to the movies. I like to go out and have a good time!" A Christian brother said, "But there are also many things that you can't do now. You can't eat mud!" "No," said the young man, "but I don't want to eat mud." "That's just it," said the Christian brother, "when you become a *real* Christian and love the Lord Jesus with *all* your heart, you will not like sin. You will not want the sinful things of this world."

"Take the world, but give me Jesus,
　All its joy is but a name;
But His love abideth ever,
　Through eternal years the *same!*"

God Loves Us

A young woman felt the voice of Jesus calling, "Come unto Me." This young woman loved the world, and had been following the world and its pleasures. She said, "I will *not* follow Jesus, for I will have to give up too much. I do not want to give up the sinful things of the world!"

A friend asked, "Do you think God loves you?" "Yes," she replied. Then the friend asked, "How much does He love you?" The woman replied, "Enough to give His Son, Jesus, to die for me." Then the friend asked, "If God loves you, will He ask you to give up anything that is good for you to keep?" "No," said the young woman, "He would not want me to give up anything that is good for me to keep. I will leave the world, and will come to Jesus. I will follow Him!"

The young woman did come to Jesus. She trusted Him as her Saviour. Jesus filled her life and heart so full of joy that she was never sorry that she had left the world.

Not for You

One day a teacher asked her pupils to dance. Betsy Ann said to the teacher, "I do not care to dance." That night Betsy Ann told her mother about it. She said, "Mother, I do not want to dance, because the Holy Spirit said to me, 'Betsy, dancing is not for you.'"

"How do you know that the Holy Spirit said that to you?" asked the mother.

"Because," Betsy answered, "it was the same Voice that once said to me, 'Betsy, if you will trust the Lord Jesus, He will save you.' I did trust Him, and He saved me, Mother. I know it was the same Voice that said to me today, 'Betsy, dancing is not for *you*.' So, Mother, I do not intend to dance, and I told the teacher so."

There are many customs and ways in the world which are *not* for God's children. Let us day by day keep our eyes upon God. Let us live for Him, and seek His ways.

Entanglement

A traveler who sailed along the coast of South America tells an interesting story: While his ship lay at anchor near the coast, it became "lily-bound." In that climate, the growth of vegetation is very rapid. In a few days, the vessel became the center of a great, floating island of beautiful lilies. They grew so fast that the chains became entangled. Soon, the flowery mass caused the vessel to drag her anchor and drift in the wrong direction. Then, the crew had a long and hard task. With cutlasses and hatchets, they released their ship from the flowers.

How easy it is for Christians to become entangled with the gay and golden flowers of riches and worldly pleasures, so that their lives drift in the wrong direction. We must keep ourselves free from the entanglements of this world. Paul said, "No man that warreth entangleth himself with the affairs of this life; that he may please him who hath chosen him to be a soldier" (*II Tim. 2:4*).

Bad Company

One spring, a band of crows began to pull up a farmer's young corn. He determined to put a stop to it. He loaded his shotgun, and slipped along the fence. He had a very sociable parrot, who, discovering the crows pulling up the corn, flew over and joined them. The farmer saw the crows, but he did not see the parrot. He fired among the crows, and then climbed over the fence to see what had happened. There lay three dead crows, and there lay his pet parrot also, with a broken leg! When the parrot was taken home, the children asked, "Who hurt our pretty Polly?" In a solemn voice, the parrot answered, "Bad company! Bad company!" The farmer said, "Yes, children, that was it. Polly was with those bad crows when I fired, and she received a shot intended for them."

Remember, the parrot and what the bird would teach us, "Beware of bad company!"